It's another great book from CGP...

OK, so GCSE Maths can be seriously challenging — and the latest exams are tougher than ever. But help is at hand...

This life-saving CGP book is totally up-to-date for the new GCSE course. It's packed with no nonsense explanations, plus worked examples, grade info and exam-style practice questions for every topic.

It even includes a free Online Edition to read on your computer or tablet!

How to get your free Online Edition

Just go to **cgpbooks.co.uk/extras** and enter this code...

0996 4471 7583 2877

By the way, this code only works for one person. If somebody else has used this book before you, they might have already claimed the Online Edition.

CGP — still the best! ☺

Our sole aim here at CGP is to produce the highest quality books — carefully written, immaculately presented and dangerously close to being funny.

Then we work our socks off to get them out to you
— at the cheapest possible prices.

Contents

Throughout this book you'll see grade stamps like these:
You can use these to focus your revision on easier or harder work.
But remember — to get a top grade you have to know **everything**, not just the hardest topics.

Section Six — Pythagoras and Trigonometry

Section Seven — Probability and Statistics

Published by CGP

Written by Richard Parsons

Updated by: Rob Harrison, Shaun Harrogate, Alison Palin, Dave Ryan, Caley Simpson, Ruth Wilbourne

With thanks to Alastair Duncombe and Simon Little for the proofreading

Printed by Elanders Ltd, Newcastle upon Tyne.
Clipart from Corel®

Types of Number and BODMAS

Ah, the glorious world of GCSE Maths. OK maybe it's more like whiffy socks at times, but learn it you must.
Here are some handy definitions of different types of number, and a bit about what order to do things in.

Integers:

You need to make sure you know the <u>meaning</u> of this word — it'll come up <u>all the time</u> in GCSE Maths.
An <u>integer</u> is another name for a <u>whole number</u> — either a positive or negative number, or zero.

<u>Examples</u>

Integers:	–365, 0, 1, 17, 989, 1 234 567 890
Not integers:	0.5, $\dfrac{2}{3}$, $\sqrt{7}$, $13\dfrac{3}{4}$, -1000.1, 66.66, π

All Numbers are Either Rational or Irrational

<u>Rational numbers</u> can be written as <u>fractions</u>. Most numbers you deal with are rational.

Rational numbers come in 3 different forms:
1) <u>Integers</u> e.g. $4\ (=\frac{4}{1})$, $-5\ (=\frac{-5}{1})$, $-12\ (=\frac{-12}{1})$
2) <u>Fractions</u> p/q, where p and q are (non-zero) integers, e.g. $\frac{1}{4}$, $-\frac{1}{2}$, $\frac{7}{4}$
3) <u>Terminating or recurring decimals</u> e.g. $0.125\ (=\frac{1}{8})$, $0.33333333...\ (=\frac{1}{3})$, $0.143143143...\ (=\frac{143}{999})$

<u>Irrational numbers</u> are messy. They <u>can't</u> be written as fractions — they're <u>never-ending</u>, <u>non-repeating</u>
<u>decimals</u>. <u>Square roots</u> of +ve integers are either integers or irrational (e.g. $\sqrt{2}$ and $\sqrt{3}$ are irrational, but
$\sqrt{4} = 2$ isn't). <u>Surds</u> (see p.20) are numbers or expressions containing irrational roots. π is also irrational.

BODMAS

Brackets, Other, Division, Multiplication, Addition, Subtraction

<u>BODMAS</u> tells you the <u>ORDER</u> in which these operations should be done:
Work out <u>Brackets</u> first, then <u>Other</u> things like squaring, then <u>Divide</u> / <u>Multiply</u>
groups of numbers before <u>Adding</u> or <u>Subtracting</u> them.

You can use BODMAS when it's <u>not clear</u> what to do <u>next</u>,
or if there's <u>more than one</u> thing you could do.

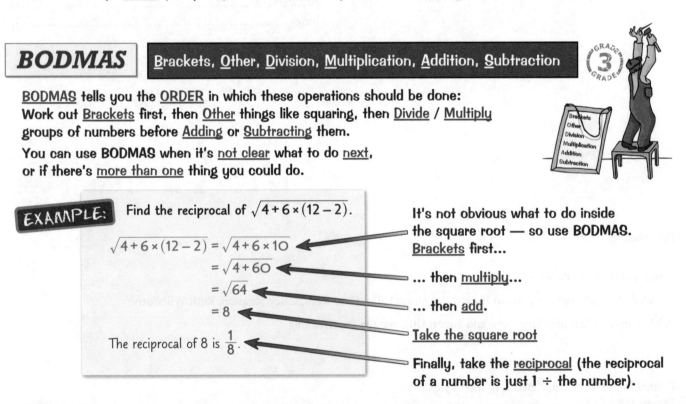

EXAMPLE: Find the reciprocal of $\sqrt{4 + 6 \times (12 - 2)}$.

$$\sqrt{4 + 6 \times (12 - 2)} = \sqrt{4 + 6 \times 10}$$
$$= \sqrt{4 + 60}$$
$$= \sqrt{64}$$
$$= 8$$

The reciprocal of 8 is $\frac{1}{8}$.

It's not obvious what to do inside
the square root — so use BODMAS.
<u>Brackets</u> first...

... then <u>multiply</u>...

... then <u>add</u>.

<u>Take the square root</u>

Finally, take the <u>reciprocal</u> (the reciprocal
of a number is just 1 ÷ the number).

What's your BODMAS? About 50 kg, dude...

It's really important to check your working on BODMAS questions. You might be certain you did it
right, but it's surprisingly easy to make a slip. Try this Exam Practice Question and see how you do.

Q1   Without using a calculator, find the value of $3 + 22 \times 3 - 14$.   [2 marks]

Multiples, Factors and Prime Factors

If you think 'factor' is short for 'fat actor', you should give this page a read. Stop thinking about fat actors.

Multiples and Factors (3)

The MULTIPLES of a number are just its <u>times table</u>.

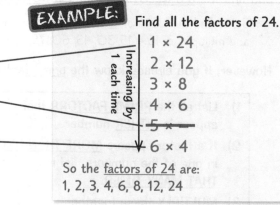

EXAMPLE: Find the first 8 multiples of 13.

You just need to find the first 8 numbers in the 13 times table:

13   26   39   52   65   78   91   104

The FACTORS of a number are all the numbers that <u>divide into it</u>.

There's a method that guarantees you'll find them all:

1) Start off with 1 × the number itself, then try 2 ×, then 3 × and so on, listing the pairs in rows.

2) Try each one in turn. Cross out the row if it doesn't divide exactly.

3) Eventually, when you get a number <u>repeated</u>, <u>stop</u>.

4) The numbers in the rows you haven't crossed out make up the list of factors.

EXAMPLE: Find all the factors of 24.

Increasing by 1 each time →

1 × 24
2 × 12
3 × 8
4 × 6
5 ×
6 × 4

So the <u>factors of 24</u> are:
1, 2, 3, 4, 6, 8, 12, 24

Prime Numbers: (3)

| 2 | 3 | 5 | 7 | 11 | 13 | 17 | 19 | 23 | 29 | 31 | 37 | 41 | 43... |

A <u>prime number</u> is a number which <u>doesn't divide by anything</u>, apart from itself and 1 —
i.e. its only <u>factors</u> are itself and 1. (The only exception is <u>1</u>, which is <u>NOT</u> a prime number.)

Finding Prime Factors — The Factor Tree (4)

<u>Any number</u> can be broken down into a string of prime factors all multiplied together —
this is called '<u>prime factor decomposition</u>' or '<u>prime factorisation</u>'.

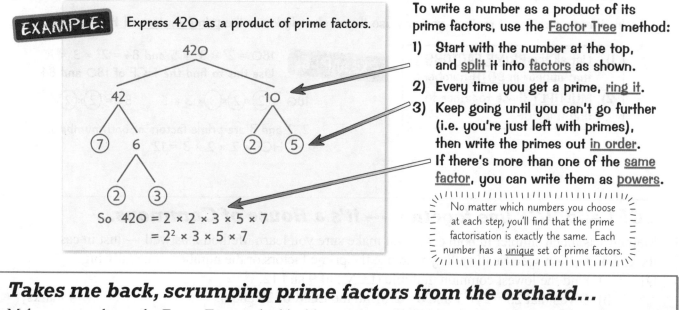

EXAMPLE: Express 420 as a product of prime factors.

420
42   10
⑦ 6   ② ⑤
② ③

So 420 = 2 × 2 × 3 × 5 × 7
       = $2^2 × 3 × 5 × 7$

To write a number as a product of its prime factors, use the <u>Factor Tree</u> method:

1) Start with the number at the top, and <u>split</u> it into <u>factors</u> as shown.

2) Every time you get a prime, <u>ring it</u>.

3) Keep going until you can't go further (i.e. you're just left with primes), then write the primes out <u>in order</u>. If there's more than one of the <u>same factor</u>, you can write them as <u>powers</u>.

No matter which numbers you choose at each step, you'll find that the prime factorisation is exactly the same. Each number has a <u>unique</u> set of prime factors.

Takes me back, scrumping prime factors from the orchard...

Make sure you know the Factor Tree method inside out, then give this Exam Practice Question a go...

Q1   Express as products of their prime factors: a) 990   [2 marks]   b) 160   [2 marks] (4)

LCM and HCF

As if the previous page wasn't enough excitement, here's some more factors and multiples fun...

LCM — 'Least Common Multiple' (5)

The SMALLEST number that will DIVIDE BY ALL the numbers in question.

If you're given two numbers and asked to find their LCM, just LIST the MULTIPLES of BOTH numbers and find the SMALLEST one that's in BOTH lists.

So, to find the LCM of 12 and 15, list their multiples (multiples of 12 = 12, 24, 36, 48, 60, 72, ... and multiples of 15 = 15, 30, 45, 60, 75, ...) and find the smallest one that's in both lists — so LCM = 60.

However, if you already know the prime factors of the numbers, you can use this method instead:

1) List all the PRIME FACTORS that appear in EITHER number.
2) If a factor appears MORE THAN ONCE in one of the numbers, list it THAT MANY TIMES.
3) MULTIPLY these together to give the LCM.

EXAMPLE: $18 = 2 \times 3^2$ and $30 = 2 \times 3 \times 5$. Find the LCM of 18 and 30.

$18 = 2 \times 3 \times 3$ $30 = 2 \times 3 \times 5$

So the prime factors that appear in either number are: 2, 3, 3, 5 — List 3 twice as it appears twice in 18.

$LCM = 2 \times 3 \times 3 \times 5 = 90$

HCF — 'Highest Common Factor' (5)

The BIGGEST number that will DIVIDE INTO ALL the numbers in question.

If you're given two numbers and asked to find their HCF, just LIST the FACTORS of BOTH numbers and find the BIGGEST one that's in BOTH lists.

Take care listing the factors — make sure you use the proper method (as shown on the previous page).

So, to find the HCF of 36 and 54, list their factors (factors of 36 = 1, 2, 3, 4, 6, 9, 12, 18 and 36 and factors of 54 = 1, 2, 3, 6, 9, 18, 27 and 54) and find the biggest one that's in both lists — so HCF = 18.

Again, there's a different method you can use if you already know the prime factors of the numbers:

1) List all the PRIME FACTORS that appear in BOTH numbers.
2) MULTIPLY these together to find the HCF.

EXAMPLE: $180 = 2^2 \times 3^2 \times 5$ and $84 = 2^2 \times 3 \times 7$. Use this to find the HCF of 180 and 84.

$180 = ②\times②\times③\times 3 \times 5$ $84 = ②\times②\times③\times 7$

2, 2 and 3 are prime factors of both numbers, so HCF = $2 \times 2 \times 3 = 12$

LCM and HCF live together — it's a House of Commons...

Method 1 is much simpler in both cases, but make sure you learn Method 2 as well — just in case the exam question specifically tells you to use the prime factors or the numbers are really big.

Q1   a) Find the lowest common multiple (LCM) of 9 and 12.
       b) Given that $28 = 2^2 \times 7$ and $8 = 2^3$, find the LCM of 28 and 8.   [4 marks] (5)
Q2   a) Find the highest common factor (HCF) of 36 and 84.
       b) Given that $150 = 2 \times 3 \times 5^2$ and $60 = 2^2 \times 3 \times 5$, find the HCF of 150 and 60.   [3 marks] (5)

Fractions

These pages show you how to cope with fraction calculations without your <u>beloved calculator</u>.

1) Cancelling down

To <u>cancel down</u> or <u>simplify</u> a fraction, <u>divide top and bottom by the same number</u>, till they won't go further:

EXAMPLE: Simplify $\frac{18}{24}$.

Cancel down in a series of <u>easy steps</u> — keep going till the top and bottom don't have <u>any</u> common factors.

$$\frac{18}{24} = \frac{6}{8} = \frac{3}{4}$$

The number on the top of the fraction is the <u>numerator</u>, and the number on the bottom is the <u>denominator</u>.

2) Mixed numbers

<u>Mixed numbers</u> are things like $3\frac{1}{3}$, with an integer part and a fraction part. <u>Improper fractions</u> are ones where the top number is larger than the bottom number. You need to be able to convert between the two.

EXAMPLES:

1. Write $4\frac{2}{3}$ as an improper fraction.

1) Think of the <u>mixed number</u> as an <u>addition</u>:
$$4\frac{2}{3} = 4 + \frac{2}{3}$$

2) Turn the <u>integer part</u> into a <u>fraction</u>:
$$4 + \frac{2}{3} = \frac{12}{3} + \frac{2}{3} = \frac{12+2}{3} = \frac{14}{3}$$

2. Write $\frac{31}{4}$ as a mixed number.

<u>Divide</u> the top number by the bottom.
1) The <u>answer</u> gives the <u>whole number part</u>.
2) The <u>remainder</u> goes <u>on top</u> of the fraction.
$$31 \div 4 = 7 \text{ remainder } 3 \text{ so } \frac{31}{4} = 7\frac{3}{4}$$

3) Multiplying

Multiply top and bottom separately. It usually helps to cancel down first if you can.

EXAMPLE: Find $\frac{8}{15} \times \frac{5}{12}$.

<u>Cancel down</u> by dividing top and bottom by any common factors you find in <u>either</u> fraction:

Now multiply the top and bottom numbers <u>separately</u>:

8 and 12 both divide by 4

15 and 5 both divide by 5

$$\frac{8}{15} \times \frac{5}{12} = \frac{2}{15} \times \frac{5}{3} = \frac{2}{3} \times \frac{1}{3} = \frac{2 \times 1}{3 \times 3} = \frac{2}{9}$$

4) Dividing

Turn the 2nd fraction <u>UPSIDE DOWN</u> and then <u>multiply</u>:

When you're multiplying or dividing with mixed numbers, <u>always</u> turn them into improper fractions first.

EXAMPLE: Find $2\frac{1}{3} \div 3\frac{1}{2}$.

Rewrite the <u>mixed numbers</u> as <u>fractions</u>: $2\frac{1}{3} \div 3\frac{1}{2} = \frac{7}{3} \div \frac{7}{2}$

Turn $\frac{7}{2}$ <u>upside down</u> and <u>multiply</u>: $= \frac{7}{3} \times \frac{2}{7}$

<u>Simplify</u> by cancelling the 7s: $= \frac{1}{3} \times \frac{2}{1} = \frac{2}{3}$

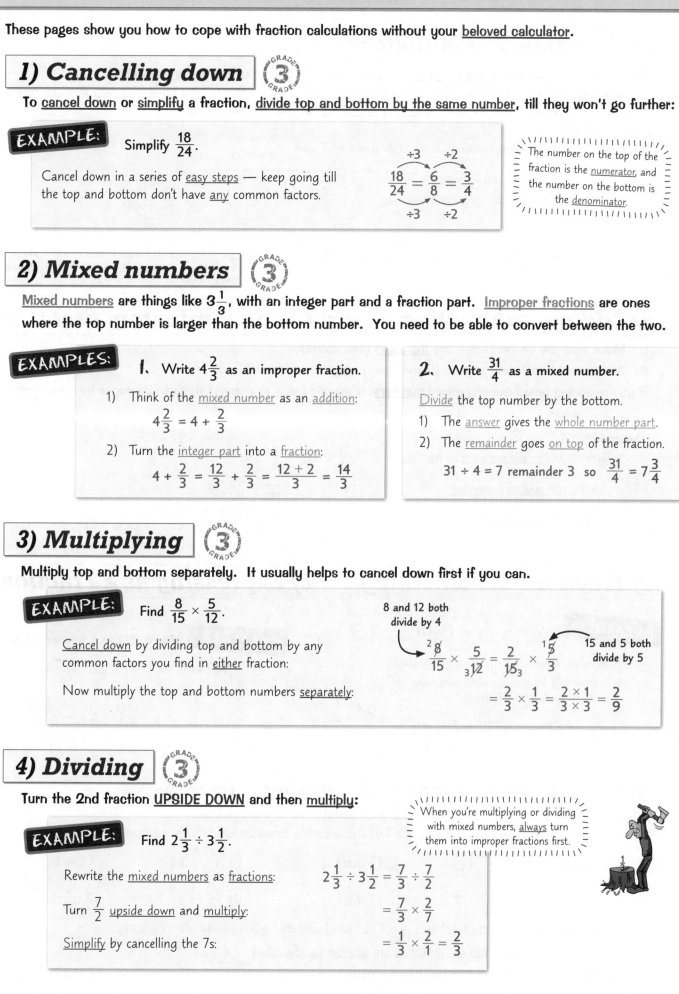

Fractions

5) Common denominators

This comes in handy for ordering fractions by size, and for adding or subtracting fractions.
You need to find a number that all the denominators divide into — this will be your common denominator.
The simplest way is to find the lowest common multiple of the denominators:

EXAMPLE: Put these fractions in ascending order of size: $\frac{8}{3}, \frac{5}{4}, \frac{12}{5}$

The LCM of 3, 4 and 5 is 60, so make 60 the common denominator:

$$\frac{8}{3} = \frac{160}{60} \quad (\times 20) \qquad \frac{5}{4} = \frac{75}{60} \quad (\times 15) \qquad \frac{12}{5} = \frac{144}{60} \quad (\times 12)$$

So the correct order is $\frac{75}{60}, \frac{144}{60}, \frac{160}{60}$ i.e. $\frac{5}{4}, \frac{12}{5}, \frac{8}{3}$

Don't forget to use the original fractions in the final answer.

6) Adding, subtracting — sort the denominators first

1) Make sure the denominators are the same (see above).
2) Add (or subtract) the top lines (numerators) only.

If you're adding or subtracting mixed numbers, it usually helps to convert them to improper fractions first.

EXAMPLE: Calculate $2\frac{1}{5} - 1\frac{1}{2}$.

Rewrite the mixed numbers as fractions: $2\frac{1}{5} - 1\frac{1}{2} = \frac{11}{5} - \frac{3}{2}$

Find a common denominator: $= \frac{22}{10} - \frac{15}{10}$

Combine the top lines: $= \frac{22 - 15}{10} = \frac{7}{10}$

7) Fractions of something

EXAMPLE: What is $\frac{9}{20}$ of £360?

'$\frac{9}{20}$ of' means '$\frac{9}{20} \times$', so multiply the 'something' by the top of the fraction, and divide it by the bottom.

It doesn't matter which order you do those two steps in — just start with whatever's easiest.

$\frac{9}{20}$ of £360 = (£360 ÷ 20) × 9
$= £18 \times 9 = £162$

8) Expressing as a Fraction

EXAMPLE: Write 180 as a fraction of 80.

Just write the first number over the second and cancel down.

$$\frac{180}{80} = \frac{9}{4}$$

No fractions were harmed in the making of these pages...

...although one was slightly frightened for a while, and several were tickled.
When you think you've learnt all this, try all of these Exam Practice Questions without a calculator.

Q1 Calculate:

a) $\frac{3}{8} \times 1\frac{5}{12}$ [3 marks]

b) $1\frac{7}{9} \div 2\frac{2}{3}$ [3 marks]

c) $4\frac{1}{9} + 2\frac{2}{27}$ [3 marks]

d) $5\frac{2}{3} - 9\frac{1}{4}$ [3 marks]

Q2 Dean has made 30 sandwiches. $\frac{7}{15}$ of the sandwiches he has made are vegetarian, and $\frac{3}{7}$ of the vegetarian sandwiches are cheese sandwiches.
How many cheese sandwiches has he made? [2 marks]

Fractions, Decimals and Percentages

The one word that describes all these three is <u>PROPORTION</u>. Fractions, decimals and percentages are simply <u>three different ways</u> of expressing a <u>proportion</u> of something — and it's pretty important you should see them as <u>closely related and completely interchangeable</u> with each other. These tables show the really common conversions which you should know straight off without having to work them out:

Fraction	Decimal	Percentage
$\frac{1}{2}$	0.5	50%
$\frac{1}{4}$	0.25	25%
$\frac{3}{4}$	0.75	75%
$\frac{1}{3}$	0.333333...	$33\frac{1}{3}$%
$\frac{2}{3}$	0.666666...	$66\frac{2}{3}$%
$\frac{1}{10}$	0.1	10%
$\frac{2}{10}$	0.2	20%

Fraction	Decimal	Percentage
$\frac{1}{5}$	0.2	20%
$\frac{2}{5}$	0.4	40%
$\frac{1}{8}$	0.125	12.5%
$\frac{3}{8}$	0.375	37.5%
$\frac{5}{2}$	2.5	250%
$\frac{7}{2}$	3.5	350%
$\frac{9}{4}$	2.25	225%

The more of those conversions you learn, the better — but for those that you <u>don't know</u>, you must <u>also learn</u> how to <u>convert</u> between the three types. These are the methods:

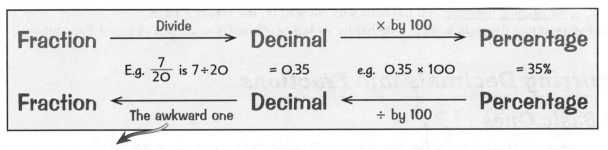

Fraction $\xrightarrow{\text{Divide}}$ **Decimal** $\xrightarrow{\times \text{ by 100}}$ **Percentage**

E.g. $\frac{7}{20}$ is 7÷20   = 0.35   e.g. 0.35 × 100   = 35%

Fraction $\xleftarrow{\text{The awkward one}}$ **Decimal** $\xleftarrow{\div \text{ by 100}}$ **Percentage**

<u>Converting decimals to fractions</u> is awkward, because it's different for different types of decimal. There are two different methods you need to learn:

1) <u>Terminating decimals</u> to fractions — this is fairly easy. The digits after the decimal point go on the top, and a <u>power of 10</u> on the bottom — with the same number of zeros as there were decimal places.

$$0.6 = \frac{6}{10} \qquad 0.3 = \frac{3}{10} \qquad 0.7 = \frac{7}{10} \quad \text{etc.}$$

$$0.12 = \frac{12}{100} \qquad 0.78 = \frac{78}{100} \qquad 0.05 = \frac{5}{100} \quad \text{etc.}$$

$$0.345 = \frac{345}{1000} \qquad 0.908 = \frac{908}{1000} \qquad 0.024 = \frac{24}{1000} \quad \text{etc.}$$

These can often be <u>cancelled down</u> — see p.5.

2) <u>Recurring decimals</u> to fractions — this is trickier. See next page...

Eight out of ten cats prefer the perfume Eighty Purr Scent...

Learn the top tables and the 4 conversion processes. Then it's time to break into a mild sweat...

Q1   Turn the following decimals into fractions and reduce them to their simplest form.
      a) 0.4   b) 0.02   c) 0.77   d) 0.555   e) 5.6   [5 marks]

Q2   Which is greater: a) 57% or $\frac{5}{9}$,   b) 0.2 or $\frac{6}{25}$,   c) $\frac{7}{8}$ or 90%?   [3 marks]

Fractions and Recurring Decimals

You might think that a decimal is just a decimal. But oh no — things get a lot more juicy than that...

Recurring or Terminating...

1) <u>Recurring</u> decimals have a <u>pattern</u> of numbers which repeats forever, e.g. $\frac{1}{3}$ is the decimal 0.333333... Note, it doesn't have to be a single digit that repeats. You could have, for instance: 0.143143143...

2) The <u>repeating part</u> is usually marked with <u>dots</u> or a <u>bar</u> on top of the number. If there's one dot, then only one digit is repeated. If there are two dots, then everything from the first dot to the second dot is the repeating bit. E.g. $0.2\dot{5} = 0.2555555...$, $0.\dot{2}\dot{5} = 0.25252525...$, $0.\dot{2}5\dot{5} = 0.255255255...$

3) <u>Terminating</u> decimals are <u>finite</u> (they come to an end), e.g $\frac{1}{20}$ is the decimal 0.05.

The <u>denominator</u> (bottom number) of a fraction in its simplest form tells you if it converts to a <u>recurring</u> or <u>terminating decimal</u>. Fractions where the denominator has <u>prime factors</u> of <u>only 2 or 5</u> will give <u>terminating decimals</u>. All <u>other fractions</u> will give <u>recurring decimals</u>.

For prime factors, see p.3.

	Only prime factors: 2 and 5				Also other prime factors			
FRACTION	$\frac{1}{5}$	$\frac{1}{125}$	$\frac{1}{2}$	$\frac{1}{20}$	$\frac{1}{7}$	$\frac{1}{35}$	$\frac{1}{3}$	$\frac{1}{6}$
EQUIVALENT DECIMAL	0.2	0.008	0.5	0.05	$0.\dot{1}4285\dot{7}$	$0.0\dot{2}8571\dot{4}$	$0.\dot{3}$	$0.1\dot{6}$
	Terminating decimals				Recurring decimals			

Converting <u>terminating decimals</u> into fractions was covered on the previous page.
Converting <u>recurring decimals</u> is quite a bit harder — but you'll be OK once you've learnt the method...

Recurring Decimals into Fractions

1) Basic Ones

Turning a recurring decimal into a fraction uses a really clever trick. Just watch this...

EXAMPLE: Write $0.\dot{2}3\dot{4}$ as a fraction.

1) Name your decimal — I've called it <u>r</u>.

Let r = $0.\dot{2}3\dot{4}$

2) Multiply r by a <u>power of ten</u> to move it past the decimal point by <u>one full repeated lump</u> — here that's 1000:

$1000r = 234.\dot{2}3\dot{4}$

3) Now you can <u>subtract</u> to <u>get rid</u> of the decimal part:

$$1000r = 234.\dot{2}3\dot{4}$$
$$-\quad\quad r = 0.\dot{2}3\dot{4}$$
$$999r = 234$$

4) Then just <u>divide</u> to leave r, and <u>cancel</u> if possible:

$$r = \frac{234}{999} = \frac{26}{111}$$

The 'Just Learning the Result' Method:

1) For converting recurring decimals to fractions, you <u>could</u> just learn the result that the fraction always has the <u>repeating unit</u> on the top and <u>the same number of nines</u> on the bottom...

2) <u>BUT</u> this <u>only</u> works if the repeating bit starts <u>straight after</u> the decimal point (see the next page for an example where it doesn't).

3) <u>AND</u> some exam questions will ask you to 'show that' or 'prove' that a fraction and a recurring decimal are equivalent — and that means you have to use the <u>proper method</u>.

Fractions and Recurring Decimals

2) The Trickier Type 〔GRADE 7〕

If the recurring bit doesn't come right after the decimal point, things are slightly trickier — but only slightly.

EXAMPLE:

Write $0.1\dot{6}$ as a fraction.

1) Name your decimal.   Let $r = 0.1\dot{6}$

2) Multiply r by a <u>power of ten</u> to move the <u>non-repeating part</u> past the decimal point. $10r = 1.\dot{6}$

3) Now multiply again to move <u>one full repeated lump</u> past the decimal point. $100r = 16.\dot{6}$

4) <u>Subtract</u> to <u>get rid</u> of the decimal part:

$$100r = 16.\dot{6}$$
$$-\ \ \ 10r = \ \ 1.\dot{6}$$
$$90r = 15$$

5) <u>Divide</u> to leave r, and <u>cancel</u> if possible: $r = \dfrac{15}{90} = \dfrac{1}{6}$

Fractions into Recurring Decimals 〔GRADE 7〕

You might find this cropping up in your exam too — and if they're being really unpleasant, they'll stick it in a <u>non-calculator</u> paper.

EXAMPLE:

Write $\dfrac{8}{33}$ as a recurring decimal.

There are <u>two ways</u> you can do this:

1 Find an equivalent fraction with <u>all nines</u> on the bottom. The number on the top will tell you the <u>recurring part</u>.

$$\overset{\times 3}{\dfrac{8}{33} = \dfrac{24}{99}}$$
$\times 3$

Watch out — the <u>number of nines</u> on the bottom tells you the <u>number of digits</u> in the recurring part. E.g. $\dfrac{24}{99} = 0.\dot{2}\dot{4}$, but $\dfrac{24}{999} = 0.\dot{0}2\dot{4}$

$$\dfrac{24}{99} = 0.\dot{2}\dot{4}$$

2 Remember, $\dfrac{8}{33}$ means $8 \div 33$, so you could just <u>do the division</u>: (This is OK if you're allowed your calculator, but a bit tricky if not... you can use <u>short or long division</u> if you're feeling bold, but I recommend sticking with <u>method 1</u> instead.)

$$33\overline{)8.0^{14}0^{8}0^{14}0^{8}00}$$
$$0.2\ 4\ 2\ 4...$$

$$\dfrac{8}{33} = 0.\dot{2}\dot{4}$$

Oh, what's recurrin'?...

Learn how to tell whether a fraction will be a terminating or recurring decimal, and all the methods above. Then turn over and write it all down. Now, try to answer these beauties...

Q1   Express $0.\dot{1}2\dot{6}$ as a fraction in its simplest form.   [2 marks] 〔GRADE 7〕

Q2   Show that $0.\dot{0}\dot{7} = \dfrac{7}{99}$ [2 marks] 〔GRADE 7〕

Q3   Without using a calculator, convert $\dfrac{5}{111}$ to a recurring decimal.   [2 marks] 〔GRADE 7〕

Rounding Numbers

There are <u>two different ways</u> of specifying <u>where</u> a number should be <u>rounded</u>.
They are: 'Decimal Places' and 'Significant Figures'.

Decimal Places (d.p.) (3) GRADE

To round to a given number of <u>decimal places</u>:

> 1) <u>IDENTIFY</u> the position of the '<u>LAST DIGIT</u>' from the number of decimal places.
> 2) Then look at the next digit to the <u>RIGHT</u> — called <u>THE DECIDER</u>.
> 3) If the <u>DECIDER</u> is <u>5 OR MORE</u>, then <u>ROUND UP</u> the <u>LAST DIGIT</u>.
>   If the <u>DECIDER</u> is <u>4 OR LESS</u>, then <u>LEAVE</u> the <u>LAST DIGIT</u> as it is.
> 4) There must be <u>NO MORE DIGITS</u> after the last digit (not even zeros).

'Last digit' = last one in the <u>rounded version</u>, not the original number.

EXAMPLE: What is 7.45839 to 2 decimal places?

$$7.4\underline{58}39 = \underline{7.46}$$

LAST DIGIT   DECIDER

The <u>LAST DIGIT</u> rounds <u>UP</u> because the <u>DECIDER</u> is <u>5 or more</u>.

If you have to <u>round up</u> a <u>9</u> (to 10), replace the 9 with 0, and <u>carry 1</u> to the left.
Remember to keep enough <u>zeros</u> to fill the right number of decimal places
— so to 2 d.p. <u>45.699</u> would be rounded to <u>45.70</u>, and <u>64.996</u> would
be rounded to <u>65.00</u>.

65 has the <u>same value</u> as 65.00, but 65 <u>isn't</u> expressed to <u>2 d.p.</u> so it would be marked <u>wrong</u>.

Significant Figures (s.f.) (3) GRADE

The method for significant figures is <u>identical</u> to that for decimal places except that
locating the <u>last digit</u> is more difficult — it wouldn't be so bad, but for the <u>zeros</u>...

> 1) The <u>1st significant figure</u> of any number is simply <u>the first digit which isn't a zero</u>.

> 2) The <u>2nd, 3rd, 4th, etc. significant figures</u> follow on immediately after the 1st, <u>regardless of being zeros or not zeros</u>.

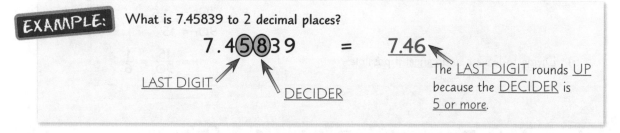

0.002309   2.03070

SIG. FIGS: 1st 2nd 3rd 4th   1st 2nd 3rd 4th
(If we're rounding to say, 3 s.f., then the LAST DIGIT is simply the 3rd sig. fig.)

I asked Stacey for her significant figures.
Data?
Nah, we're just friends.

> 3) After <u>rounding</u> the <u>last digit</u>, <u>end zeros</u> must be filled in up to, <u>but not beyond</u>, the decimal point.

No <u>extra zeros</u> must ever be put in <u>after</u> the decimal point.

EXAMPLES:

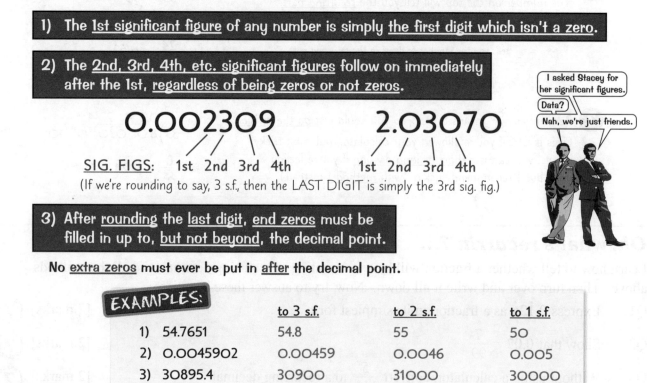

		to 3 s.f.	to 2 s.f.	to 1 s.f.
1)	54.7651	54.8	55	50
2)	0.0045902	0.00459	0.0046	0.005
3)	30895.4	30900	31000	30000

Estimating

'Estimating' doesn't mean 'take a wild guess', it means 'look at the numbers, make them a bit easier, then do the calculation'. Your answer won't be as accurate as the real thing but hey, it's easier on your brain.

Estimating Calculations

It's time to put your rounding skills to use and do some estimating.

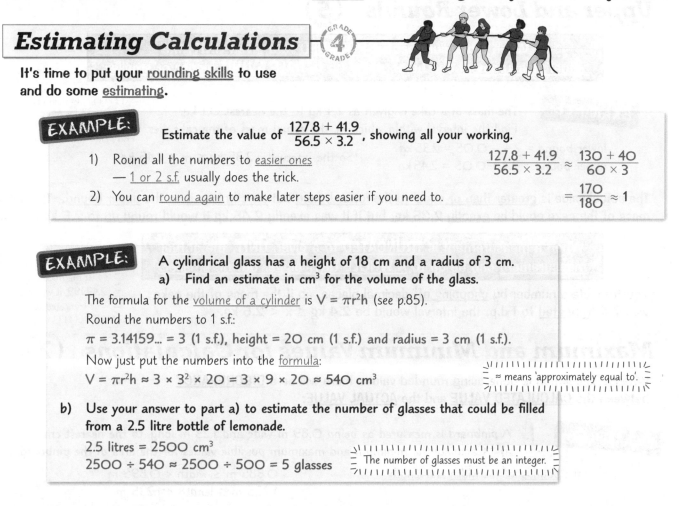

EXAMPLE: Estimate the value of $\frac{127.8 + 41.9}{56.5 \times 3.2}$, showing all your working.

1) Round all the numbers to easier ones — 1 or 2 s.f. usually does the trick.

2) You can round again to make later steps easier if you need to.

$$\frac{127.8 + 41.9}{56.5 \times 3.2} \approx \frac{130 + 40}{60 \times 3}$$
$$= \frac{170}{180} \approx 1$$

EXAMPLE: A cylindrical glass has a height of 18 cm and a radius of 3 cm.
a) Find an estimate in cm³ for the volume of the glass.

The formula for the volume of a cylinder is $V = \pi r^2 h$ (see p.85).

Round the numbers to 1 s.f.:

$\pi = 3.14159... = 3$ (1 s.f.), height = 20 cm (1 s.f.) and radius = 3 cm (1 s.f.).

Now just put the numbers into the formula:

$V = \pi r^2 h \approx 3 \times 3^2 \times 20 = 3 \times 9 \times 20 \approx 540$ cm³

≈ means 'approximately equal to'.

b) Use your answer to part a) to estimate the number of glasses that could be filled from a 2.5 litre bottle of lemonade.

2.5 litres = 2500 cm³
$2500 \div 540 \approx 2500 \div 500 = 5$ glasses

The number of glasses must be an integer.

Estimating Square Roots ⑤

Estimating square roots can be a bit tricky, but there are only 2 steps:

1) Find two square numbers, one either side of the number you're given.

2) Decide which number it's closest to, and make a sensible estimate of the digit after the decimal point.

EXAMPLE: Estimate the value of $\sqrt{87}$ to 1 d.p.

87 is between 81 (= 9^2) and 100 (= 10^2).

It's closer to 81, so its square root will be closer to 9 than 10: $\sqrt{87} \approx 9.3$
(the actual value of $\sqrt{87}$ is 9.32737..., so this is a reasonable estimate).

By my estimate, it's time to go home...

If you're asked to estimate something in the exam, make sure you show all your steps (including what each number is rounded to) to prove that you didn't just use a calculator. That would be naughty.

Q1   Estimate the value of: a) $\frac{4.23 \times 11.8}{7.7}$ [2 marks]   b) $\sqrt{136}$ [2 marks]

Q2   The volume of a sphere is given by the formula $V = \frac{4}{3}\pi r^3$.
a) Use this formula to estimate the volume of a sphere of radius 9 cm.   [2 marks]
b) Will your estimate be bigger or smaller than the actual value?   [1 mark]

Bounds

Finding <u>upper and lower bounds</u> is pretty easy, but using them in <u>calculations</u> is a bit trickier.

Upper and Lower Bounds (5)

> When a measurement is <u>ROUNDED</u> to a given <u>UNIT</u>, the
> <u>actual measurement</u> can be anything up to <u>HALF A UNIT</u> bigger or smaller.

EXAMPLE: The mass of a cake is given as 2.4 kg to the nearest 0.1 kg.
Find the interval within which m, the actual mass of the cake, lies.

See p.33 for more on inequalities.

lower bound = 2.4 − 0.05 = 2.35 kg
upper bound = 2.4 + 0.05 = 2.45 kg

So the interval is 2.35 kg $\leq$ m < 2.45 kg

The actual value is <u>greater than or equal to</u> the <u>lower bound</u> but <u>strictly less than</u> the <u>upper bound</u>. The actual mass of the cake could be <u>exactly</u> 2.35 kg, but if it was exactly 2.45 kg it would <u>round up</u> to 2.5 kg instead.

> When a measurement is <u>TRUNCATED</u> to a given <u>UNIT</u>, the <u>actual</u>
> <u>measurement</u> can be up to <u>A WHOLE UNIT</u> bigger but no smaller.

You truncate a number by <u>chopping off</u> decimal places, so if the mass of the cake
was 2.4 <u>truncated</u> to 1 d.p. the interval would be 2.4 kg $\leq$ x < 2.5 kg.

If the mass was 2.49999, it would still be truncated to 2.4.

Maximum and Minimum Values for Calculations (7)

When a calculation is done using rounded values there will be a <u>DISCREPANCY</u>
between the <u>CALCULATED VALUE</u> and the <u>ACTUAL VALUE</u>:

EXAMPLES: **1.** A pinboard is measured as being 0.89 m wide and 1.23 m long, to the nearest cm.
a) Calculate the minimum and maximum possible values for the area of the pinboard.

Find the <u>bounds</u> for the <u>width</u> and <u>length</u>:

0.885 m $\leq$ width < 0.895 m
1.225 m $\leq$ length < 1.235 m

Find the <u>minimum</u> area by multiplying the <u>lower bounds</u>,
and the <u>maximum</u> by multiplying the <u>upper bounds</u>:

minimum possible area = 0.885 × 1.225
= 1.084125 m^2

maximum possible area = 0.895 × 1.235
= 1.105325 m^2

b) Use your answers to part a) to give the area of the pinboard to an appropriate degree of accuracy.
The area of the pinboard lies in the interval 1.084125 m^2 $\leq$ a < 1.105325 m^2. Both the <u>upper bound</u>
and the <u>lower bound</u> round to 1.1 m^2 to 1 d.p. so the area of the pinboard is 1.1 m^2 to 1 d.p.

2. a = 5.3 and b = 4.2, both given to 1 d.p. What are the maximum and minimum values of a ÷ b?

First find the <u>bounds</u> for a and b. $\longrightarrow$ 5.25 $\leq$ a < 5.35, 4.15 $\leq$ b < 4.25

Now the tricky bit... The <u>bigger</u> the number
you <u>divide by</u>, the <u>smaller</u> the answer, so:

max(a ÷ b) = max(a) ÷ min(b)

and min(a ÷ b) = min(a) ÷ max(b)

max. value of a ÷ b = 5.35 ÷ 4.15
= 1.289 (to 3 d.p.)

min. value of a ÷ b = 5.25 ÷ 4.25
= 1.235 (to 3 d.p.)

Bound, bound, get a bound, I get a bound...

Be careful with bounds if the quantity has to be a whole number. For example, the maximum value
of the bound 145 $\leq$ x < 155 is 154 for a number of people but 154.99999... for the height of a person.

Q1 Maisie runs 200 m (to the nearest m) in a time of 32.2 seconds (to the nearest 0.1 second).
By considering bounds, find her speed in m/s to an appropriate degree of accuracy. [5 marks] (7)

Standard Form

Standard form is useful for writing <u>VERY BIG</u> or <u>VERY SMALL</u> numbers in a more convenient way, e.g.

$56\,000\,000\,000$ would be 5.6×10^{10} in standard form.

$0.000\,000\,003\,45$ would be 3.45×10^{-9} in standard form.

But <u>ANY NUMBER</u> can be written in standard form and you need to know how to do it:

What it Actually is: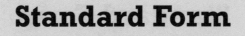

A number written in standard form must <u>always</u> be in <u>exactly</u> this form:

This <u>number</u> must <u>always</u> be <u>between 1 and 10</u>.

$$\boxed{\text{A} \times 10^n}$$

This number is just the <u>number of places</u> the <u>decimal point</u> moves.

(The fancy way of saying this is $1 \le A < 10$)

Learn the Three Rules:

1) The <u>front number</u> must always be <u>between 1 and 10</u>.

2) The power of 10, n, is <u>how far the decimal point moves</u>.

3) n is <u>positive for BIG numbers</u>, n is <u>negative for SMALL numbers</u>.

(This is much better than rules based on which way the decimal point moves.)

Four Important Examples:

1 Express 35 600 in standard form.

1) <u>Move the decimal point</u> until 35 600 becomes 3.56 ($1 \le A < 10$)

2) The decimal point has moved <u>4 places</u> so n = 4, giving: 10^4

3) 35 600 is a <u>big number</u> so n is +4, not −4

3.5600

$= 3.56 \times 10^4$

2 Express 0.0000623 in standard form.

1) The decimal point must move <u>5 places</u> to give 6.23 ($1 \le A < 10$). So the power of 10 is 5.

2) Since 0.0000623 is a <u>small number</u> it must be 10^{-5} not 10^{+5}

$0.00006 23$

$= 6.23 \times 10^{-5}$

3 Express 4.95×10^{-3} as an ordinary number.

1) The power of 10 is <u>negative</u>, so it's a <u>small number</u> — the answer will be less than 1.

2) The power is −3, so the decimal point moves <u>3 places</u>.

004.95×10^{-3}

$= 0.00495$

4 What is 146.3 million in standard form?

Too many people get this type of question <u>wrong</u>. Just take your time and do it in <u>two stages</u>:

146.3 million = $146.3 \times 1\,000\,000$

$= 146\,300\,000$ ——— 1) Write the number out in full.

$= 1.463 \times 10^8$ ——— 2) Convert to standard form.

The two favourite <u>wrong answers</u> for this are:

146.3×10^6 — which is kind of right but it's not in <u>standard form</u> because 146.3 is not between 1 and 10

1.463×10^6 — this one <u>is</u> in standard form but it's <u>not big enough</u>

Standard Form

Calculations with Standard Form (GRADE 5)

These are really popular <u>exam questions</u> — you might be asked to add, subtract, multiply or divide using numbers in standard form <u>without</u> using a calculator.

Multiplying and Dividing — not too bad

1) Rearrange to put the <u>front numbers</u> and the <u>powers of 10 together</u>.
2) Multiply or divide the front numbers, and use the <u>power rules</u> (see p.17) to multiply or divide the powers of 10.
3) Make sure your answer is still in <u>standard form</u>.

EXAMPLES:

1. Find $(2 \times 10^3) \times (6.75 \times 10^5)$ without using a calculator.
Give your answer in standard form.

$(2 \times 10^3) \times (6.75 \times 10^5)$
Multiply front numbers and powers separately
$= (2 \times 6.75) \times (10^3 \times 10^5)$
$= 13.5 \times 10^{3+5}$ — Add the powers (see p.17)
$= 13.5 \times 10^8$
Not in standard form — convert it
$= 1.35 \times 10 \times 10^8$
$= 1.35 \times 10^9$

2. Calculate $240\,000 \div (4.8 \times 10^{10})$ without using a calculator.
Give your answer in standard form.

$240\,000 \div (4.8 \times 10^{10})$
Convert 240 000 to standard form
$= \dfrac{2.4 \times 10^5}{4.8 \times 10^{10}} = \dfrac{2.4}{4.8} \times \dfrac{10^5}{10^{10}}$
Divide front numbers and powers separately
$= 0.5 \times 10^{5-10}$ — Subtract the powers (see p.17)
$= 0.5 \times 10^{-5}$
Not in standard form — convert it
$= 5 \times 10^{-1} \times 10^{-5}$
$= 5 \times 10^{-6}$

Adding and Subtracting — a bit trickier

1) Make sure the <u>powers of 10</u> are <u>the same</u> — you'll probably need to rewrite one of them.
2) Add or subtract the <u>front numbers</u>.
3) Convert the answer to <u>standard form</u> if necessary.

EXAMPLE:

Calculate $(9.8 \times 10^4) + (6.6 \times 10^3)$ without using a calculator.
Give your answer in standard form.

$(9.8 \times 10^4) + (6.6 \times 10^3)$

1) <u>Rewrite one number</u> so both powers of 10 are equal: $= (9.8 \times 10^4) + (0.66 \times 10^4)$
2) Now add the <u>front numbers</u>: $= (9.8 + 0.66) \times 10^4$
3) 10.46×10^4 isn't in standard form, so <u>convert it</u>: $= 10.46 \times 10^4 = 1.046 \times 10^5$

To put standard form numbers into your <u>calculator</u>, use the [EXP] or the [×10ˣ] button.
E.g. enter 2.67×10^{15} by pressing [2.67] [EXP] [15] [=] or [2.67] [×10ˣ] [15] [=] .

Or for just £25, you can upgrade to luxury form...

Make sure you understand all the examples on these pages. Then answer these Exam Practice Questions:

Q1 Express 0.854 million and 0.00018 in standard form. [2 marks] (GRADE 4)

Q2 Work out the following without using a calculator. Give your answers in standard form.
a) $(3.2 \times 10^7) \div (1.6 \times 10^{-4})$ [2 marks] b) $(6.7 \times 10^{10}) + (5.8 \times 10^{11})$ [2 marks] (GRADE 5)

Q3 Write $2^{25} \times 5^{27}$ in standard form. [3 marks] (GRADE 7)

Revision Questions for Section One

Well, that wraps up <u>Section One</u> — time to put yourself to the test and find out <u>how much you really know</u>.

- Try these questions and <u>tick off each one</u> when you <u>get it right</u>.
- When you've done <u>all the questions</u> for a topic and are <u>completely happy</u> with it, tick off the topic.

Types of Number, Factors and Multiples (p2-4) ☑

1) What are: a) integers   b) rational numbers   c) prime numbers?
2) Use BODMAS to answer the following questions: a) $7 + 8 \div 2$ b) $7 \div (5 + 9)$ c) $(2 - 5 \times 3)^2$
3) Buns are sold in packs of 6, cheese slices are sold in packs of 16 and hot dogs are sold in packs of 12. Noah wants to buy the same number of each item. What is the smallest number of packs of buns, cheese slices and hot dogs he can buy?
4) Find: a) the HCF of 42 and 28   b) the LCM of 8 and 10
5) a) Write 320 and 880 as products of their prime factors.
   b) Use the prime factorisations to find the LCM and HCF of 320 and 880.

Fractions (p5-6) ☑

You're not allowed to use a calculator for q6-18 and 23-26. Sorry.

6) How do you simplify a fraction?
7) a) Write $\frac{74}{9}$ as a mixed number   b) Write $4\frac{5}{7}$ as an improper fraction
8) What are the rules for multiplying, dividing and adding/subtracting fractions?
9) Calculate: a) $\frac{2}{11} \times \frac{7}{9}$ b) $5\frac{1}{2} \div 1\frac{3}{4}$ c) $\frac{5}{8} - \frac{1}{6}$ d) $3\frac{3}{10} + 4\frac{1}{4}$
10) a) Find $\frac{7}{9}$ of 270 kg.   b) Write 88 as a fraction of 56.
11) Which of $\frac{5}{8}$ and $\frac{7}{10}$ is closer in value to $\frac{3}{4}$?

Fractions, Decimals and Percentages (p7-9) ☑

12) How do you convert: a) a fraction to a decimal?   b) a terminating decimal to a fraction?
13) Write: a) 0.04 as: (i) a fraction (ii) a percentage   b) 65% as: (i) a fraction (ii) a decimal
14) 25 litres of fruit punch is made up of 50% orange juice, $\frac{2}{5}$ lemonade and $\frac{1}{10}$ cranberry juice. How many litres of orange juice, lemonade and cranberry juice are there in the punch?
15) Show that $0.5\dot{1} = \frac{17}{33}$

Rounding, Estimating and Bounds (p10-12) ☑

16) Round 427.963 to: a) 2 d.p.   b) 1 d.p.   c) 2 s.f.   d) 4 s.f.
17) Estimate the value of $(104.6 + 56.8) \div 8.4$
18) Estimate the value of $\sqrt{45}$ to 1 d.p.
19) How do you determine the upper and lower bounds of a rounded and truncated measurement?
20) The volume of water in a jug is given as 2.4 litres to the nearest 100 ml. Find the upper and lower bounds for the volume of the jug. Give your answer as an inequality.
21) A rectangle measures 15.6 m by 8.4 m, to the nearest 0.1 m. Find its maximum possible area.

Standard Form (p13-14) ☑

22) What are the three rules for writing numbers in standard form?
23) Write these numbers in standard form: a) 970 000   b) 3 560 000 000   c) 0.00000275
24) Express 4.56×10^{-3} and 2.7×10^5 as ordinary numbers.
25) Calculate: a) $(3.2 \times 10^6) \div (1.6 \times 10^3)$ b) $(1.75 \times 10^{12}) + (9.89 \times 10^{11})$ Give your answers in standard form.
26) At the start of an experiment, there are 3.1×10^8 bacteria on a petri dish. The number of bacteria doubles every 10 minutes. How many bacteria will there be after 30 minutes?

Algebra Basics

Before you can really get your teeth into <u>algebra</u>, there are some basics you need to get your head around.

Negative Numbers

Negative numbers crop up everywhere so you need to learn these rules for dealing with them:

+	+	makes	+
+	−	makes	−
−	+	makes	−
−	−	makes	+

Use these rules when:

1) <u>Multiplying or dividing</u>.
   e.g. $-2 \times 3 = -6$, $-8 \div -2 = +4$

2) <u>Two signs are together</u>.
   e.g. $x + -y - -z = x - y + z$

Be careful when squaring or cubing. <u>Squaring</u> a negative number gives a <u>positive</u> number, e.g. $(-2)^2 = 4$ but <u>cubing</u> a negative number gives a <u>negative</u> number, e.g. $(-3)^3 = -27$.

Letters Multiplied Together

Watch out for these combinations of letters in algebra that regularly catch people out:

1) abc means $a \times b \times c$.   The ×'s are often left out to make it clearer.

2) gn^2 means $g \times n \times n$.   Note that only the n is squared, not the g as well — e.g. πr^2 means $\pi \times r \times r$.

3) $(gn)^2$ means $g \times g \times n \times n$.   The brackets mean that <u>BOTH</u> letters are squared.

4) $p(q - r)^3$ means $p \times (q - r) \times (q - r) \times (q - r)$.   Only the brackets get cubed.

5) -3^2 is a bit ambiguous.   It should either be written $(-3)^2 = 9$, or $-(3^2) = -9$ (you'd usually take -3^2 to be -9).

Terms

Before you can do anything else with algebra, you must understand what a term is:

A TERM IS A COLLECTION OF NUMBERS, LETTERS AND BRACKETS, ALL MULTIPLIED/DIVIDED TOGETHER

Terms are separated by <u>+ and − signs</u>. Every term has a + or − attached to the <u>front of it</u>.

If there's no sign in front of the first term, it means there's an invisible + sign.

$4xy$ + $5x^2$ − $2y$ + $6y^2$ + 4

'xy' term   'x²' term   'y' term   'y²' term   'number' term

Simplifying or 'Collecting Like Terms'

To <u>simplify</u> an algebraic expression, you combine '<u>like terms</u>' — terms that have the <u>same combination of letters</u> (e.g. all the x terms, all the y terms, all the number terms etc.).

EXAMPLE: Simplify $2x - 4 + 5x + 6$

number terms

Invisible + sign

x-terms

$2x$ -4 $+5x$ $+6$ = $+2x$ $+5x$ -4 $+6$
   = $7x$ $+2$ = $7x + 2$

1) Put <u>bubbles</u> round each term — be sure you capture the <u>+/− sign</u> in front of each.
2) Then you can move the bubbles into the <u>best order</u> so that <u>like terms</u> are together.
3) <u>Combine like terms</u>.

Ahhh algebra, it's as easy as abc, or 2(ab) + c, or something...

Nothing too tricky on this page, but you'll have to simplify in the exam, so here's some practice:

Q1   A rectangle has sides measuring $5x$ cm and $(3y + 1)$ cm.
       Find an expression for its perimeter.   [2 marks]

Powers and Roots

Powers are a very useful <u>shorthand</u>: $2 \times 2 \times 2 \times 2 \times 2 \times 2 \times 2 = 2^7$ ('two to the power 7')

That bit is easy to remember. Unfortunately, there are also <u>ten special rules</u> for powers that you need to learn.

The Seven Easy Rules: (5)

> **Warning:** Rules 1 & 2 <u>don't work</u> for things like $2^3 \times 3^7$, only for <u>powers of the same number</u>.

1) When <u>MULTIPLYING</u>, you <u>ADD THE POWERS</u>.
   e.g. $3^6 \times 3^4 = 3^{6+4} = 3^{10}$, $a^2 \times a^7 = a^{2+7} = a^9$

2) When <u>DIVIDING</u>, you <u>SUBTRACT THE POWERS</u>.
   e.g. $5^4 \div 5^2 = 5^{4-2} = 5^2$, $b^8 \div b^5 = b^{8-5} = b^3$

3) When <u>RAISING one power to another</u>, you <u>MULTIPLY THEM</u>.
   e.g. $(3^2)^4 = 3^{2 \times 4} = 3^8$, $(c^3)^6 = c^{3 \times 6} = c^{18}$

4) $x^1 = x$, <u>ANYTHING</u> to the <u>POWER 1</u> is just <u>ITSELF</u>.
   e.g. $3^1 = 3$, $d \times d^3 = d^1 \times d^3 = d^{1+3} = d^4$

5) $x^0 = 1$, <u>ANYTHING</u> to the <u>POWER 0</u> is just <u>1</u>.
   e.g. $5^0 = 1$, $67^0 = 1$, $e^0 = 1$

6) $1^x = 1$, <u>1 TO ANY POWER</u> is <u>STILL JUST 1</u>.
   e.g. $1^{23} = 1$, $1^{89} = 1$, $1^2 = 1$

7) <u>FRACTIONS</u> — Apply the power to both <u>TOP</u> and <u>BOTTOM</u>.
   e.g. $\left(1\frac{3}{5}\right)^3 = \left(\frac{8}{5}\right)^3 = \frac{8^3}{5^3} = \frac{512}{125}$, $\left(\frac{u}{v}\right)^5 = \frac{u^5}{v^5}$

The Three Tricky Rules: (7)

8) <u>NEGATIVE Powers — Turn it Upside-Down</u>

People have real difficulty remembering this — whenever you see a negative power you need to immediately think: "Aha, that means turn it the other way up and make the power positive".

e.g. $7^{-2} = \frac{1}{7^2} = \frac{1}{49}$, $a^{-4} = \frac{1}{a^4}$, $\left(\frac{3}{5}\right)^{-2} = \left(\frac{5}{3}\right)^{+2} = \frac{5^2}{3^2} = \frac{25}{9}$

9) <u>FRACTIONAL POWERS</u>

> The power $\frac{1}{2}$ means <u>Square Root</u>,
> The power $\frac{1}{3}$ means <u>Cube Root</u>,
> The power $\frac{1}{4}$ means <u>Fourth Root</u> etc.

e.g. $25^{\frac{1}{2}} = \sqrt{25} = 5$
$64^{\frac{1}{3}} = \sqrt[3]{64} = 4$
$81^{\frac{1}{4}} = \sqrt[4]{81} = 3$
$z^{\frac{1}{5}} = \sqrt[5]{z}$

> The one to really watch is when you get a <u>negative fraction</u> like $49^{-\frac{1}{2}}$ — people get mixed up and think that the minus is the square root, and forget to turn it upside down as well.

10) <u>TWO-STAGE FRACTIONAL POWERS</u>

With fractional powers like $64^{\frac{5}{6}}$ always <u>split the fraction</u> into a <u>root</u> and a <u>power</u>, and do them in that order: <u>root first</u>, then <u>power</u>: $(64)^{\frac{1}{6} \times 5} = \left(64^{\frac{1}{6}}\right)^5 = (2)^5 = 32$.

> **EXAMPLE:** Simplify $(3a^2b^4c)^3$
>
> Just deal with each bit separately:
>
> $= (3)^3 \times (a^2)^3 \times (b^4)^3 \times (c)^3$
> $= 27 \times a^{2 \times 3} \times b^{4 \times 3} \times c^3$
> $= 27a^6b^{12}c^3$

> You simplify algebraic fractions using the power rules (though you might not realise it).
>
> So if you had to simplify e.g. $\frac{p^3 q^6}{p^2 q^3}$,
> you'd just cancel using the power rules to get $p^{3-2}q^{6-3} = pq^3$.

Don't let the power go to your head...

Learn all ten exciting rules on this page, then have a go at these Exam Practice Questions.

Q1 Simplify: a) $e^4 \times e^7$ [1 mark]   b) $f^9 \div f^5$ [1 mark] (5)
            c) $(g^6)^{\frac{1}{2}}$ [1 mark]   d) $2h^5j^{-2} \times 3h^2j^4$ [2 marks]

Q2 Evaluate without a calculator:
    a) $625^{\frac{3}{4}}$ [2 marks]   b) $25^{-\frac{1}{2}}$ [2 marks]   c) $\left(\frac{27}{216}\right)^{-\frac{1}{3}}$ [2 marks] (7)

Multiplying Out Brackets

I usually use brackets to make witty comments (I'm very witty), but in algebra they're useful for simplifying things. First of all, you need to know how to expand brackets (multiply them out).

Single Brackets

The main thing to remember when multiplying out brackets is that the thing <u>outside</u> the bracket multiplies <u>each separate term</u> inside the bracket.

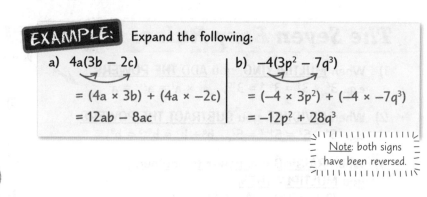

EXAMPLE: Expand the following:

a) $4a(3b - 2c)$

$= (4a \times 3b) + (4a \times -2c)$
$= 12ab - 8ac$

b) $-4(3p^2 - 7q^3)$

$= (-4 \times 3p^2) + (-4 \times -7q^3)$
$= -12p^2 + 28q^3$

Note: both signs have been reversed.

Double Brackets

<u>Double</u> brackets are trickier than single brackets — this time, you have to multiply <u>everything</u> in the <u>first bracket</u> by <u>everything</u> in the <u>second bracket</u>. You'll get <u>4 terms</u>, and usually 2 of them will combine to leave <u>3 terms</u>. There's a handy way to multiply out double brackets — it's called the <u>FOIL method</u>:

<u>F</u>irst — multiply the first term in each bracket together

<u>O</u>utside — multiply the outside terms (i.e. the first term in the first bracket by the second term in the second bracket)

<u>I</u>nside — multiply the inside terms (i.e. the second term in the first bracket by the first term in the second bracket)

<u>L</u>ast — multiply the second term in each bracket together

EXAMPLE: Expand and simplify $(2p - 4)(3p + 1)$

$(2p - 4)(3p + 1) = (2p \times 3p) + (2p \times 1) + (-4 \times 3p) + (-4 \times 1)$
$\qquad = 6p^2 + 2p - 12p - 4$
$\qquad = 6p^2 - 10p - 4$

The two p terms combine together.

Always write out <u>SQUARED BRACKETS</u> as <u>TWO BRACKETS</u> (to avoid mistakes), then multiply out as above.
So $(3x + 5)^2 = (3x + 5)(3x + 5) = 9x^2 + 15x + 15x + 25 = 9x^2 + 30x + 25$.
(DON'T make the mistake of thinking that $(3x + 5)^2 = 9x^2 + 25$ — this is <u>wrong wrong wrong</u>.)

Triple Brackets

1) For <u>three</u> brackets, just multiply <u>two</u> together as above, then multiply the result by the remaining bracket.

It doesn't matter which pair of brackets you multiply together first.

2) If you end up with <u>three terms</u> in one bracket, you <u>won't</u> be able to use FOIL. Instead, you can reduce it to a <u>series</u> of <u>single bracket multiplications</u> — like in the example below.

EXAMPLE: Expand and simplify $(x + 2)(x + 3)(2x - 1)$

$(x + 2)(x + 3)(2x - 1) = (x + 2)(2x^2 + 5x - 3) = x(2x^2 + 5x - 3) + 2(2x^2 + 5x - 3)$
$\qquad = (2x^3 + 5x^2 - 3x) + (4x^2 + 10x - 6)$
$\qquad = 2x^3 + 9x^2 + 7x - 6$

Go forth and multiply out brackets...

You can expand cubed brackets by writing them out as three brackets and expanding as above.

Q1   Expand and simplify: a) $(y + 4)(y - 5)$ [2 marks]   b) $(2p - 3)^2$ [2 marks] (4)

Q2   Expand and simplify: a) $(2t + \sqrt{2})(t - 3\sqrt{2})$ [3 marks]   b) $(x - 2)^3$ [3 marks] (7)

Factorising

Right, now you know how to expand brackets, it's time to put them back in. This is known as <u>factorising</u>.

Factorising — Putting Brackets In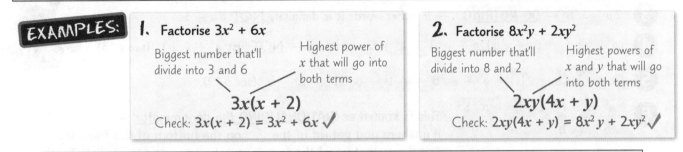

This is the <u>exact reverse</u> of multiplying out brackets. Here's the method to follow:

1) Take out the <u>biggest number</u> that goes into all the terms.
2) <u>For each letter in turn</u>, take out the <u>highest power</u> (e.g. x, x^2 etc.) that will go into EVERY term.
3) Open the bracket and fill in all the bits needed to <u>reproduce each term</u>.
4) <u>Check</u> your answer by <u>multiplying out</u> the bracket and making sure it matches the original expression.

EXAMPLES:

1. Factorise $3x^2 + 6x$

Biggest number that'll divide into 3 and 6

Highest power of x that will go into both terms

$$3x(x + 2)$$

Check: $3x(x + 2) = 3x^2 + 6x$ ✓

2. Factorise $8x^2y + 2xy^2$

Biggest number that'll divide into 8 and 2

Highest powers of x and y that will go into both terms

$$2xy(4x + y)$$

Check: $2xy(4x + y) = 8x^2y + 2xy^2$ ✓

<u>REMEMBER</u>: The bits <u>taken out</u> and put at the front are the <u>common factors</u>. The bits <u>inside the bracket</u> are what's needed to get back to the <u>original terms</u> if you multiply the bracket out again.

D.O.T.S. — The Difference Of Two Squares (6)

The 'difference of two squares' (D.O.T.S. for short) is where you have 'one thing squared' <u>take away</u> 'another thing squared'. There's a quick and easy way to factorise it — just use the rule below:

$$a^2 - b^2 = (a + b)(a - b)$$

EXAMPLE: Factorise:

a) $9p^2 - 16q^2$ Answer: $9p^2 - 16q^2 = (3p + 4q)(3p - 4q)$
Here you had to spot that 9 and 16 are square numbers.

b) $3x^2 - 75y^2$ Answer: $3x^2 - 75y^2 = 3(x^2 - 25y^2) = 3(x + 5y)(x - 5y)$
This time, you had to take out a factor of 3 first.

c) $x^2 - 5$ Answer: $x^2 - 5 = (x + \sqrt{5})(x - \sqrt{5})$
Although 5 isn't a square number, you can write it as $(\sqrt{5})^2$.

Watch out — the difference of two squares can creep into other algebra questions. A popular <u>exam question</u> is to put a difference of two squares on the top or bottom of a <u>fraction</u> and ask you to simplify it. There's more on algebraic fractions on p.30.

EXAMPLE: Simplify $\dfrac{x^2 - 36}{5x + 30}$

The numerator is a difference of two squares.

$$\frac{x^2 - 36}{5x + 30} = \frac{(x + 6)(x - 6)}{5(x + 6)} = \frac{x - 6}{5}$$

Factorise the denominator.

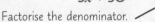

Well, one's green and one's yellow...

As factorising is the reverse process of expanding brackets, you <u>must check</u> your answer by multiplying out the brackets. Make sure you can spot differences of two squares as well — they can be a bit sneaky.

Q1   Factorise $6xy + 15y^2$ [2 marks] (5)
Q2   Factorise $x^2 - 16y^2$ [2 marks] (6)

Q3   Factorise $x^2 - 11$ [2 marks] (7)
Q4   Simplify $\dfrac{6x - 42}{x^2 - 49}$ [3 marks] (7)

Manipulating Surds

<u>Surds</u> are expressions with <u>irrational square roots</u> in them (remember from p.2 that irrational numbers are ones which <u>can't</u> be written as <u>fractions</u>, such as most square roots, cube roots and π).

Manipulating Surds — 6 Rules to Learn (7 GRADE)

There are 6 rules you need to learn for dealing with surds...

1 $\sqrt{a} \times \sqrt{b} = \sqrt{a \times b}$ e.g. $\sqrt{2} \times \sqrt{3} = \sqrt{2 \times 3} = \sqrt{6}$ — also $(\sqrt{b})^2 = \sqrt{b} \times \sqrt{b} = \sqrt{b \times b} = b$

2 $\dfrac{\sqrt{a}}{\sqrt{b}} = \sqrt{\dfrac{a}{b}}$ e.g. $\dfrac{\sqrt{8}}{\sqrt{2}} = \sqrt{\dfrac{8}{2}} = \sqrt{4} = 2$

3 $\sqrt{a} + \sqrt{b}$ — <u>DO NOTHING</u> — in other words it is definitely <u>NOT</u> $\sqrt{a+b}$

4 $(a + \sqrt{b})^2 = (a + \sqrt{b})(a + \sqrt{b}) = a^2 + 2a\sqrt{b} + b$ — <u>NOT</u> just $a^2 + (\sqrt{b})^2$ (see p.18)

5 $(a + \sqrt{b})(a - \sqrt{b}) = a^2 + a\sqrt{b} - a\sqrt{b} - (\sqrt{b})^2 = a^2 - b$ (see p.19).

6 $\dfrac{a}{\sqrt{b}} = \dfrac{a}{\sqrt{b}} \times \dfrac{\sqrt{b}}{\sqrt{b}} = \dfrac{a\sqrt{b}}{b}$ This is known as '<u>RATIONALISING the denominator</u>' — it's where you get rid of the $\sqrt{}$ on the bottom of the fraction. For denominators of the form $a \pm \sqrt{b}$, you always multiply by the denominator but <u>change the sign</u> in front of the root (see example 3 below).

Use the Rules to Simplify Expressions (8 GRADE)

EXAMPLES:

1. Write $\sqrt{300} + \sqrt{48} - 2\sqrt{75}$ in the form $a\sqrt{3}$, where a is an integer.

Write each surd in terms of $\sqrt{3}$: $\sqrt{300} = \sqrt{100 \times 3} = \sqrt{100} \times \sqrt{3} = 10\sqrt{3}$

$\sqrt{48} = \sqrt{16 \times 3} = \sqrt{16} \times \sqrt{3} = 4\sqrt{3}$

$2\sqrt{75} = 2\sqrt{25 \times 3} = 2 \times \sqrt{25} \times \sqrt{3} = 10\sqrt{3}$

Then do the sum (leaving your answer in terms of $\sqrt{3}$):

$\sqrt{300} + \sqrt{48} - 2\sqrt{75} = 10\sqrt{3} + 4\sqrt{3} - 10\sqrt{3} = 4\sqrt{3}$

2. A rectangle with length $4x$ cm and width x cm has an area of 32 cm². Find the exact value of x, giving your answer in its simplest form.

Area of rectangle = length × width = $4x \times x = 4x^2$

So $4x^2 = 32$

$x^2 = 8$

$x = \pm\sqrt{8}$ You can ignore the negative square root (see p.22) as length must be positive.

'Exact value' means you have to leave your answer in surd form, so get $\sqrt{8}$ into its simplest form:

$\sqrt{8} = \sqrt{4 \times 2} = \sqrt{4}\sqrt{2}$

$= 2\sqrt{2}$ So $x = 2\sqrt{2}$

3. Write $\dfrac{3}{2 + \sqrt{5}}$ in the form $a + b\sqrt{5}$, where a and b are integers. (9 GRADE)

To <u>rationalise the denominator</u>, multiply top and bottom by $2 - \sqrt{5}$:

$\dfrac{3}{2 + \sqrt{5}} = \dfrac{3(2 - \sqrt{5})}{(2 + \sqrt{5})(2 - \sqrt{5})}$

$= \dfrac{6 - 3\sqrt{5}}{2^2 - 2\sqrt{5} + 2\sqrt{5} - (\sqrt{5})^2}$

$= \dfrac{6 - 3\sqrt{5}}{4 - 5} = \dfrac{6 - 3\sqrt{5}}{-1} = -6 + 3\sqrt{5}$

(so $a = -6$ and $b = 3$)

Rationalise the denominator? How absurd...

Learn the 6 rules for manipulating surds, then give these Exam Practice Questions a go...

Q1   Simplify $\sqrt{180} + \sqrt{20} + (\sqrt{5})^3$ [3 marks] (8 GRADE)

Q2   Write $\dfrac{2}{2 + \sqrt{3}}$ in the form $a + b\sqrt{3}$, where a and b are integers.   [3 marks] (9 GRADE)

Solving Equations

The basic idea of <u>solving equations</u> is very simple — keep <u>rearranging</u> until you end up with x = number. The two most common methods for <u>rearranging</u> equations are: 1) 'same to both sides' and 2) do the <u>opposite</u> when you cross the '=' We'll use the 'same to both sides' method on these pages.

Rearrange Until You Have x = Number ③

The easiest ones to solve are where you just have a <u>mixture</u> of x's and numbers.

1) First, <u>rearrange</u> the equation so that all the <u>x's</u> are on one side and the <u>numbers</u> are on the other. <u>Combine</u> terms where you can.

2) Then <u>divide</u> both sides by the <u>number multiplying x</u> to find the value of x.

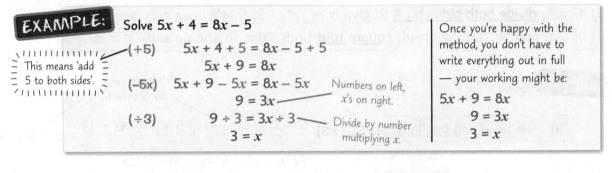

EXAMPLE: Solve $5x + 4 = 8x - 5$

This means 'add 5 to both sides'.

(+5) $5x + 4 + 5 = 8x - 5 + 5$
        $5x + 9 = 8x$
(−5x) $5x + 9 - 5x = 8x - 5x$ Numbers on left, x's on right.
        $9 = 3x$
(÷3) $9 \div 3 = 3x \div 3$ Divide by number multiplying x.
        $3 = x$

Once you're happy with the method, you don't have to write everything out in full — your working might be:

$5x + 9 = 8x$
$9 = 3x$
$3 = x$

Multiply Out Brackets First

If your equation has <u>brackets</u> in it... ④

1) <u>Multiply</u> them out <u>before rearranging</u>.

2) <u>Solve it</u> in the same way as above.

EXAMPLE: Solve $3(3x - 2) = 5x + 10$

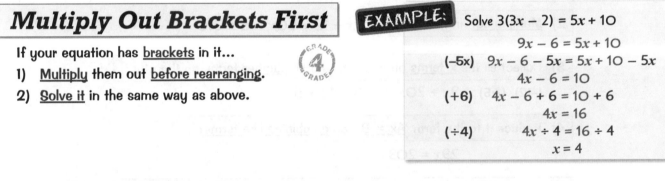

        $9x - 6 = 5x + 10$
(−5x) $9x - 6 - 5x = 5x + 10 - 5x$
        $4x - 6 = 10$
(+6) $4x - 6 + 6 = 10 + 6$
        $4x = 16$
(÷4) $4x \div 4 = 16 \div 4$
        $x = 4$

Get Rid of Fractions (before they take over the world) ⑤

1) <u>Fractions</u> make everything more complicated — so you need to get rid of them <u>before doing anything else</u> (yep, even before multiplying out brackets).

2) To get rid of fractions, multiply <u>every term</u> of the equation by whatever's on the <u>bottom</u> of the fraction. If there are <u>two</u> fractions, you'll need to multiply by <u>both</u> denominators.

EXAMPLES:

1. Solve $\dfrac{x+2}{4} = 4x - 7$

(×4) $\dfrac{4(x+2)}{4} = 4(4x) - 4(7)$

Multiply <u>every term</u> by 4 to get rid of the fraction.

$x + 2 = 16x - 28$
$30 = 15x$ — And solve.
$2 = x$

2. Solve $\dfrac{3x+5}{2} = \dfrac{4x+10}{3}$ Multiply <u>everything</u> by 2 then by 3.

(×2), (×3) $\dfrac{2 \times 3 \times (3x+5)}{2} = \dfrac{2 \times 3 \times (4x+10)}{3}$

And solve.
$3(3x + 5) = 2(4x + 10)$
$9x + 15 = 8x + 20$
$x = 5$

Solving equations — more fun than greasing a seal...

Here's a handy final tip — you can always check your answer by sticking it in both sides of the original equation. They should both give the same number. Now practise what you've learned on these beauts:

Q1   Solve $2x + 5 = 17 - 4x$ [2 marks] ③

Q2   Solve $4(y + 3) = 3y + 16$ [3 marks] ④

Q3   Solve $\dfrac{3x+2}{5} = \dfrac{5x+6}{9}$ [3 marks] ⑤

Solving Equations

Now you know the basics of solving equations, it's time to put it all together into a handy step-by-step method.

Solving Equations Using the 6-Step Method (5)

Here's the method to follow (just ignore any steps that don't apply to your equation):

1) Get rid of any <u>fractions</u>.
2) <u>Multiply out</u> any brackets.
3) Collect all the <u>x-terms</u> on one side and all <u>number terms</u> on the other.
4) Reduce it to the form '<u>Ax = B</u>' (by <u>combining like terms</u>).
5) Finally <u>divide both sides by A</u> to give 'x =   ', and that's your answer.
6) If you had '$x^2 =$ ' instead, <u>square root</u> both sides to end up with 'x = ±   '.

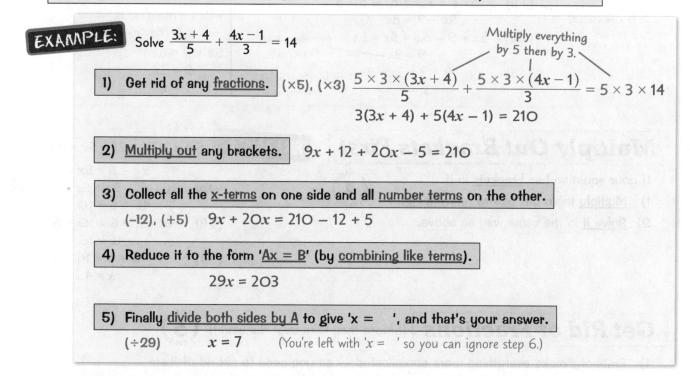

EXAMPLE: Solve $\dfrac{3x+4}{5} + \dfrac{4x-1}{3} = 14$

Multiply everything by 5 then by 3.

1) Get rid of any <u>fractions</u>. (×5), (×3) $\dfrac{5 \times 3 \times (3x+4)}{5} + \dfrac{5 \times 3 \times (4x-1)}{3} = 5 \times 3 \times 14$

$3(3x+4) + 5(4x-1) = 210$

2) <u>Multiply out</u> any brackets. $9x + 12 + 20x - 5 = 210$

3) Collect all the <u>x-terms</u> on one side and all <u>number terms</u> on the other.

(−12), (+5) $9x + 20x = 210 - 12 + 5$

4) Reduce it to the form '<u>Ax = B</u>' (by <u>combining like terms</u>).

$29x = 203$

5) Finally <u>divide both sides by A</u> to give 'x =   ', and that's your answer.

(÷29) $x = 7$ (You're left with 'x =   ' so you can ignore step 6.)

Dealing With Squares (5)

If you're unlucky, you might get an $\underline{x^2}$ in an equation. If this happens, you'll end up with '$x^2 = ...$' at step 5, and then step 6 is to take <u>square roots</u>. There's one very important thing to remember: whenever you take the square root of a number, the answer can be <u>positive</u> or <u>negative</u> (unless there's a reason it can't be −ve).

EXAMPLE: There are 75 tiles on a roof. Each row contains three times the number of tiles as each column. How many tiles are there in one column?

Let the number of tiles in a column be x. Write an equation for the total number of tiles in terms of x.

$3x \times x = 75$
$3x^2 = 75$
(÷3) $x^2 = 25$
($\sqrt{\ }$) $x = \pm 5$

Ignore the negative square root — you can't have a negative number of tiles.

So there are 5 tiles in one column.

You always get a +ve and −ve version of the <u>same number</u> (your calculator only gives the +ve answer). This shows why: $5^2 = 5 \times 5 = 25$ but also $(-5)^2 = (-5) \times (-5) = 25$.

Square Roots? Must be a geomer-tree...

In a lot of exam questions, you'll be given a wordy question and have to set up your own equation. Once you've got your equation, just use the methods from the previous two pages to solve it.

Q1   Solve $2x^2 + 8 = 80$ [2 marks] (5)   Q2   Solve $\dfrac{3x-2}{2} - \dfrac{4x-5}{3} = 2$ [3 marks] (5)

*winner of Best Maths Gag in a Supporting Role, International Algebra Awards 2014

Rearranging Formulas

Rearranging formulas means making one letter the subject, e.g. getting 'y = ' from '2x + z = 3(y + 2p)' — you have to get the subject on its own.

Rearrange Formulas with the Solving Equations Method

Rearranging formulas is remarkably similar to solving equations. The method below is identical to the method for solving equations, except that I've added an extra step at the start.

1) Get rid of any square root signs by squaring both sides.
2) Get rid of any fractions.
3) Multiply out any brackets.
4) Collect all the subject terms on one side and all non-subject terms on the other.
5) Reduce it to the form 'Ax = B' (by combining like terms). You might have to do some factorising here too.
6) Divide both sides by A to give 'x =   '.
7) If you're left with 'x² =   ', square root both sides to get 'x = ±   ' (don't forget the ±).

x is the subject term here. A and B could be numbers or letters (or a mix of both).

What To Do If...

...the Subject Appears in a Fraction

You won't always need to use all 7 steps in the method above — just ignore the ones that don't apply.

EXAMPLE: Make b the subject of the formula $a = \frac{5b + 3}{4}$.

There aren't any square roots, so ignore step 1.

2) Get rid of any fractions. (by multiplying every term by 4, the denominator)

$(\times 4)$ $4a = \frac{4(5b + 3)}{4}$

$4a = 5b + 3$

There aren't any brackets so ignore step 3.

4) Collect all the subject terms on one side and all non-subject terms on the other.

(remember that you're trying to make b the subject) (-3) $5b = 4a - 3$

5) It's now in the form $Ab = B$. (where A = 5 and B = 4a − 3)

6) Divide both sides by 5 to give 'b =   '. $(\div 5)$ $b = \frac{4a - 3}{5}$

b isn't squared, so you don't need step 7.

If I could rearrange my subjects, I'd have maths all day...

Learn the 7 steps for rearranging formulas. Then get rearrangin' with these snazzy practice questions:

Q1 Make q the subject of the formula $p = \frac{q}{7} + 2r$ [2 marks]

Q2 Make v the subject of the formula $a = \frac{v - u}{t}$ [2 marks]

Rearranging Formulas

Carrying straight on from the previous page, now it's time for what to do if...

...there's a Square or Square Root Involved (5)

If the subject appears as a square or in a square root, you'll have to use steps 1 and 7 (not necessarily both).

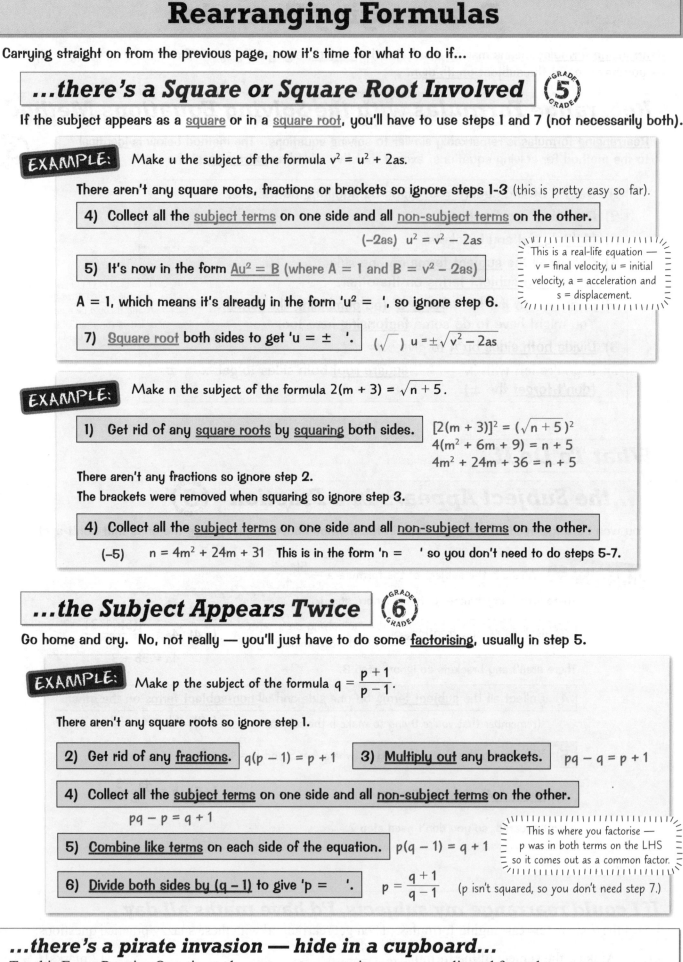

EXAMPLE: Make u the subject of the formula $v^2 = u^2 + 2as$.

There aren't any square roots, fractions or brackets so ignore steps 1-3 (this is pretty easy so far).

4) Collect all the subject terms on one side and all non-subject terms on the other.

$(-2as)$ $u^2 = v^2 - 2as$

This is a real-life equation —
v = final velocity, u = initial
velocity, a = acceleration and
s = displacement.

5) It's now in the form $Au^2 = B$ (where A = 1 and B = $v^2 - 2as$)

A = 1, which means it's already in the form '$u^2 =$ ', so ignore step 6.

7) Square root both sides to get '$u = \pm$ '. $(\sqrt{\ })$ $u = \pm\sqrt{v^2 - 2as}$

EXAMPLE: Make n the subject of the formula $2(m + 3) = \sqrt{n + 5}$.

1) Get rid of any square roots by squaring both sides. $[2(m + 3)]^2 = (\sqrt{n + 5})^2$
$4(m^2 + 6m + 9) = n + 5$
$4m^2 + 24m + 36 = n + 5$

There aren't any fractions so ignore step 2.
The brackets were removed when squaring so ignore step 3.

4) Collect all the subject terms on one side and all non-subject terms on the other.

(-5) $n = 4m^2 + 24m + 31$ This is in the form '$n =$ ' so you don't need to do steps 5-7.

...the Subject Appears Twice (6)

Go home and cry. No, not really — you'll just have to do some factorising, usually in step 5.

EXAMPLE: Make p the subject of the formula $q = \dfrac{p + 1}{p - 1}$.

There aren't any square roots so ignore step 1.

2) Get rid of any fractions. $q(p - 1) = p + 1$ 3) Multiply out any brackets. $pq - q = p + 1$

4) Collect all the subject terms on one side and all non-subject terms on the other.

$pq - p = q + 1$

This is where you factorise —
p was in both terms on the LHS
so it comes out as a common factor.

5) Combine like terms on each side of the equation. $p(q - 1) = q + 1$

6) Divide both sides by (q – 1) to give '$p =$ '. $p = \dfrac{q + 1}{q - 1}$ (p isn't squared, so you don't need step 7.)

...there's a pirate invasion — hide in a cupboard...

Try this Exam Practice Question to have a go at rearranging more complicated formulas...

Q1   Make y the subject of: a) $x = \dfrac{y^2}{4}$ [2 marks] (5)   b) $x = \dfrac{y}{y - z}$ [4 marks] (6)

Factorising Quadratics

There are several ways of solving a quadratic equation as detailed on the following pages.

Factorising a Quadratic (5)

1) 'Factorising a quadratic' means 'putting it into 2 brackets'.
2) The standard format for quadratic equations is: $ax^2 + bx + c = 0$.
3) If $a = 1$, the quadratic is much easier to deal with. E.g. $x^2 + 3x + 2 = 0$
4) As well as factorising a quadratic, you might be asked to solve the equation. This just means finding the values of x that make each bracket 0 (see example below).

See next page for when 'a' is not 1.

Factorising Method when a = 1 (5)

1) **ALWAYS** rearrange into the **STANDARD FORMAT**: $x^2 + bx + c = 0$.

2) Write down the **TWO BRACKETS** with the x's in: (x   )(x   ) = 0.

3) Then find 2 numbers that **MULTIPLY to give 'c'** (the end number) but also **ADD/SUBTRACT to give 'b'** (the coefficient of x).

Ignore any minus signs at this stage.

4) Fill in the +/− signs and make sure they work out properly.

5) As an **ESSENTIAL CHECK**, expand the brackets to make sure they give the original equation.

6) Finally, **SOLVE THE EQUATION** by setting each bracket equal to 0.

You only need to do step 6) if the question asks you to solve the equation — if it just tells you to factorise, you can stop at step 5).

EXAMPLE: Solve $x^2 − x = 12$.

1) $x^2 − x − 12 = 0$ ← 1) Rearrange into the standard format.

2) $(x$ $)(x$ $) = 0$ ← 2) Write down the initial brackets.

3) | | |
|---|---|
| 1 × 12 Add/subtract to give: | 13 or 11 |
| 2 × 6 Add/subtract to give: | 8 or 4 |
| 3 × 4 Add/subtract to give: | 7 or ① |

3) Find the right pairs of numbers that multiply to give c (= 12), and add or subtract to give b (= 1) (remember, we're ignoring the +/− signs for now).

$(x$ $3)(x$ $4) = 0$ This is what we want.

4) $(x + 3)(x − 4) = 0$ ← 4) Now fill in the +/− signs so that 3 and 4 add/subtract to give −1 (= b).

5) Check:
$(x + 3)(x − 4) = x^2 − 4x + 3x − 12$
$= x^2 − x − 12$ ✓

5) **ESSENTIAL check** — **EXPAND the brackets** to make sure they give the original expression.

But we're not finished yet — we've only factorised it, we still need to...

6) $(x + 3) = 0 \Rightarrow x = −3$
$(x − 4) = 0 \Rightarrow x = 4$

6) **SOLVE THE EQUATION** by setting each bracket equal to 0.

Bring me a biscuit or I'll factorise your quadratic...

Handy tip: to help you work out which signs you need, look at c. If c is positive, the signs will be the same (both positive or both negative), but if c is negative the signs will be different (one positive and one negative).

Q1   Factorise $x^2 + 2x − 15$ [2 marks] (5)   Q2   Solve $x^2 − 9x + 20 = 0$ [3 marks] (5)

Factorising Quadratics

So far so good. It gets a bit more complicated when 'a' isn't 1, but it's all good fun, right? Right?
Well, I think it's fun anyway.

When 'a' is Not 1 (7)

The basic method is still the same but it's <u>a bit messier</u> — the initial brackets are <u>different</u> as the first terms in
each bracket have to multiply to give '<u>a</u>'. This means finding the <u>other</u> numbers to go in the brackets is harder
as there are more <u>combinations</u> to try. The best way to get to grips with it is to have a look at an <u>example</u>.

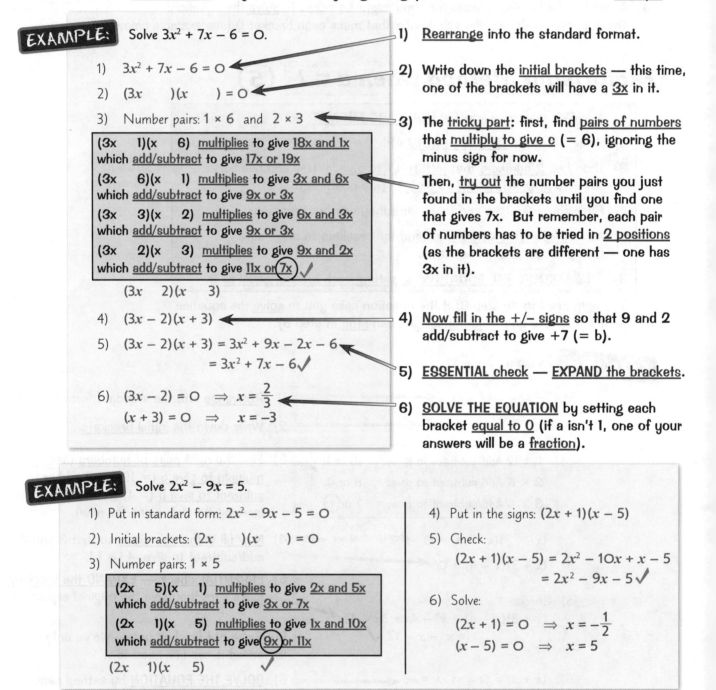

EXAMPLE: Solve $3x^2 + 7x - 6 = 0$.

1) $3x^2 + 7x - 6 = 0$

2) $(3x\quad)(x\quad) = 0$

3) Number pairs: 1×6 and 2×3

> $(3x\quad 1)(x\quad 6)$ multiplies to give $18x$ and $1x$
> which add/subtract to give $17x$ or $19x$
>
> $(3x\quad 6)(x\quad 1)$ multiplies to give $3x$ and $6x$
> which add/subtract to give $9x$ or $3x$
>
> $(3x\quad 3)(x\quad 2)$ multiplies to give $6x$ and $3x$
> which add/subtract to give $9x$ or $3x$
>
> $(3x\quad 2)(x\quad 3)$ multiplies to give $9x$ and $2x$
> which add/subtract to give $11x$ or $7x$ ✓

$(3x\quad 2)(x\quad 3)$

4) $(3x - 2)(x + 3)$

5) $(3x - 2)(x + 3) = 3x^2 + 9x - 2x - 6$
$= 3x^2 + 7x - 6$ ✓

6) $(3x - 2) = 0 \Rightarrow x = \dfrac{2}{3}$
$(x + 3) = 0 \Rightarrow x = -3$

1) <u>Rearrange</u> into the standard format.

2) Write down the <u>initial brackets</u> — this time,
one of the brackets will have a <u>3x</u> in it.

3) The <u>tricky part</u>: first, find <u>pairs of numbers</u>
that <u>multiply to give c</u> (= 6), ignoring the
minus sign for now.

Then, <u>try out</u> the number pairs you just
found in the brackets until you find one
that gives 7x. But remember, each pair
of numbers has to be tried in <u>2 positions</u>
(as the brackets are different — one has
3x in it).

4) <u>Now fill in the +/– signs</u> so that 9 and 2
add/subtract to give +7 (= b).

5) <u>ESSENTIAL check</u> — <u>EXPAND the brackets</u>.

6) <u>SOLVE THE EQUATION</u> by setting each
bracket <u>equal to 0</u> (if a isn't 1, one of your
answers will be a <u>fraction</u>).

EXAMPLE: Solve $2x^2 - 9x = 5$.

1) Put in standard form: $2x^2 - 9x - 5 = 0$

2) Initial brackets: $(2x\quad)(x\quad) = 0$

3) Number pairs: 1×5

> $(2x\quad 5)(x\quad 1)$ multiplies to give $2x$ and $5x$
> which add/subtract to give $3x$ or $7x$
>
> $(2x\quad 1)(x\quad 5)$ multiplies to give $1x$ and $10x$
> which add/subtract to give $9x$ or $11x$

$(2x\quad 1)(x\quad 5)$ ✓

4) Put in the signs: $(2x + 1)(x - 5)$

5) Check:
$(2x + 1)(x - 5) = 2x^2 - 10x + x - 5$
$= 2x^2 - 9x - 5$ ✓

6) Solve:
$(2x + 1) = 0 \Rightarrow x = -\dfrac{1}{2}$
$(x - 5) = 0 \Rightarrow x = 5$

It's not scary — just think of it as brackets giving algebra a hug...

Learn the step-by-step method above, then have a go at these nice practice questions.

Q1 Factorise $2x^2 - 5x - 12$ [2 marks] (7) Q2 Solve $3x^2 + 10x - 8 = 0$ [3 marks] (7)

Q3 Factorise $3x^2 + 32x + 20$ [2 marks] (7) Q4 Solve $5x^2 - 13x = 6$ [3 marks] (7)

The Quadratic Formula

The solutions to ANY quadratic equation $ax^2 + bx + c = 0$ are given by this formula:

$$x = \frac{-b \pm \sqrt{b^2 - 4ac}}{2a}$$

<u>LEARN THIS FORMULA</u> — and <u>how to use it</u>. Using it isn't that hard, but there are a few pitfalls — so <u>TAKE HEED of these crucial details</u>:

Quadratic Formula — Five Crucial Details

1) Take it nice and slowly — always write it down in stages as you go.

2) WHENEVER YOU GET A MINUS SIGN, <u>THE ALARM BELLS SHOULD ALWAYS RING!</u>

> If either 'a' or 'c' is negative, the -4ac effectively becomes +4ac, so watch out. Also, be careful if b is negative, as -b will be positive.

3) Remember it's '<u>2a</u>' on the bottom line, not just 'a' — and you <u>divide ALL of the top line by 2a</u>.

4) The $\pm$ sign means you end up with <u>two solutions</u> (by replacing it in the final step with '+' and '−').

5) If you get a <u>negative</u> number inside your square root, go back and <u>check your working</u>. Some quadratics do have a negative value in the square root, but they won't come up at GCSE.

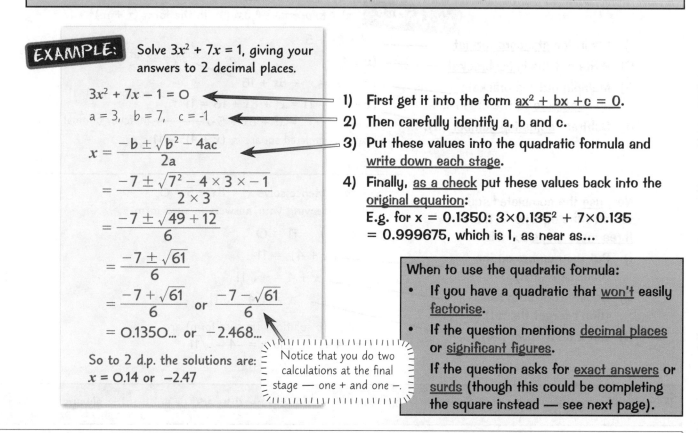

EXAMPLE: Solve $3x^2 + 7x = 1$, giving your answers to 2 decimal places.

$3x^2 + 7x - 1 = 0$

$a = 3$, $b = 7$, $c = -1$

$x = \dfrac{-b \pm \sqrt{b^2 - 4ac}}{2a}$

$= \dfrac{-7 \pm \sqrt{7^2 - 4 \times 3 \times -1}}{2 \times 3}$

$= \dfrac{-7 \pm \sqrt{49 + 12}}{6}$

$= \dfrac{-7 \pm \sqrt{61}}{6}$

$= \dfrac{-7 + \sqrt{61}}{6}$ or $\dfrac{-7 - \sqrt{61}}{6}$

$= 0.1350...$ or $-2.468...$

So to 2 d.p. the solutions are:
$x = 0.14$ or -2.47

> Notice that you do two calculations at the final stage — one + and one −.

1) First get it into the form <u>$ax^2 + bx + c = 0$</u>.

2) Then carefully identify a, b and c.

3) Put these values into the quadratic formula and <u>write down each stage</u>.

4) Finally, <u>as a check</u> put these values back into the <u>original equation</u>:
E.g. for x = 0.1350: $3 \times 0.135^2 + 7 \times 0.135$
$= 0.999675$, which is 1, as near as...

When to use the quadratic formula:

- If you have a quadratic that <u>won't</u> easily <u>factorise</u>.

- If the question mentions <u>decimal places</u> or <u>significant figures</u>.

- If the question asks for <u>exact answers</u> or <u>surds</u> (though this could be completing the square instead — see next page).

Enough number crunches? Now it's time to work on your quads...

You might have to do a bit of fancy rearranging to get your quadratic into the form $ax^2 + bx + c$.
In Q2 below, it doesn't even look like a quadratic until you start rearranging it and get rid of the fraction.

Q1 Find $x^2 + 10x - 4 = 0$, giving your answers to 2 decimal places. [3 marks]

Q2 Find the exact solutions of $2x + \dfrac{3}{x - 2} = -2$. [4 marks]

Completing the Square

There's just one more method to learn for solving quadratics — and it's a bit of a nasty one.
It's called 'completing the square', and takes a bit to get your head round it.

Solving Quadratics by 'Completing the Square' (8)

To 'complete the square' you have to:

    1) Write down a <u>SQUARED</u> bracket, and then   2) Stick a number on the end to '<u>COMPLETE</u>' it.

$$x^2 + 12x - 5 = (x + 6)^2 - 41$$

                     The SQUARE...   ...COMPLETED

It's not that bad if you learn all the steps — some of them aren't all that obvious.

1) As always, <u>REARRANGE THE QUADRATIC INTO THE STANDARD FORMAT</u>: $ax^2 + bx + c$
(the rest of this method is for a = 1).

2) <u>WRITE OUT THE INITIAL BRACKET</u>: $(x + \frac{b}{2})^2$ — just divide the value of b by 2.

3) <u>MULTIPLY OUT THE BRACKETS</u> and <u>COMPARE TO THE ORIGINAL</u>
to find what you need to add or subtract to complete the square.

If a isn't 1, you have to divide through by 'a' or take out a factor of 'a' at the start — see next page.

4) Add or subtract the <u>ADJUSTING NUMBER</u> to make it <u>MATCH THE ORIGINAL</u>.

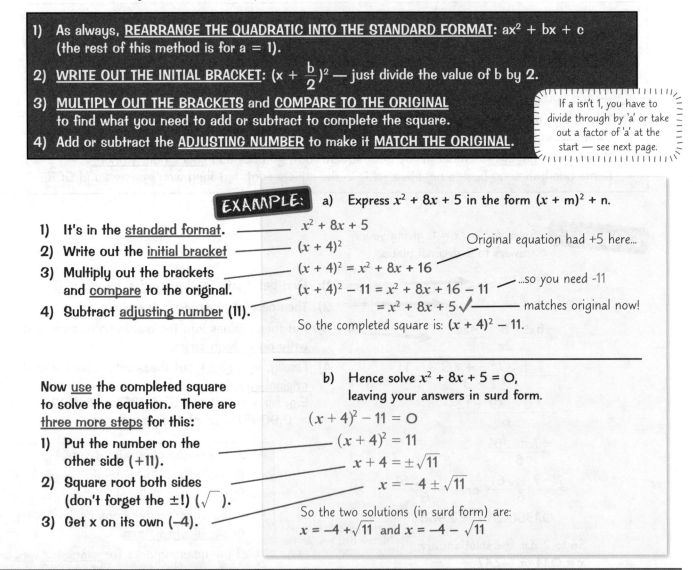

EXAMPLE: a)   Express $x^2 + 8x + 5$ in the form $(x + m)^2 + n$.

1) It's in the <u>standard format</u>. —— $x^2 + 8x + 5$

2) Write out the <u>initial bracket</u> —— $(x + 4)^2$ *Original equation had +5 here...*

3) Multiply out the brackets
and <u>compare</u> to the original. —— $(x + 4)^2 = x^2 + 8x + 16$ *...so you need -11*

        $(x + 4)^2 - 11 = x^2 + 8x + 16 - 11$

4) Subtract <u>adjusting number</u> (11). $= x^2 + 8x + 5$ ✓ —— matches original now!

So the completed square is: $(x + 4)^2 - 11$.

Now <u>use</u> the completed square to solve the equation. There are <u>three more steps</u> for this:

   b)   Hence solve $x^2 + 8x + 5 = 0$,
       leaving your answers in surd form.

1) Put the number on the other side (+11). —— $(x + 4)^2 - 11 = 0$

     $(x + 4)^2 = 11$

2) Square root both sides (don't forget the ±!) ($\sqrt{\ }$). —— $x + 4 = \pm\sqrt{11}$

3) Get x on its own (−4). —— $x = -4 \pm \sqrt{11}$

So the two solutions (in surd form) are:
$x = -4 + \sqrt{11}$ and $x = -4 - \sqrt{11}$

If you really don't like steps 3-4, just remember that the value you need to add or subtract is <u>always</u> $c - \left(\frac{b}{2}\right)^2$.

But if a square's not complete, is it really a square...?

Go over this carefully, 'cos it's pretty gosh darn confusing at first, then try these Exam Practice Questions.

Q1   Write $x^2 - 12x + 23$ in the form $(x + p)^2 + q$.   [3 marks] (8)

Q2   Solve $x^2 + 10x + 7 = 0$, by first writing it in the form $(x + m)^2 + n = 0$.
       Give your answers as simplified surds.   [5 marks] (8)

Completing the Square

If you're a fan of <u>completing the square</u>, good news — there's another page on it here.
If you're not a fan of completing the square, bad news — there's another page on it here.

Completing the Square When 'a' Isn't 1

If 'a' isn't 1, completing the square is a bit trickier. You follow the <u>same method</u> as on the previous page, but you have to take out a <u>factor of 'a'</u> from the x^2 and x-terms before you start (which often means you end up with awkward <u>fractions</u>). This time, the number in the brackets is $\frac{b}{2a}$.

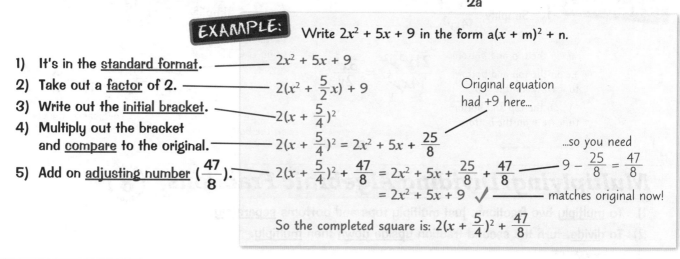

EXAMPLE: Write $2x^2 + 5x + 9$ in the form $a(x + m)^2 + n$.

1) It's in the <u>standard format</u>. $\longrightarrow$ $2x^2 + 5x + 9$

2) Take out a <u>factor</u> of 2. $\longrightarrow$ $2(x^2 + \frac{5}{2}x) + 9$

3) Write out the <u>initial bracket</u>. $\longrightarrow$ $2(x + \frac{5}{4})^2$

4) Multiply out the bracket and <u>compare</u> to the original. $\longrightarrow$ $2(x + \frac{5}{4})^2 = 2x^2 + 5x + \frac{25}{8}$

5) Add on <u>adjusting number</u> ($\frac{47}{8}$). $\longrightarrow$ $2(x + \frac{5}{4})^2 + \frac{47}{8} = 2x^2 + 5x + \frac{25}{8} + \frac{47}{8}$

$$= 2x^2 + 5x + 9 \checkmark \text{ —— matches original now!}$$

Original equation had +9 here...

...so you need $9 - \frac{25}{8} = \frac{47}{8}$

So the completed square is: $2(x + \frac{5}{4})^2 + \frac{47}{8}$

The Completed Square Helps You Sketch the Graph

There's more about <u>sketching</u> quadratic graphs on p.48, but you can use the <u>completed square</u> to work out key details about the graph — like the <u>turning point</u> (maximum or minimum) and whether it <u>crosses</u> the x-axis.

1) For a <u>positive</u> quadratic (where the x^2 coefficient is positive), the <u>adjusting number</u> tells you the <u>minimum</u> y-value of the graph. If the completed square is $a(x + m)^2 + n$, this minimum y-value will occur when the brackets are equal to 0 (because the bit in brackets is squared, so is never negative) — i.e. when $x = -m$.

2) The <u>solutions</u> to the equation tell you where the graph <u>crosses</u> the <u>x-axis</u>. If the adjusting number is <u>positive</u>, the graph will <u>never</u> cross the x-axis as it will always be greater than 0 (this means that the quadratic has <u>no real roots</u>).

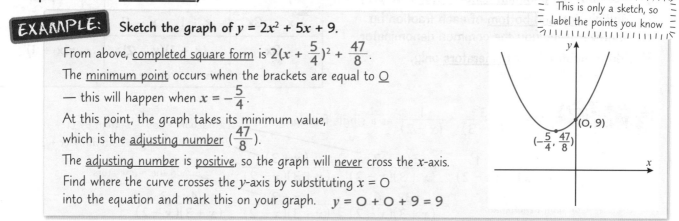

EXAMPLE: Sketch the graph of $y = 2x^2 + 5x + 9$.

From above, <u>completed square form</u> is $2(x + \frac{5}{4})^2 + \frac{47}{8}$.

The <u>minimum point</u> occurs when the brackets are equal to <u>0</u> — this will happen when $x = -\frac{5}{4}$.

At this point, the graph takes its minimum value, which is the <u>adjusting number</u> ($\frac{47}{8}$).

The <u>adjusting number</u> is <u>positive</u>, so the graph will <u>never</u> cross the x-axis.

Find where the curve crosses the y-axis by substituting $x = 0$ into the equation and mark this on your graph. $y = 0 + 0 + 9 = 9$

This is only a sketch, so label the points you know

$(0, 9)$

$(-\frac{5}{4}, \frac{47}{8})$

Complete the following square:

I'm not going to lie, this page was rather challenging (I got a bit confused myself). Be careful taking out the factor of a — you only do it for the first two terms. Take care with your fractions too.

Q1   a) Write $2x^2 + 3x - 5$ in the form $a(x + b)^2 + c$.   [4 marks]

     b) Hence solve $2x^2 + 3x - 5 = 0$.   [2 marks]

     c) Use your answer to part a) to find the coordinates of the minimum point of the graph of $y = 2x^2 + 3x - 5$.   [1 mark]

Algebraic Fractions

Unfortunately, fractions aren't limited to numbers — you can get <u>algebraic fractions</u> too.
Fortunately, everything you learnt about fractions on p.5-6 can be applied to algebraic fractions as well.

Simplifying Algebraic Fractions (6)

You can <u>simplify</u> algebraic fractions by <u>cancelling</u> terms on the top and bottom — just deal with each <u>letter</u> individually and cancel as much as you can. You might have to <u>factorise</u> first (see pages 19 and 25-26).

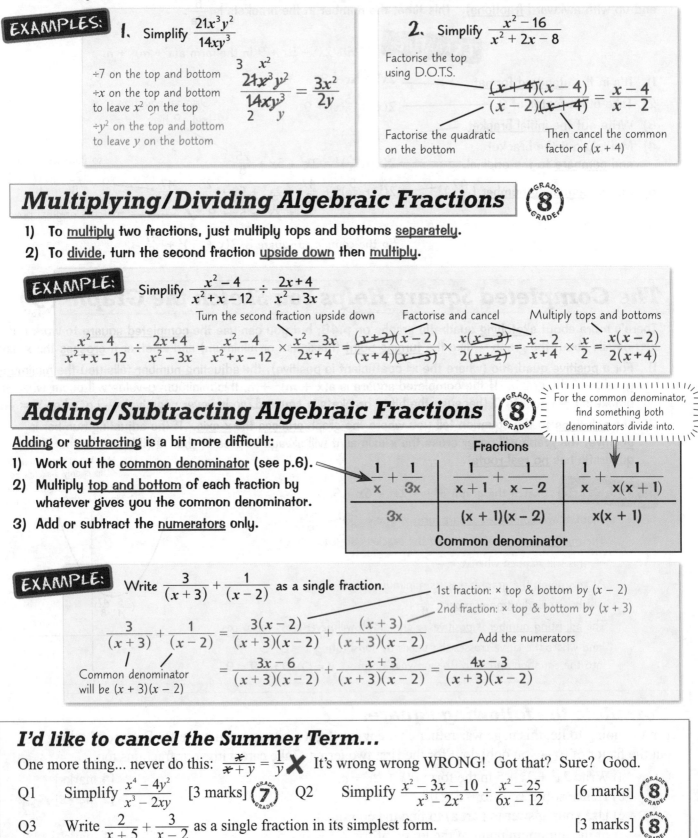

EXAMPLES:

1. Simplify $\dfrac{21x^3y^2}{14xy^3}$

÷7 on the top and bottom
÷x on the top and bottom to leave x^2 on the top
÷y^2 on the top and bottom to leave y on the bottom

$$\frac{21x^3y^2}{14xy^3} = \frac{3x^2}{2y}$$

2. Simplify $\dfrac{x^2-16}{x^2+2x-8}$

Factorise the top using D.O.T.S.

$$\frac{(x+4)(x-4)}{(x-2)(x+4)} = \frac{x-4}{x-2}$$

Factorise the quadratic on the bottom

Then cancel the common factor of $(x+4)$

Multiplying/Dividing Algebraic Fractions (8)

1) To <u>multiply</u> two fractions, just multiply tops and bottoms <u>separately</u>.

2) To <u>divide</u>, turn the second fraction <u>upside down</u> then <u>multiply</u>.

EXAMPLE: Simplify $\dfrac{x^2-4}{x^2+x-12} \div \dfrac{2x+4}{x^2-3x}$

Turn the second fraction upside down   Factorise and cancel   Multiply tops and bottoms

$$\frac{x^2-4}{x^2+x-12} \div \frac{2x+4}{x^2-3x} = \frac{x^2-4}{x^2+x-12} \times \frac{x^2-3x}{2x+4} = \frac{(x+2)(x-2)}{(x+4)(x-3)} \times \frac{x(x-3)}{2(x+2)} = \frac{x-2}{x+4} \times \frac{x}{2} = \frac{x(x-2)}{2(x+4)}$$

Adding/Subtracting Algebraic Fractions (8)

Adding or subtracting is a bit more difficult:

1) Work out the <u>common denominator</u> (see p.6).

2) Multiply <u>top and bottom</u> of each fraction by whatever gives you the common denominator.

3) Add or subtract the <u>numerators</u> only.

For the common denominator, find something both denominators divide into.

Fractions		
$\dfrac{1}{x}+\dfrac{1}{3x}$	$\dfrac{1}{x+1}+\dfrac{1}{x-2}$	$\dfrac{1}{x}+\dfrac{1}{x(x+1)}$
$3x$	$(x+1)(x-2)$	$x(x+1)$
Common denominator		

EXAMPLE: Write $\dfrac{3}{(x+3)} + \dfrac{1}{(x-2)}$ as a single fraction.

1st fraction: × top & bottom by $(x-2)$
2nd fraction: × top & bottom by $(x+3)$

$$\frac{3}{(x+3)} + \frac{1}{(x-2)} = \frac{3(x-2)}{(x+3)(x-2)} + \frac{(x+3)}{(x+3)(x-2)}$$

Common denominator will be $(x+3)(x-2)$

Add the numerators

$$= \frac{3x-6}{(x+3)(x-2)} + \frac{x+3}{(x+3)(x-2)} = \frac{4x-3}{(x+3)(x-2)}$$

I'd like to cancel the Summer Term...

One more thing... never do this: $\dfrac{x}{x+y} = \dfrac{1}{y}$ ✗ It's wrong wrong WRONG! Got that? Sure? Good.

Q1   Simplify $\dfrac{x^4-4y^2}{x^3-2xy}$ [3 marks] (7)   Q2   Simplify $\dfrac{x^2-3x-10}{x^3-2x^2} \div \dfrac{x^2-25}{6x-12}$ [6 marks] (8)

Q3   Write $\dfrac{2}{x+5} + \dfrac{3}{x-2}$ as a single fraction in its simplest form.   [3 marks] (8)

Sequences

You might be asked to "find an <u>expression</u> for the <u>nth term</u> of a sequence" — this is just a formula with n in, like 5n – 3. It gives you <u>every term in a sequence</u> when you put in different values for n.

Finding the nth Term of a Linear Sequence (GRADE 4)

This method works for <u>linear sequences</u> — ones with a <u>common difference</u> (where the terms <u>increase</u> or <u>decrease</u> by the <u>same amount</u> each time). Linear sequences are also known as <u>arithmetic sequences</u>.

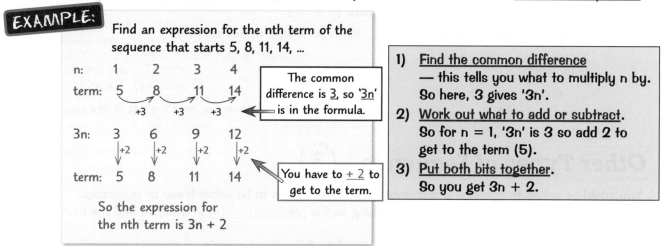

EXAMPLE:

Find an expression for the nth term of the sequence that starts 5, 8, 11, 14, ...

n:	1	2	3	4
term:	5	8	11	14

+3 +3 +3

The common difference is <u>3</u>, so '<u>3n</u>' is in the formula.

3n:	3	6	9	12
	+2	+2	+2	+2
term:	5	8	11	14

You have to <u>+ 2</u> to get to the term.

So the expression for the nth term is 3n + 2

1) <u>Find the common difference</u> — this tells you what to multiply n by. So here, 3 gives '<u>3n</u>'.
2) <u>Work out what to add or subtract</u>. So for n = 1, '3n' is 3 so add 2 to get to the term (5).
3) <u>Put both bits together</u>. So you get 3n + 2.

Always <u>check</u> your expression by putting the first few values of n back in, e.g. putting n = 1 into 3n + 2 gives 5, n = 2 gives 8, etc. which is the <u>original sequence</u> you were given — hooray!

Finding the nth Term of a Quadratic Sequence (GRADE 7)

A <u>quadratic sequence</u> has an n^2 term — the <u>difference</u> between the terms <u>changes</u> as you go through the sequence, but the <u>difference</u> between the <u>differences</u> is the <u>same</u> each time.

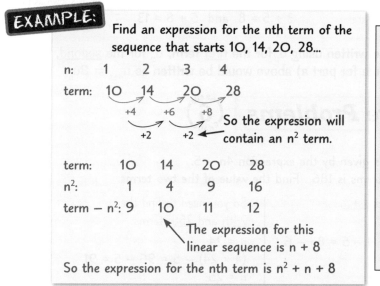

EXAMPLE:

Find an expression for the nth term of the sequence that starts 10, 14, 20, 28...

n:	1	2	3	4
term:	10	14	20	28

+4 +6 +8

+2 +2

So the expression will contain an n^2 term.

term:	10	14	20	28
n^2:	1	4	9	16
term – n^2:	9	10	11	12

The expression for this linear sequence is n + 8

So the expression for the nth term is $n^2 + n + 8$

1) Find the <u>difference</u> between each pair of terms.
2) The difference is <u>changing</u>, so work out the difference between the <u>differences</u>.
3) <u>Divide</u> this value by <u>2</u> — this gives the coefficient of the n^2 term (here it's 2 ÷ 2 = 1).
4) <u>Subtract</u> the n^2 term from each term in the sequence. This will give you a <u>linear sequence</u>.
5) Find the <u>rule</u> for the nth term of the linear sequence (see above) and <u>add</u> this on to the n^2 term.

Again, make sure you <u>check</u> your expression by putting the first few values of n back in — so n = 1 gives $1^2 + 1 + 8 = 10$, n = 2 gives $2^2 + 2 + 8 = 14$ and so on.

It's our differences that make us unique (or linear, or quadratic)...

If you have to use your expression to find a term, just replace *n* with the number of the term.

Q1   Find an expression for the *n*th term of the linear sequence 2, 9, 16, 23, ...   [2 marks] (GRADE 4)

Q2   A quadratic sequence starts 6, 10, 18, 30. Find an expression for the *n*th term.   [4 marks] (GRADE 7)

Sequences

Now you know how to find the nth terms of linear and quadratic sequences, it's time to use your skills to solve problems involving sequences. Oh what fun.

Deciding if a Term is in a Sequence

You might be given the nth term and asked if a certain value is in the sequence. The trick here is to set the expression equal to that value and solve to find n. If n is a whole number, the value is in the sequence.

> **EXAMPLE:** The nth term of a sequence is given by $n^2 - 2$.
>
> **a) Find the 6th term in the sequence.**
>
> This is dead easy — just put $n = 6$ into the expression:
>
> $6^2 - 2 = 36 - 2$
> $= 34$
>
> **b) Is 45 a term in this sequence?**
>
> Set it equal to 45... $n^2 - 2 = 45$
> $n^2 = 47$ ...and solve for n.
> $n = \sqrt{47} = 6.8556...$
>
> n is not a whole number, so 45 is not in the sequence.
>
> *Have a look at p.21-22 for more on solving equations.*

Other Types of Sequence (3)

You could be asked to continue a sequence that doesn't seem to be either linear or quadratic. These sequences usually involve doing something to the previous term(s) in order to find the next one.

> **EXAMPLE:** Find the next two terms in each of the following sequences.
>
> **a) 0.2, 0.6, 1.8, 5.4, 16.2...**
>
> 1) This is an example of a geometric progression — there is a common ratio (where you multiply or divide by the same number each time).
>
> Common Ratio $= 0.6 \div 0.2 = 3$
>
> 2) So the next two terms are:
>
> $16.2 \times 3 = 48.6$ and $48.6 \times 3 = 145.8$
>
> **b) 1, 1, 2, 3, 5...**
>
> The rule for this sequence is 'add together the two previous terms', so the next two terms are:
>
> $3 + 5 = 8$ and $5 + 8 = 13$
>
> *This is known as the Fibonacci sequence.*

You might sometimes see sequences like these written using u_1 for the first term, u_2 for the second, u_n for the nth term. Using this notation, the rule for part a) above would be written as $u_{n+1} = 3u_n$.

Using Sequences to Solve Problems (6)

> **EXAMPLE:** The nth term of a sequence is given by the expression $4n - 5$.
> The sum of two consecutive terms is 186. Find the value of the two terms.
>
> Call the two terms you're looking for n and $n + 1$.
> Then their sum is:
>
> $4n - 5 + 4(n + 1) - 5 = 4n - 5 + 4n + 4 - 5 = 8n - 6$
>
> This is equal to 186, so solve the equation:
>
> $8n - 6 = 186$
> $8n = 192$
> $n = 24$
>
> So you need to find the 24th and 25th terms:
>
> $n = 24$:
> $(4 \times 24) - 5 = 96 - 5 = 91$
> $n = 25$:
> $(4 \times 25) - 5 = 100 - 5 = 95$

If I've told you n times, I've told you n + 1 times — learn this page...

There's no limit to the type of sequences you might be given, so just work out the pattern for each one.

Q1 A linear sequence has common difference of 8. Three consecutive terms in the sequence are added together to give a total of 126. Find the three terms. **[4 marks]** (6)

Section Two — Algebra

Inequalities

...y look. Once you've learned the tricks involved, most of the algebra ...ns (have a look back at p.21-22 if you need a reminder).

...bols (Grade 3)

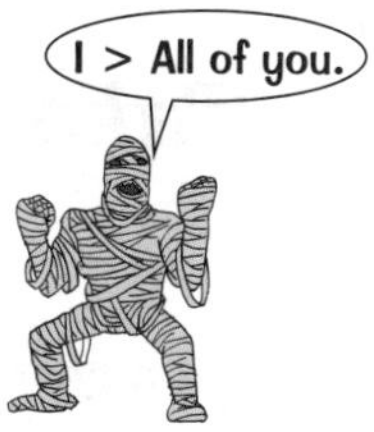
I > All of you.

...er than' $\geq$ means 'Greater than or equal to'
...than' $\leq$ means 'Less than or equal to'

...alities (Grade 5)

...solve them just like regular equations but WITH ONE BIG EXCEPTION:

...DE by a NEGATIVE NUMBER, you must FLIP THE INEQUALITY SIGN.

...such that $-4 < x \leq 3$.
...sible values of x.
...f the inequality is telling you:
...: is greater than -4',
...s less than or equal to 3'.
...he values that x can take.
...ust +ve or −ve whole numbers)
...-1, 0, 1, 2, 3

2. Solve $6x + 7 > x + 22$.

Just solve it like an equation:

(−7) $6x + 7 - 7 > x + 22 - 7$
$6x > x + 15$
(−x) $6x - x > x + 15 - x$
$5x > 15$
(÷5) $5x \div 5 > 15 \div 5$
$x > 3$

...5.
...there are two inequality signs —
...each bit of the inequality:
...$3 \leq 5 - 3$
...4×2

4. Solve $9 - 2x > 15$.

Again, solve it like an equation:

(−9) $9 - 2x - 9 > 15 - 9$
$-2x > 6$
(÷−2) $-2x \div -2 < 6 \div -2$
$x < -3$

The > has turned into a <, because we divided by a negative number.

...ualities on Number Lines (Grade 4)

...e is dead easy — all you have to remember is that you use ...coloured-in circle (●) for $\geq$ or $\leq$.

...$-4 < x \leq 3$ on a number line.

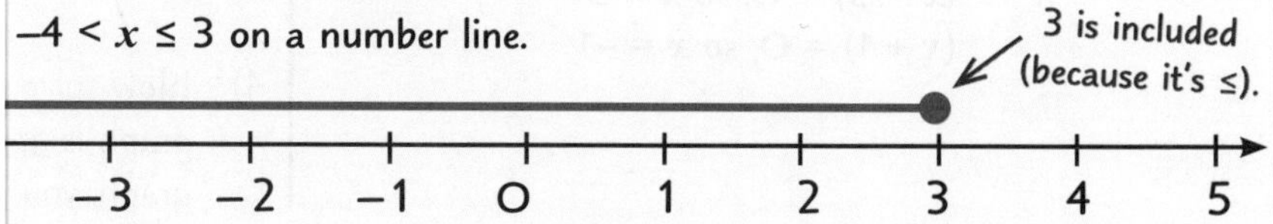
3 is included (because it's ≤).
−3
−2
−1
0
1
2
3
4
5

...lity sign — how rude...

...n right, pop in a value for x and check the inequality's true.

... [2 marks] b) $6 - 4x \geq 18$ [2 marks] (Grade 5)

Q2 Solve the inequality $-8 \leq 5x + 2 \leq 22$ and represent the solution on a number line. [3 marks] (Grade 5)

Inequalities

Quadratic inequalities are a bit tricky — you have to remember that there are <u>two solutions</u> (just like quadratic equations), so you might end up with a solution in <u>two separate bits</u>, or an <u>enclosed region</u>.

Take Care with Quadratic Inequalities (8)

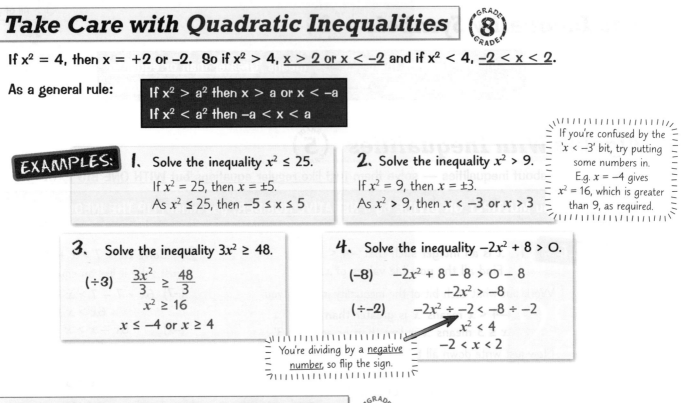

If $x^2 = 4$, then $x = +2$ or -2. So if $x^2 > 4$, <u>$x > 2$ or $x < -2$</u> and if $x^2 < 4$, <u>$-2 < x < 2$</u>.

As a general rule:

> If $x^2 > a^2$ then $x > a$ or $x < -a$
> If $x^2 < a^2$ then $-a < x < a$

If you're confused by the '$x < -3$' bit, try putting some numbers in. E.g. $x = -4$ gives $x^2 = 16$, which is greater than 9, as required.

EXAMPLES:

1. Solve the inequality $x^2 \leq 25$.

If $x^2 = 25$, then $x = \pm 5$.
As $x^2 \leq 25$, then $-5 \leq x \leq 5$

2. Solve the inequality $x^2 > 9$.

If $x^2 = 9$, then $x = \pm 3$.
As $x^2 > 9$, then $x < -3$ or $x > 3$

3. Solve the inequality $3x^2 \geq 48$.

$(\div 3) \quad \dfrac{3x^2}{3} \geq \dfrac{48}{3}$

$x^2 \geq 16$

$x \leq -4$ or $x \geq 4$

4. Solve the inequality $-2x^2 + 8 > 0$.

$(-8) \quad -2x^2 + 8 - 8 > 0 - 8$

$-2x^2 > -8$

$(\div -2) \quad -2x^2 \div -2 < -8 \div -2$

$x^2 < 4$

$-2 < x < 2$

You're dividing by a <u>negative number</u>, so flip the sign.

Sketch the Graph to Help You (9)

Worst case scenario — you have to solve a quadratic inequality such as $-x^2 + 2x + 3 > 0$. Don't panic — you can use the <u>graph</u> of the quadratic to help (there's more on sketching quadratic graphs on p.48).

EXAMPLE: Solve the inequality $-x^2 + 2x + 3 > 0$.

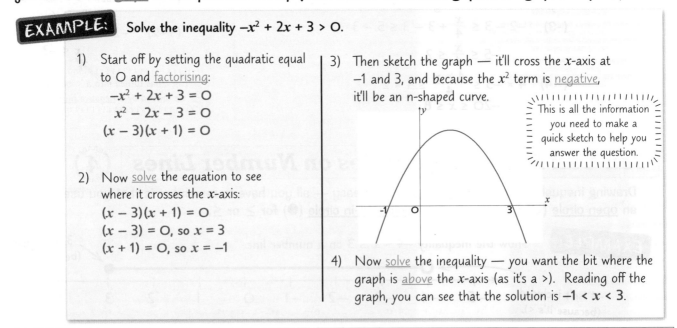

1) Start off by setting the quadratic equal to 0 and <u>factorising</u>:

$-x^2 + 2x + 3 = 0$

$x^2 - 2x - 3 = 0$

$(x - 3)(x + 1) = 0$

2) Now <u>solve</u> the equation to see where it crosses the x-axis:

$(x - 3)(x + 1) = 0$

$(x - 3) = 0$, so $x = 3$

$(x + 1) = 0$, so $x = -1$

3) Then sketch the graph — it'll cross the x-axis at -1 and 3, and because the x^2 term is <u>negative</u>, it'll be an n-shaped curve.

This is all the information you need to make a quick sketch to help you answer the question.

4) Now <u>solve</u> the inequality — you want the bit where the graph is <u>above</u> the x-axis (as it's a >). Reading off the graph, you can see that the solution is $-1 < x < 3$.

There's too much inequality in the world — especially in Maths...

Don't worry about drawing the graphs perfectly — all you need to know is where the graph crosses the x-axis and whether it's u-shaped or n-shaped so you can see which bit of the graph you want.

Q1   Solve these inequalities: a) $p^2 < 49$ [2 marks]   b) $-\frac{1}{2}p^2 \leq -32$ [3 marks] (8)

Q2   Write down all the integer values that satisfy the inequality $x^2 - 4x \leq 0$.   [3 marks] (9)

Graphical Inequalities

These questions always involve <u>shading a region on a graph</u>. The method sounds very complicated, but once you've seen it in action with an example, you'll see that it's OK...

Showing Inequalities on a Graph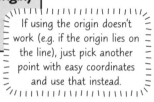

Here's the method to follow:

> 1) <u>CONVERT each INEQUALITY to an EQUATION</u>
> by simply putting an '=' in place of the inequality sign.
>
> 2) <u>DRAW THE GRAPH FOR EACH EQUATION</u> — if the inequality sign is < or > draw a <u>dotted line</u>, but if it's ≥ or ≤ draw a <u>solid line</u>.
>
> 3) <u>Work out WHICH SIDE of each line you want</u> — put a point (usually the origin) into the inequality to see if it's on the correct side of the line.
>
> 4) <u>SHADE THE REGION this gives you</u>.

If using the origin doesn't work (e.g. if the origin lies on the line), just pick another point with easy coordinates and use that instead.

EXAMPLE: Shade the region that satisfies all three of the following inequalities:
$x + y < 5$ $y \leq x + 2$ $y > 1$.

1) **CONVERT EACH INEQUALITY TO AN EQUATION:**
$x + y = 5$, $y = x + 2$ and $y = 1$

2) **DRAW THE GRAPH FOR EACH EQUATION (see p.45)**
You'll need a <u>dotted</u> line for $x + y = 5$ and $y = 1$ and a <u>solid</u> line for $y = x + 2$.

3) **WORK OUT WHICH SIDE OF EACH LINE YOU WANT**
This is the fiddly bit. Put $x = 0$ and $y = 0$ (the origin) into each inequality and see if this makes the inequality <u>true</u> or <u>false</u>.

<u>$x + y < 5$:</u>
$x = 0$, $y = 0$ gives $0 < 5$ which is <u>true</u>.
This means the <u>origin</u> is on the <u>correct</u> side of the line.

<u>$y \leq x + 2$:</u>
$x = 0$, $y = 0$ gives $0 \leq 2$ which is <u>true</u>.
So the origin is on the <u>correct</u> side of this line.

<u>$y > 1$:</u>
$x = 0$, $y = 0$ gives $0 > 1$ which is <u>false</u>.
So the origin is on the <u>wrong side</u> of this line.

4) **SHADE THE REGION**
You want the region that satisfies all of these:
— below $x + y = 5$ (because the origin <u>is</u> on this side)
— right of $y = x + 2$ (because the origin <u>is</u> on this side)
— above $y = 1$ (because the origin <u>isn't</u> on this side).

<u>Dotted lines</u> mean the region <u>doesn't</u> include the points on the line.

A <u>solid line</u> means the region <u>does</u> include the points on the line

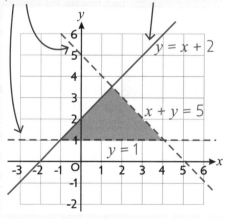

Make sure you read the question <u>carefully</u> — you might be asked to <u>label</u> the region instead of shade it, or just <u>mark on points</u> that satisfy all three inequalities. No point throwing away marks because you didn't read the question properly.

Graphical inequalities — it's a shady business...

Once you've found the region, it's a good idea to pick a point inside it and check that it satisfies ALL the inequalities. Try it out on this Exam Practice Question:

Q1   On a grid, shade the region that satisfies $x \leq 5$, $y > -1$ and $y < x + 1$.   [3 marks]

Iterative Methods

Iterative methods are techniques where you keep repeating a calculation in order to get closer and closer to the solution you want. You usually put the value you've just found back into the calculation to find a better value.

Where There's a Sign Change, There's a Solution (7)

If you're trying to solve an equation that equals 0, there's one very important thing to remember:

> If there's a sign change (i.e. from positive to negative or vice versa) when you put two numbers into the equation, there's a solution between those numbers.

Think about the equation $x^3 - 3x - 1 = 0$. When $x = \underline{-1}$, the expression gives $(-1)^3 - 3(-1) - 1 = \underline{1}$, which is positive, and when $x = \underline{-2}$ the expression gives $(-2)^3 - 3(-2) - 1 = \underline{-3}$, which is negative. This means that the expression will be $\underline{0}$ for some value between $x = -1$ and $x = -2$ (the solution).

Use Iteration When an Equation is Too Hard to Solve (7)

Not all equations can be solved using the methods you've seen so far in this section (e.g. factorising, the quadratic formula etc.). But if you know an interval that contains a solution to an equation, you can use an iterative method to find the approximate value of the solution.

This is known as the decimal search method.

EXAMPLE: A solution to the equation $x^3 - 3x - 1 = 0$ lies between -1 and -2. By considering values in this interval, find a solution to this equation to 1 d.p.

1) Try (in order) the values of x with 1 d.p. that lie between -1 and -2. There's a sign change between $\underline{-1.5}$ and $\underline{-1.6}$, so the solution lies in this interval.

2) Now try values of x with 2 d.p. between -1.5 and -1.6. There's a sign change between $\underline{-1.53}$ and $\underline{-1.54}$, so the solution lies in this interval.

3) Both -1.53 and -1.54 round to -1.5 to 1 d.p. so a solution to $x^3 - 3x - 1 = 0$ is $x = -1.5$ to 1 d.p.

Each time you find a sign change, you narrow the interval that the solution lies within. Keep going until you know the solution to the accuracy you want.

x	$x^3 - 3x - 1$	
-1.0	1	Positive
-1.1	0.969	Positive
-1.2	0.872	Positive
-1.3	0.703	Positive
-1.4	0.456	Positive
-1.5	0.125	Positive
-1.6	-0.296	Negative
-1.51	0.087049	Positive
-1.52	0.048192	Positive
-1.53	0.008423	Positive
-1.54	-0.032264	Negative

EXAMPLE: Use the iteration machine below to find a solution to the equation $x^3 - 3x - 1 = 0$ to 1 d.p. Use the starting value $x_0 = -1$.

Look back at p.32 for more on the x_n notation.

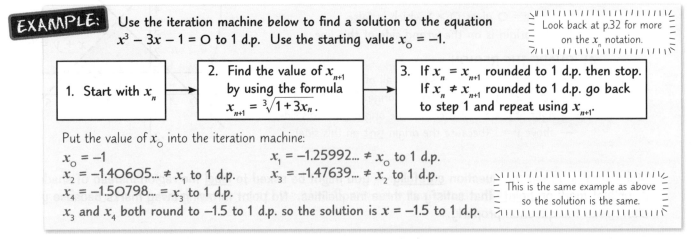

1. Start with x_n

2. Find the value of x_{n+1} by using the formula $x_{n+1} = \sqrt[3]{1 + 3x_n}$.

3. If $x_n = x_{n+1}$ rounded to 1 d.p. then stop. If $x_n \neq x_{n+1}$ rounded to 1 d.p. go back to step 1 and repeat using x_{n+1}.

Put the value of x_0 into the iteration machine:

$x_0 = -1$
$x_1 = -1.25992... \neq x_0$ to 1 d.p.
$x_2 = -1.40605... \neq x_1$ to 1 d.p.
$x_3 = -1.47639... \neq x_2$ to 1 d.p.
$x_4 = -1.50798... = x_3$ to 1 d.p.

x_3 and x_4 both round to -1.5 to 1 d.p. so the solution is $x = -1.5$ to 1 d.p.

This is the same example as above so the solution is the same.

A little less iteration, a little more action please...

Don't worry — in the exam you'll almost certainly be given a method to use (e.g. an iteration machine).

Q1 The equation above has another solution in the interval $1 < x < 2$. Use the iteration machine given with $x_0 = 2$, but this time compare values to 2 d.p. to find this solution to 2 d.p. **[4 marks]** (7)

Simultaneous Equations

There are two types of simultaneous equations you could get
— EASY ONES (where both equations are linear) and TRICKY ONES (where one's quadratic).

1 $2x = 6 - 4y$ and $-3 - 3y = 4x$ **2** $7x + y = 1$ and $2x^2 - y = 3$

1 Six Steps for Easy Simultaneous Equations   (5)

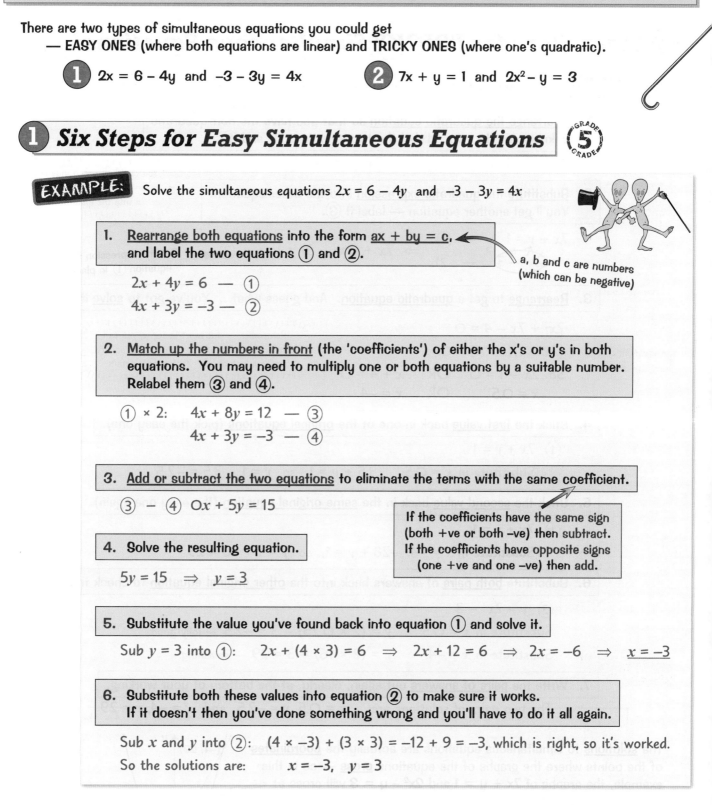

EXAMPLE: Solve the simultaneous equations $2x = 6 - 4y$ and $-3 - 3y = 4x$

1. Rearrange both equations into the form $ax + by = c$, and label the two equations ① and ②.

     a, b and c are numbers (which can be negative)

     $2x + 4y = 6$ — ①
     $4x + 3y = -3$ — ②

2. Match up the numbers in front (the 'coefficients') of either the x's or y's in both equations. You may need to multiply one or both equations by a suitable number. Relabel them ③ and ④.

     ① × 2: $4x + 8y = 12$ — ③
              $4x + 3y = -3$ — ④

3. Add or subtract the two equations to eliminate the terms with the same coefficient.

     ③ − ④ $0x + 5y = 15$

     If the coefficients have the same sign (both +ve or both −ve) then subtract. If the coefficients have opposite signs (one +ve and one −ve) then add.

4. Solve the resulting equation.

     $5y = 15 \Rightarrow y = 3$

5. Substitute the value you've found back into equation ① and solve it.

     Sub $y = 3$ into ①: $2x + (4 \times 3) = 6 \Rightarrow 2x + 12 = 6 \Rightarrow 2x = -6 \Rightarrow x = -3$

6. Substitute both these values into equation ② to make sure it works. If it doesn't then you've done something wrong and you'll have to do it all again.

     Sub x and y into ②: $(4 \times -3) + (3 \times 3) = -12 + 9 = -3$, which is right, so it's worked.
     So the solutions are: $x = -3$, $y = 3$

Sunday morning, lemon squeezy & simultaneous linear equations...

You need to learn the 6 steps on this page. When you think you've got them, try them out on these Exam Practice Questions.

Q1   Issy buys two cups of tea and three slices of cake for £9.
       Rudy buys four cups of tea and one slice of cake from the same cafe for £8.
       Find the cost of one cup of tea and the cost of one slice of cake.   [3 marks] (5)

Q2   Find x and y given that $2x - 10 = 4y$ and $3y = 5x - 18$.   [3 marks] (5)

Simultaneous Equations

② *Seven Steps for TRICKY Simultaneous Equations* (8)

EXAMPLE: Solve these two equations simultaneously: $7x + y = 1$ and $2x^2 - y = 3$

1. **Rearrange the quadratic equation** so that you have the non-quadratic unknown on its own.   Label the two equations ① and ②.

   $7x + y = 1$ — ① $y = 2x^2 - 3$ — ②

   You could also rearrange the linear equation and substitute it into the quadratic.

2. **Substitute** the quadratic expression into the other equation. You'll get another equation — label it ③.

   $7x + y = 1$ — ①
   $y = \boxed{2x^2 - 3}$ — ② $\Rightarrow 7x + (2x^2 - 3) = 1$ — ③ ← *Put the expression for y into equation ① in place of y.*

3. **Rearrange to get a quadratic equation.** And guess what... You've got to **solve** it.

   $2x^2 + 7x - 4 = 0$

   $(2x - 1)(x + 4) = 0$

   So $2x - 1 = 0$ OR $x + 4 = 0$
   $x = 0.5$ OR $x = -4$

   Remember — if it won't factorise, you can either use the formula or complete the square. Have a look at p.27-29 for more details.

4. **Stick the first value** back in one of the **original equations** (pick the easy one).

   ① $7x + y = 1$

   Substitute in $x = 0.5$: $3.5 + y = 1$, so $y = 1 - 3.5 = -2.5$

5. **Stick the second value** back in the **same original equation** (the easy one again).

   ① $7x + y = 1$

   Substitute in $x = -4$: $-28 + y = 1$, so $y = 1 + 28 = 29$

6. **Substitute both pairs** of answers back into the **other original equation** to check they work.

   ② $y = 2x^2 - 3$

   Substitute in $x = 0.5$: $y = (2 \times 0.25) - 3 = -2.5$ — jolly good.
   Substitute in $x = -4$: $y = (2 \times 16) - 3 = 29$ — smashing.

7. **Write the pairs of answers** out again, clearly, at the bottom of your working.

   The two pairs of solutions are: $x = 0.5$, $y = -2.5$ and $x = -4$, $y = 29$

The **solutions** to simultaneous equations are actually the **coordinates** of the points where the graphs of the equations **cross** — so in this example, the graphs of $7x + y = 1$ and $2x^2 - y = 3$ will cross at (0.5, -2.5) and (-4, 29).   There's more on this on p.52.

(-4, 29)

(0.5, -2.5)

Simultaneous pain and pleasure — it must be algebra...

Don't get confused and think that there are 4 <u>separate</u> solutions — you end up with <u>2 pairs</u> of solutions.

Q1   Solve the simultaneous equations $y = 2 - 3x$ and $y + 2 = x^2$ [4 marks] (8)

Q2   Find the coordinates of *A* and *B*, the points where the graphs of $y = x^2 + 4$ and
$y - 6x - 4 = 0$ intersect, and use your answer to find the exact length of *AB*.   [5 marks] (8)

Proof

I'm not going to lie — <u>proof questions</u> can look a bit terrifying. There are <u>all sorts</u> of things you could be asked to prove — I'll start with some <u>algebraic</u> proofs on this page, then move on to <u>wild and wonderful</u> topics.

Show Things Are Odd, Even or Multiples by Rearranging

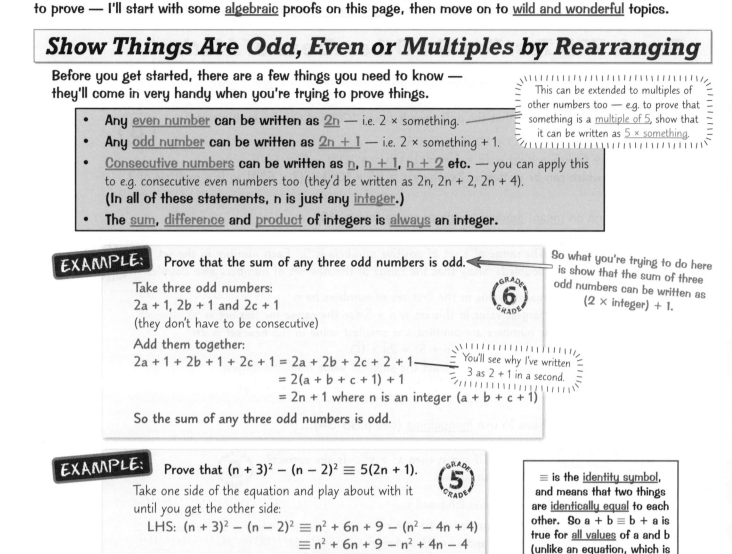

Before you get started, there are a few things you need to know — they'll come in very handy when you're trying to prove things.

This can be extended to multiples of other numbers too — e.g. to prove that something is a <u>multiple of 5</u>, show that it can be written as <u>5 × something</u>.

- Any <u>even number</u> can be written as <u>2n</u> — i.e. 2 × something.
- Any <u>odd number</u> can be written as <u>2n + 1</u> — i.e. 2 × something + 1.
- <u>Consecutive numbers</u> can be written as <u>n</u>, <u>n + 1</u>, <u>n + 2</u> etc. — you can apply this to e.g. consecutive even numbers too (they'd be written as 2n, 2n + 2, 2n + 4).
  (In all of these statements, n is just any <u>integer</u>.)
- The <u>sum</u>, <u>difference</u> and <u>product</u> of integers is <u>always</u> an integer.

EXAMPLE: Prove that the sum of any three odd numbers is odd.

So what you're trying to do here is show that the sum of three odd numbers can be written as (2 × integer) + 1.

Take three odd numbers:
$2a + 1$, $2b + 1$ and $2c + 1$
(they don't have to be consecutive)
Add them together:
$2a + 1 + 2b + 1 + 2c + 1 = 2a + 2b + 2c + 2 + 1$

You'll see why I've written 3 as 2 + 1 in a second.

$\qquad = 2(a + b + c + 1) + 1$
$\qquad = 2n + 1$ where n is an integer $(a + b + c + 1)$

So the sum of any three odd numbers is odd.

EXAMPLE: Prove that $(n + 3)^2 - (n - 2)^2 \equiv 5(2n + 1)$.

Take one side of the equation and play about with it until you get the other side:

LHS: $(n + 3)^2 - (n - 2)^2 \equiv n^2 + 6n + 9 - (n^2 - 4n + 4)$
$\qquad\qquad\qquad\qquad\qquad \equiv n^2 + 6n + 9 - n^2 + 4n - 4$
$\qquad\qquad\qquad\qquad\qquad \equiv 10n + 5$
$\qquad\qquad\qquad\qquad\qquad \equiv 5(2n + 1) = $ RHS ✓

$\equiv$ is the <u>identity symbol</u>, and means that two things are <u>identically equal</u> to each other. So $a + b \equiv b + a$ is true for <u>all values</u> of a and b (unlike an equation, which is only true for certain values).

Disprove Things by Finding a Counter Example

If you're asked to prove a statement <u>isn't</u> true, all you have to do is find <u>one example</u> that the statement doesn't work for — this is known as <u>disproof by counter example</u>.

EXAMPLE: Ross says "the difference between any two consecutive square numbers is always a prime number". Prove that Ross is wrong.

Just keep trying pairs of consecutive square numbers (e.g. 1^2 and 2^2) until you find one that doesn't work:

1 and 4 — difference = 3 (a prime number)
4 and 9 — difference = 5 (a prime number)
9 and 16 — difference = 7 (a prime number)
16 and 25 — difference = 9 (NOT a prime number) so Ross is wrong.

You don't have to go through loads of examples if you can spot one that's wrong straightaway — you could go straight to 16 and 25.

Prove that maths isn't fun...

The only way to get on top of proof questions is practice — so start with these:

Q1   Prove that the sum of two consecutive even numbers is even.   [3 marks] (6)

Q2 $4x + 2 = 3(3a + x)$. For odd integer values of a, prove that x is never a multiple of 8.   [3 marks] (7)

Proof

There's <u>no set method</u> for proof questions — you have to think about all the things you're <u>told</u> in the question (or that you <u>know</u> from other areas of maths) and <u>jiggle them around</u> until you've come up with a proof.

Proofs Will Test You On Other Areas of Maths

You could get asked just about anything in a proof question, from <u>power laws</u>...

EXAMPLE: Show that the difference between 10^{18} and 6^{21} is a multiple of 2. *(GRADE 8)*

$10^{18} - 6^{21} = (10 \times 10^{17}) - (6 \times 6^{20})$
$= (2 \times 5 \times 10^{17}) - (2 \times 3 \times 6^{20}) = 2[(5 \times 10^{17}) - (3 \times 6^{20})]$
which can be written as $2x$ where $x = [(5 \times 10^{17}) - (3 \times 6^{20})]$ so is a multiple of 2.

... to questions on <u>mean</u>, <u>median</u>, <u>mode</u> or <u>range</u> (see p.116)...

EXAMPLE: The range of a set of positive numbers is 5. Each number in the set is doubled. Show that the range of the new set of numbers also doubles. *(GRADE 6)*

Let the smallest value in the first set of numbers be n.
Then the largest value in this set is n + 5 (as the range for this set is 5).
When the numbers are doubled, the smallest value in the new set is 2n
and the largest value is 2(n + 5) = 2n + 10.
To find the new range, subtract the smallest value from the largest:
2n + 10 − 2n = 10 = 2 × 5, which is double the original range.

... or ones where you have to use <u>inequalities</u> (see p.33-34)...

EXAMPLE: Ellie says, "If $x > y$, then $x^2 > y^2$". Is she correct? Explain your answer. *(GRADE 5)*

Try some different values for x and y:
$x = 2, y = 1$: $x > y$ and $x^2 = 4 > 1 = y^2$
$x = 5, y = 2$: $x > y$ and $x^2 = 25 > 4 = y^2$

> This is an example of finding a counter example — see previous page.

At first glance, Ellie seems to be correct. BUT... $x = -1, y = -2$: $x > y$ but $x^2 = 1 < 4 = y^2$, so Ellie is wrong as the statement does not hold for all values of x and y.

... or even <u>geometric proofs</u> (see section 5 for more on geometry).

EXAMPLE: Prove that the sum of the exterior angles of a triangle is 360°. *(GRADE 5)*

First sketch a triangle with angles a, b and c:

Then the exterior angles are:
180° − a, 180° − b and 180° − c

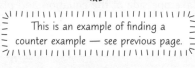

So their sum is:
(180° − a) + (180° − b) + (180° − c)
= 540° − (a + b + c) = 540° − 180° (as the angles in a triangle add up to 180°)
= 360°

The proof of the pudding is in the eating...

You might get a proof question hidden inside another question — don't let it catch you out.

Q1 Prove that the difference between two consecutive square numbers is always odd. [3 marks] *(GRADE 6)*

Q2 Triangle numbers are formed from the expression $\frac{1}{2}n(n + 1)$.
Prove that the ratio between two consecutive triangle numbers is always $n : n + 2$. [2 marks] *(GRADE 7)*

Functions

A <u>function</u> takes an <u>input</u>, <u>processes</u> it and <u>outputs</u> a value. There are two main ways of writing a function: <u>f(x) = 5x + 2</u> or <u>f: x → 5x + 2</u>. Both of these say 'the function f takes a value for x, <u>multiplies</u> it by <u>5</u> and <u>adds 2</u>. Functions can look a bit scary-mathsy, but they're just like <u>equations</u> but with y replaced by <u>f(x)</u>.

Evaluating Functions

This is easy — just shove the numbers into the function and you're away.

> **EXAMPLE:** $f(x) = x^2 - x + 7$. Find a) f(3) and b) f(−2)
>
> a) $f(3) = (3)^2 - (3) + 7 = 9 - 3 + 7 = 13$ b) $f(-2) = (-2)^2 - (-2) + 7 = 4 + 2 + 7 = 13$

Combining Functions (8)

1) You might get a question with <u>two functions</u>, e.g. f(x) and g(x), <u>combined</u> into a single function (called a <u>composite function</u>).

2) Composite functions are written e.g. <u>fg(x)</u>, which means 'do g first, then do <u>f</u>' — you always do the function <u>closest</u> to x first.

3) To find a composite function, rewrite fg(x) as <u>f(g(x))</u>, then replace g(x) with the <u>expression</u> it represents and then put this into f.

> Watch out — usually fg(x) ≠ gf(x). Never assume that they're the same.

> **EXAMPLE:** If $f(x) = 2x - 10$ and $g(x) = -\frac{x}{2}$, find: a) fg(x) and b) gf(x).
>
> a) $fg(x) = f(g(x)) = f(-\frac{x}{2}) = 2(-\frac{x}{2}) - 10 = -x - 10$
>
> b) $gf(x) = g(f(x)) = g(2x - 10) = -\left(\frac{2x-10}{2}\right) = -(x - 5) = 5 - x$

Inverse Functions (8)

The <u>inverse</u> of a function f(x) is another function, $f^{-1}(x)$, which <u>reverses</u> f(x). Here's the <u>method</u> to find it:

> 1) Write out the equation <u>x = f(y)</u> ◄
> 2) <u>Rearrange</u> the equation to <u>make y the subject</u>.
> 3) Finally, <u>replace</u> y with $f^{-1}(x)$.

f(y) is just the expression f(x), but with y's instead of x's

> **EXAMPLE:** If $f(x) = \frac{12+x}{3}$, find $f^{-1}(x)$.
>
> 1) Write out x = f(y): $x = \frac{12+y}{3}$
> 2) Rearrange to make y the subject: $3x = 12 + y$
> $y = 3x - 12$
> 3) Replace y with $f^{-1}(x)$: $f^{-1}(x) = 3x - 12$

So here you just rewrite the function replacing f(x) with x and x with y.

You can check your answer by seeing if $f^{-1}(x)$ does reverse f(x): e.g. $f(9) = \frac{21}{3} = 7$, $f^{-1}(7) = 21 - 12 = 9$

That page has really put the 'fun' into 'functions'...

Sorry, that joke just had to be made. This is another topic where practice really does make perfect.

Q1   If $f(x) = 5x - 1$, $g(x) = 8 - 2x$ and $h(x) = x^2 + 3$, find:
     a) f(4)   [1 mark]   b) h(−2)   [1 mark]   c) gf(x)   [2 marks]
     d) fh(x)   [2 marks]   e) gh(−3)   [2 marks]   f) $f^{-1}(x)$ [3 marks] (8)

Revision Questions for Section Two

There's no denying, Section Two is grisly grimsdike algebra — so check now how much you've learned.
- Try these questions and <u>tick off each one</u> when you <u>get it right</u>.
- When you've done <u>all the questions</u> for a topic and are <u>completely happy</u> with it, tick off the topic.

Algebra (p16-24) ☑

1) Simplify by collecting like terms: $3x + 2y - 5 - 6y + 2x$

2) Simplify the following: a) $x^3 \times x^6$ b) $y^7 \div y^5$ c) $(z^3)^4$

3) Multiply out these brackets: a) $3(2x + 1)$ b) $(x + 2)(x - 3)$ c) $(x - 1)(x + 3)(x + 5)$

4) Factorise: a) $8x^2 - 2y^2$ b) $49 - 81p^2q^2$ c) $12x^2 - 48y^2$

5) Simplify the following: a) $\sqrt{27}$ b) $\sqrt{125} \div \sqrt{5}$

6) Write $\sqrt{98} + 3\sqrt{8} - \sqrt{200}$ in the form $a\sqrt{2}$, where a is an integer.

7) Solve these equations: a) $5(x + 2) = 8 + 4(5 - x)$ b) $x^2 - 21 = 3(5 - x^2)$

8) Make p the subject of these: a) $\dfrac{p}{p + y} = 4$ b) $\dfrac{1}{p} = \dfrac{1}{q} + \dfrac{1}{r}$

Quadratics (p25-29) ☑

9) Solve the following by factorising them first: a) $x^2 + 9x + 18 = 0$ b) $5x^2 - 17x - 12 = 0$

10) Write down the quadratic formula.

11) Find the solutions of these equations (to 2 d.p.) using the quadratic formula:
a) $x^2 + x - 4 = 0$ b) $5x^2 + 6x = 2$ c) $(2x + 3)^2 = 15$

12) Find the exact solutions of these equations by completing the square:
a) $x^2 + 12x + 15 = 0$ b) $x^2 - 6x = 2$

13) The graph of $y = x^2 + px + q$ has a turning point at $(2, 5)$. Find the values of p and q.

Algebraic Fractions (p30) ☑

14) Write $\dfrac{2}{x + 3} + \dfrac{1}{x - 1}$ as a single fraction.

Sequences (p31-32) ☑

15) Find the expression for the nth term in the following sequences:
a) 7, 9, 11, 13   b) 11, 8, 5, 2   c) 5, 9, 15, 23.

16) The nth term of a sequence is given by $n^2 + 7$. Is 32 a term in this sequence?

Inequalities (p33-35) ☑

17) Solve the following inequalities: a) $4x + 3 \leq 6x + 7$ b) $5x^2 > 180$

18) Show on a graph the region described by these conditions: $x + y \leq 6$, $y > 0.5$, $y \leq 2x - 2$

Iterative Methods (p36) ☑

19) Show that the equation $x^3 - 4x^2 + 2x - 3 = 0$ has a solution between $x = 3$ and $x = 4$.

Simultaneous Equations (p37-38) ☑

20) Solve the following pair of simultaneous equations: $4x + 5y = 23$ and $3y - x = 7$

21) Solve these simultaneous equations: $y = 3x + 4$ and $x^2 + 2y = 0$

Proof and Functions (p39-41) ☑

22) Prove that the product of an odd number and an even number is even.

23) $f(x) = x^2 - 3$ and $g(x) = 4x$. Find: a) $f(3)$ b) $g(4.5)$ c) $fg(x)$ d) $f^{-1}(x)$.

Straight Lines and Gradients

If you thought I-spy was a fun game, wait 'til you play 'recognise the straight-line graph from the equation'.

Learn to Spot These Straight Line Equations **3**

If an equation has a y and/or x but no higher powers (like x^2 or x^3), then it's a straight line equation.

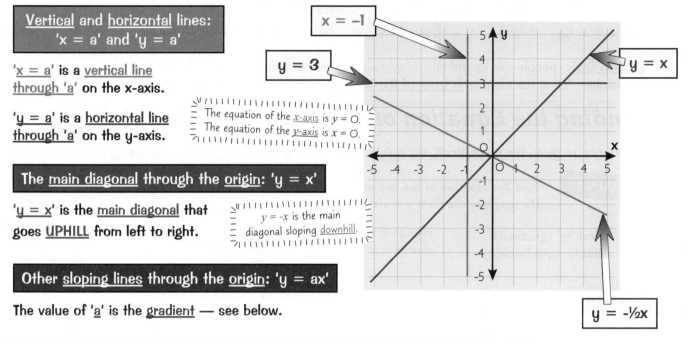

Vertical and **horizontal** lines:
'x = a' and 'y = a'

'$\underline{x = a}$' is a <u>vertical line</u> <u>through 'a'</u> on the x-axis.

'$\underline{y = a}$' is a <u>horizontal line</u> <u>through 'a'</u> on the y-axis.

The equation of the <u>x-axis</u> is $y = 0$.
The equation of the <u>y-axis</u> is $x = 0$.

The <u>main diagonal</u> through the <u>origin</u>: '**y = x**'

'$\underline{y = x}$' is the <u>main diagonal</u> that goes <u>UPHILL</u> from left to right.

$y = -x$ is the main diagonal sloping <u>downhill</u>.

Other <u>sloping lines</u> through the <u>origin</u>: '**y = ax**'

The value of '$\underline{a}$' is the <u>gradient</u> — see below.

x = –1

y = 3

y = x

y = -½x

The Gradient is the Steepness of the Line **3**

The <u>gradient</u> of the line is how <u>steep</u> it is — the <u>larger</u> the gradient, the <u>steeper</u> the slope.
A <u>negative gradient</u> tells you it slopes <u>downhill</u>. You find it by dividing the <u>change in y</u> by the <u>change in x</u>.

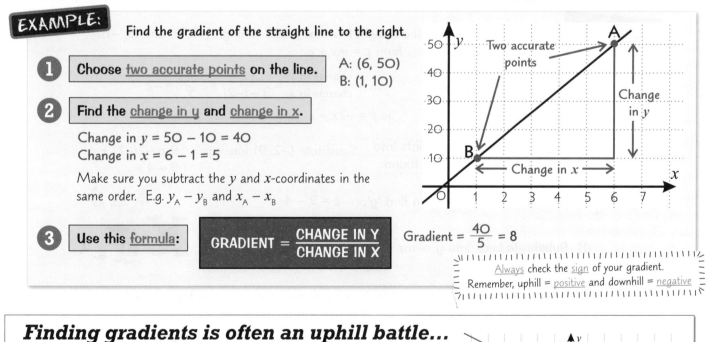

EXAMPLE: Find the gradient of the straight line to the right.

1 Choose <u>two accurate points</u> on the line.   A: (6, 50)
                                                        B: (1, 10)

2 Find the <u>change in y</u> and <u>change in x</u>.

Change in $y = 50 - 10 = 40$
Change in $x = 6 - 1 = 5$

Make sure you subtract the y and x-coordinates in the same order. E.g. $y_A - y_B$ and $x_A - x_B$

3 Use this <u>formula</u>: $$\text{GRADIENT} = \frac{\text{CHANGE IN Y}}{\text{CHANGE IN X}}$$

Two accurate points

Change in y

Change in x

Gradient $= \dfrac{40}{5} = 8$

<u>Always</u> check the <u>sign</u> of your gradient.
Remember, uphill = <u>positive</u> and downhill = <u>negative</u>

Finding gradients is often an uphill battle...

Learn the three steps for finding the gradient then have a bash at this practice question. Take care — you might not be able to pick two points with nice, positive coordinates. Fun times ahoy.

Q1   Find the gradient of the
      line shown on the right.   [2 marks] **3**

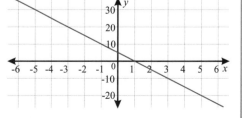

y = mx + c

Using '$y = mx + c$' is the most straightforward way of dealing with straight-line equations, and it's very useful in exams. The first thing you have to do though is <u>rearrange</u> the equation into the standard format like this:

Straight line:		Rearranged into '$y = mx + c$'		where:
$y = 2 + 3x$	$\rightarrow$	$y = 3x + 2$	($m = 3$, $c = 2$)	'm' = <u>gradient</u> of the line.
$x - y = 0$	$\rightarrow$	$y = x + 0$	($m = 1$, $c = 0$)	'c' = '<u>y-intercept</u>' (where it hits the
$4x - 3 = 5y$	$\rightarrow$	$y = \frac{4}{5}x - \frac{3}{5}$	($m = \frac{4}{5}$, $c = -\frac{3}{5}$)	y-axis)

<u>WATCH OUT</u>: people mix up 'm' and 'c' when they get something like $y = 5 + 2x$.
Remember, 'm' is the number <u>in front of the 'x'</u> and 'c' is the number <u>on its own</u>.

Finding the Equation of a Straight-Line Graph (4)

When you're given the graph itself, it's quick and easy to find the <u>equation</u> of the straight line.

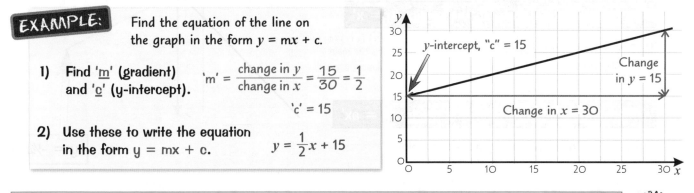

EXAMPLE: Find the equation of the line on the graph in the form $y = mx + c$.

1) Find 'm' (gradient) and 'c' (y-intercept).
$$'m' = \frac{\text{change in } y}{\text{change in } x} = \frac{15}{30} = \frac{1}{2}$$
$$'c' = 15$$

2) Use these to write the equation in the form $y = mx + c$.
$$y = \frac{1}{2}x + 15$$

y-intercept, "c" = 15
Change in y = 15
Change in x = 30

Finding the Equation of a Line Through Two Points (5)

If you're given <u>two points</u> on a line you can find the <u>gradient</u>, then you can <u>use</u> the gradient and one of the points to find the <u>equation</u> of the line. This is super handy, so practise it until you can do it in your sleep.

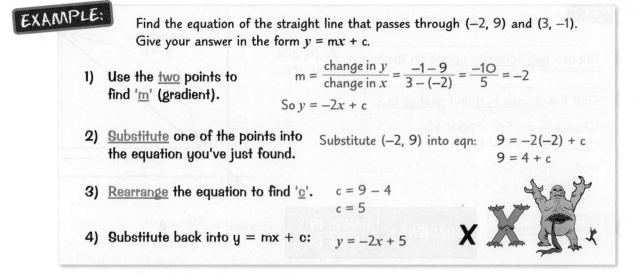

EXAMPLE: Find the equation of the straight line that passes through $(-2, 9)$ and $(3, -1)$.
Give your answer in the form $y = mx + c$.

1) Use the <u>two</u> points to find 'm' (gradient).
$$m = \frac{\text{change in } y}{\text{change in } x} = \frac{-1 - 9}{3 - (-2)} = \frac{-10}{5} = -2$$
So $y = -2x + c$

2) <u>Substitute</u> one of the points into the equation you've just found.
Substitute $(-2, 9)$ into eqn: $9 = -2(-2) + c$
$9 = 4 + c$

3) <u>Rearrange</u> the equation to find 'c'.
$c = 9 - 4$
$c = 5$

4) Substitute back into $y = mx + c$:
$y = -2x + 5$

Sometimes you'll be asked to give your equation in other forms such as $ax + by + c = 0$.
Just <u>rearrange</u> your $y = mx + c$ equation to get it in this form. It's no biggie.

Remember y = mx + c — it'll keep you on the straight and narrow...

Remember the steps for finding equations and try out your new-found graph skills.

Q1 Find the equation of the line on the graph to the right. [2 marks] (4)

Q2 Line Q goes through $(0, 5)$ and $(4, 7)$.
Find the equation of Line Q in the form $y = mx + c$. [3 marks] (5)

Drawing Straight Line Graphs

You've got three methods for <u>drawing straight-line graphs</u> on this page. Make sure you're happy with <u>all three</u>.

The 'Table of 3 Values' Method (3)

EXAMPLE: Draw the graph of $y = -2x + 4$ for values of x from -1 to 4.

1) <u>Draw up a table</u> with three suitable values of x.

2) <u>Find the y-values</u> by putting each x-value into the equation:
   When $x = 4$, $y = -2x + 4$
   $= (-2 \times 4) + 4 = -4$

x	O	2	4
y			

x	O	2	4
y	4	O	-4

3) <u>Plot the points</u> and <u>draw the line</u>.

The table gives the points (O, 4), (2, O) and (4, −4)

If it's a <u>straight-line equation</u>, the 3 points will be in a <u>dead straight line</u> with each other.
<u>If they aren't</u>, you need to go back and <u>CHECK YOUR WORKING</u>.

Using y = mx + c (4)

EXAMPLE: Draw the graph of $4y - 2x = -4$.

1 Get the equation into the form $y = mx + c$.

$4y - 2x = -4 \rightarrow y = \frac{1}{2}x - 1$

2 Put a dot on the <u>y-axis</u> at the <u>value of c</u>.

'c' = −1

3 Using <u>m</u>, go across and up or down a certain number of units. Make another dot, then repeat this step a few times in both directions.

Go <u>2 along</u> and <u>1 up</u> because 'm' = $+\frac{1}{2}$.

4 When you have 4 or 5 dots, draw a <u>straight line</u> through them.

5 Finally check that the <u>gradient</u> looks right.

A gradient of $+\frac{1}{2}$ should be <u>quite gentle</u> and <u>uphill</u> left to right — which it is, so it looks OK.

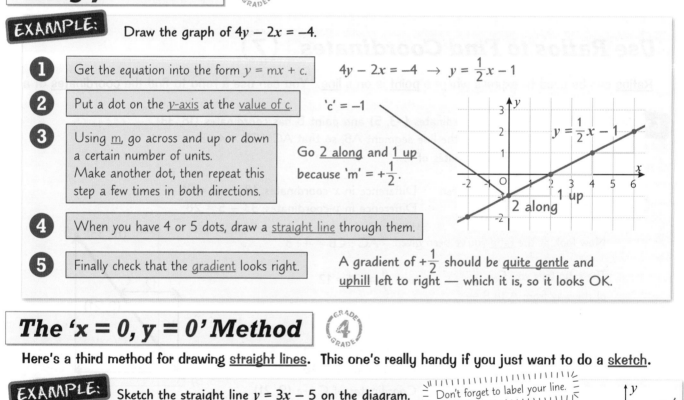

The 'x = 0, y = 0' Method (4)

Here's a third method for drawing <u>straight lines</u>. This one's really handy if you just want to do a <u>sketch</u>.

EXAMPLE: Sketch the straight line $y = 3x - 5$ on the diagram.

Don't forget to label your line.

1) <u>Set x = 0</u> in the equation, and <u>find y</u> — this is where it <u>crosses the y-axis</u>.
   $y = 3x - 5$. When $x = O$, $y = -5$.

2) <u>Set y = 0</u> in the equation and <u>find x</u> — this is where it <u>crosses the x-axis</u>.
   When $y = O$, $O = 3x - 5$. So $x = \frac{5}{3}$.

3) Mark on the two <u>points</u> and <u>draw a line</u> passing <u>through</u> them.

"No!" cried y "You won't cross me again" — extract from a Maths thriller...

Learn the details of these methods, then you'll be ready for a Practice Question.

Q1   Sketch the graph of $5y + 2x = 20$.   [3 marks] (4)

Coordinates and Ratio

Now you're all clued up on the equations of straight lines, it's time to move onto <u>line segments</u>. Instead of going on forever, a line segment is the <u>part of a line</u> between two <u>end points</u>.

Find the Mid-Point Using The Average of the End Points

To find the mid-point of a line segment, just <u>add</u> the x-coordinates and <u>divide by two</u>, then do the same for the y-coordinates.

EXAMPLE: Points A and B are given by the coordinates (7, 4) and (−1, −2) respectively. M is the mid-point of the line segment AB. Find the coordinates of M.

<u>Add</u> the x-coordinate of A to the x-coordinate of B and <u>divide by two</u> to find the x-coordinate of the <u>midpoint</u>.

Do the <u>same</u> with the y-coordinates. $\left(\dfrac{7 + -1}{2}, \dfrac{4 + -2}{2}\right) = \left(\dfrac{6}{2}, \dfrac{2}{2}\right) = (3, 1)$

So the mid-point of AB has coordinates (3, 1)

Use Ratios to Find Coordinates

Ratios can be used to express where a <u>point</u> is on a <u>line</u>. You can use a ratio to find the <u>coordinates</u> of a point.

EXAMPLE: Point A has coordinates (−3, 5) and point B has coordinates (18, 33). Point C lies on the line segment AB, so that AC : CB = 4 : 3 Find the coordinates of C.

First find the <u>difference</u> between the coordinates of <u>A and B</u>:

Difference in x-coordinates: 18 − −3 = 21
Difference in y-coordinates: 33 − 5 = 28

Now look at the <u>ratio</u> you've been given: AC : CB = 4 : 3

The ratio tells you C is $\dfrac{4}{7}$ of the way from A to B —

so find $\dfrac{4}{7}$ of each <u>difference</u>.

x: $\dfrac{4}{7} \times 21 = 12$

y: $\dfrac{4}{7} \times 28 = 16$

Now <u>add</u> these to the coordinates of <u>A</u> to find <u>C</u>.

x-coordinate: −3 + 12 = 9
y-coordinate: 5 + 16 = 21
Coordinates of C are (9, 21)

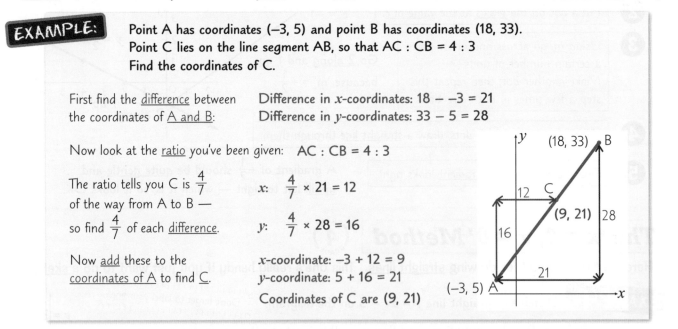

Make sure this page is segmented into your brain...

If you get a wordy line segments question, try sketching a quick diagram to help you get your head around the problem. Have a go at these questions to see if this stuff has sunk in yet:

Q1 A (−4, −1) and B (8, −3) are points on the circumference of a circle. AB is a diameter. Find the coordinates of the centre of the circle. [2 marks] **(6)**

Q2 P, Q and R lie on the straight line with equation $y − 3x = 6$, as shown on the right. PQ : QR = 1 : 2. Find the coordinates of R. [4 marks] **(7)**

Parallel and Perpendicular Lines

On p.44 you saw how to write the <u>equation of a straight line</u>. Well, you also have to be able to write the equation of a line that's <u>parallel</u> or <u>perpendicular</u> to the straight line you're given.

Parallel Lines Have the Same Gradient (5)

Parallel lines all have the <u>same gradient</u>, which means their $y = mx + c$ equations all have the same value of <u>m</u>.

So the lines: $y = 2x + 3$, $y = 2x$ and $y = 2x - 4$ are all parallel.

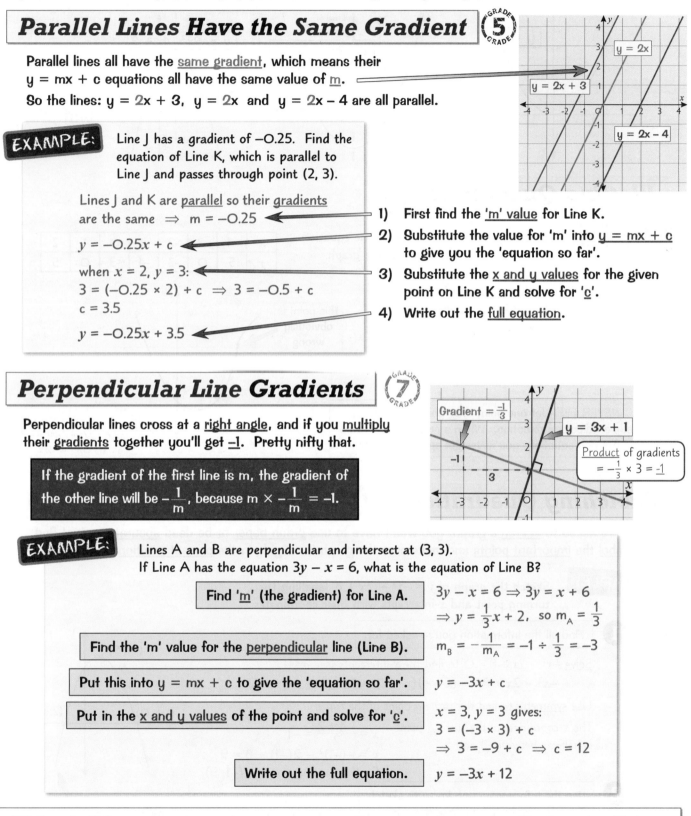

EXAMPLE: Line J has a gradient of −0.25. Find the equation of Line K, which is parallel to Line J and passes through point (2, 3).

Lines J and K are <u>parallel</u> so their <u>gradients</u> are the same $\Rightarrow$ m = −0.25 ◄

$y = -0.25x + c$ ◄

when $x = 2$, $y = 3$: ◄
$3 = (-0.25 \times 2) + c \Rightarrow 3 = -0.5 + c$
$c = 3.5$

$y = -0.25x + 3.5$ ◄

1) First find the '<u>m</u>' value for Line K.

2) Substitute the value for 'm' into <u>y = mx + c</u> to give you the 'equation so far'.

3) Substitute the <u>x and y values</u> for the given point on Line K and solve for '<u>c</u>'.

4) Write out the <u>full equation</u>.

Perpendicular Line Gradients (7)

Perpendicular lines cross at a <u>right angle</u>, and if you <u>multiply</u> their <u>gradients</u> together you'll get <u>−1</u>. Pretty nifty that.

> If the gradient of the first line is m, the gradient of the other line will be $-\frac{1}{m}$, because $m \times -\frac{1}{m} = -1$.

Gradient $= \frac{-1}{3}$

$y = 3x + 1$

Product of gradients
$= -\frac{1}{3} \times 3 = \underline{-1}$

EXAMPLE: Lines A and B are perpendicular and intersect at (3, 3). If Line A has the equation $3y - x = 6$, what is the equation of Line B?

| Find '<u>m</u>' (the gradient) for Line A. | $3y - x = 6 \Rightarrow 3y = x + 6$ $\Rightarrow y = \frac{1}{3}x + 2$, so $m_A = \frac{1}{3}$ |

| Find the 'm' value for the <u>perpendicular</u> line (Line B). | $m_B = -\frac{1}{m_A} = -1 \div \frac{1}{3} = -3$ |

| Put this into $y = mx + c$ to give the 'equation so far'. | $y = -3x + c$ |

| Put in the <u>x and y values</u> of the point and solve for '<u>c</u>'. | $x = 3$, $y = 3$ gives: $3 = (-3 \times 3) + c$ $\Rightarrow 3 = -9 + c \Rightarrow c = 12$ |

| Write out the full equation. | $y = -3x + 12$ |

This stuff is a way to get one over on the examiners (well −1 actually)...

So basically, use one gradient to find the other, then use the known x and y values to work out c.

Q1 Find the equation of the line parallel to $2x + 2y = 3$ which passes through the point (1, 4). Give your answer in the form $y = mx + c$. [3 marks] (6)

Q2 Show that the lines $y + 5x = 2$ and $5y = x + 3$ are perpendicular. [3 marks] (7)

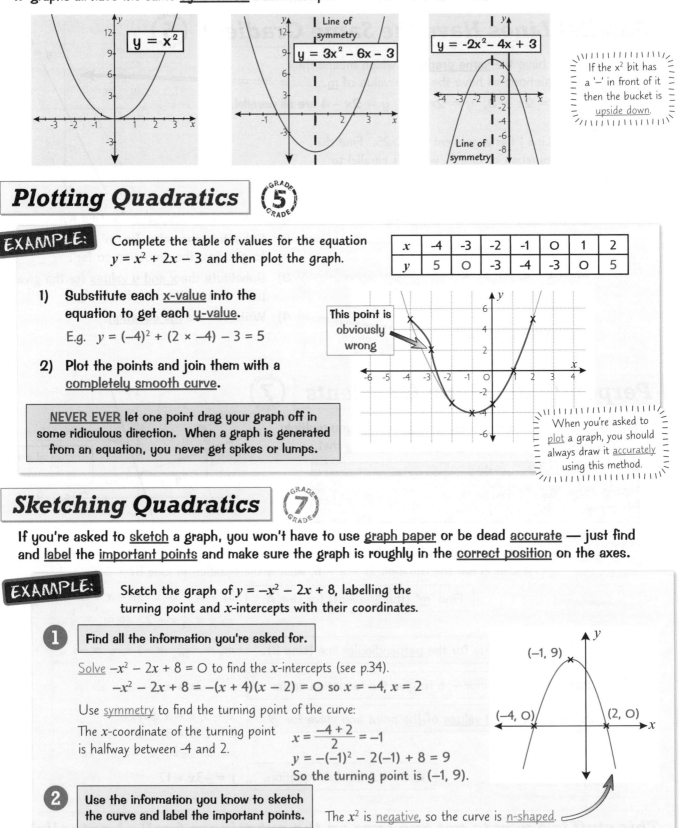

Quadratic Graphs

Quadratic functions take the form $y = \underline{anything\ with\ x^2}$ (but no higher powers of x).
x^2 graphs all have the same <u>symmetrical</u> bucket shape.

If the x^2 bit has a '–' in front of it then the bucket is <u>upside down</u>.

Plotting Quadratics

EXAMPLE: Complete the table of values for the equation $y = x^2 + 2x - 3$ and then plot the graph.

x	-4	-3	-2	-1	0	1	2
y	5	0	-3	-4	-3	0	5

1) Substitute each <u>x-value</u> into the equation to get each <u>y-value</u>.

E.g. $y = (-4)^2 + (2 \times -4) - 3 = 5$

2) Plot the points and join them with a <u>completely smooth curve</u>.

This point is obviously wrong

<u>NEVER EVER</u> let one point drag your graph off in some ridiculous direction. When a graph is generated from an equation, you never get spikes or lumps.

When you're asked to <u>plot</u> a graph, you should always draw it <u>accurately</u> using this method.

Sketching Quadratics

If you're asked to <u>sketch</u> a graph, you won't have to use <u>graph paper</u> or be dead <u>accurate</u> — just find and <u>label</u> the <u>important points</u> and make sure the graph is roughly in the <u>correct position</u> on the axes.

EXAMPLE: Sketch the graph of $y = -x^2 - 2x + 8$, labelling the turning point and x-intercepts with their coordinates.

1 Find all the information you're asked for.

<u>Solve</u> $-x^2 - 2x + 8 = 0$ to find the x-intercepts (see p.34).
$-x^2 - 2x + 8 = -(x + 4)(x - 2) = 0$ so $x = -4$, $x = 2$

Use <u>symmetry</u> to find the turning point of the curve:
The x-coordinate of the turning point is halfway between -4 and 2.
$x = \dfrac{-4 + 2}{2} = -1$
$y = -(-1)^2 - 2(-1) + 8 = 9$
So the turning point is (-1, 9).

2 Use the information you know to sketch the curve and label the important points. The x^2 is <u>negative</u>, so the curve is <u>n-shaped</u>.

(-1, 9), (-4, 0), (2, 0)

How refreshing — a page on graphs. Not seen one of those in a while...

Fun fact* — you could have also found the turning point in the example above by completing the square.

Q1 Plot the graph of $y = x^2 - 4x - 1$ for values of x between -2 and 6. [4 marks]

*fun not guaranteed.

Harder Graphs

Graphs come in all sorts of shapes, sizes and wiggles — here are the first of 7 more types you need to know:

x^3 Graphs: $y = ax^3 + bx^2 + cx + d$ (b, c and d can be zero)

All x^3 graphs (also known as <u>cubic</u> graphs) have a <u>wiggle</u> in the middle — sometimes it's a flat wiggle, sometimes it's more pronounced. $-x^3$ graphs always go down from <u>top left</u>, $+x^3$ ones go up from <u>bottom left</u>.

Note that x^3 must be the <u>highest power</u> and there must be <u>no other bits like 1/x</u> etc.

$y = x^3$

$y = x^3 + 3x^2 - 4x$

$y = -7x^3 - 7x^2 + 42x$

EXAMPLE: Draw the graph of $y = x^3 + 4x^2$ for values of x between -4 and $+2$.

Start by making a table of values.

x	-4	-3	-2	-1	0	1	2
$y = x^3 + 4x^2$	0	9	8	3	0	5	24

Plot the points and join them with a lovely <u>smooth curve</u>.
<u>DON'T</u> use your ruler — that would be a trifle daft.

Circles: $x^2 + y^2 = r^2$

The equation for a circle with <u>centre (0, 0)</u> and <u>radius r</u> is:
$$x^2 + y^2 = r^2$$

$x^2 + y^2 = 25$ is a circle with <u>centre (0, 0)</u>.
$r^2 = 25$, so the <u>radius, r, is 5</u>.

$x^2 + y^2 = 100$ is a circle with <u>centre (0, 0)</u>.
$r^2 = 100$, so the <u>radius, r, is 10</u>.

$x^2 + y^2 = 25$

EXAMPLE: Find the equation of the tangent to $x^2 + y^2 = 100$ at the point $(8, -6)$.

1) Find the gradient of the line from the origin to $(8, -6)$. This is a <u>radius</u> of the circle.

$$\text{Gradient} = \frac{\text{Change in } y}{\text{Change in } x} = \frac{-6 - 0}{8 - 0} = \frac{-3}{4}$$

2) A tangent meets a radius at 90°, (see p.76) so they are <u>perpendicular</u> — so the gradient of the tangent is $-\frac{1}{m}$.

$$\text{Gradient of tangent} = -\frac{1}{m} = -\frac{1}{\frac{-3}{4}} = \frac{4}{3}$$

3) Find the equation of the tangent by substituting $(8, -6)$ into $y = mx + c$.

$$y = mx + c \Rightarrow (-6) = \frac{4}{3}(8) + c$$
$$-6 = \frac{32}{3} + c$$
$$c = -\frac{50}{3}$$

$$y = \frac{4}{3}x - \frac{50}{3}$$

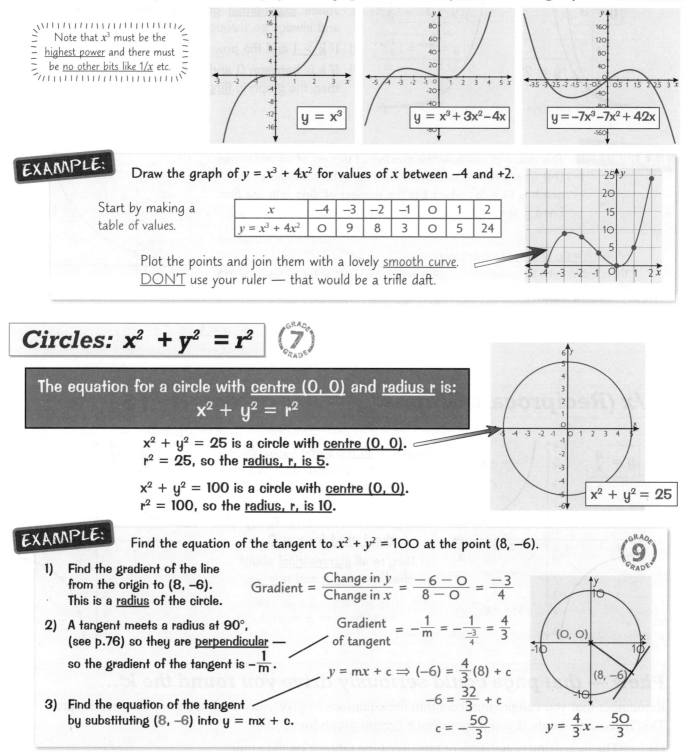

Graphs — the only place where squares make a circle...

Learn what type of graph you get from each sort of equation. Then try this Exam Practice Question.

Q1   The point (5, 12) lies on a circle with centre (0, 0).
Find the radius and equation of the circle.   [3 marks]

Harder Graphs

Here are two more graph types you need to be able to plot or sketch. Knowing what you're aiming for really helps.

k^x Graphs: $y = k^x$ or $y = k^{-x}$ (k is some positive number)

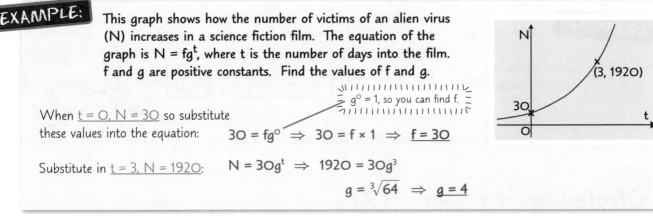

1) These 'exponential' graphs are always <u>above</u> the x-axis, and always go through the point <u>(0, 1)</u>.

2) If <u>k > 1</u> and the power is <u>+ve</u>, the graph curves <u>upwards</u>.

3) If k is <u>between 0 and 1</u> OR the power is <u>negative</u>, then the graph is <u>flipped horizontally</u>.

EXAMPLE: This graph shows how the number of victims of an alien virus (N) increases in a science fiction film. The equation of the graph is $N = fg^t$, where t is the number of days into the film. f and g are positive constants. Find the values of f and g.

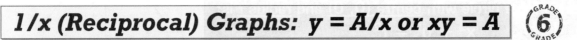

$g^0 = 1$, so you can find f.

When <u>t = 0, N = 30</u> so substitute these values into the equation:

$30 = fg^0 \Rightarrow 30 = f \times 1 \Rightarrow \underline{f = 30}$

Substitute in <u>t = 3, N = 1920</u>: $N = 30g^t \Rightarrow 1920 = 30g^3$

$g = \sqrt[3]{64} \Rightarrow \underline{g = 4}$

1/x (Reciprocal) Graphs: $y = A/x$ or $xy = A$ (6)

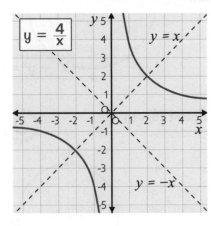

$y = \dfrac{4}{x}$

These are <u>all the same basic shape</u>, except the negative ones are in <u>opposite quadrants</u> to the positive ones (as shown). The two halves of the graph don't touch. The graphs <u>don't exist</u> for <u>x = 0</u>.

They're all <u>symmetrical</u> about the lines <u>y = x</u> and <u>y = -x</u>.

(You get this type of graph with inverse proportion — see p.63)

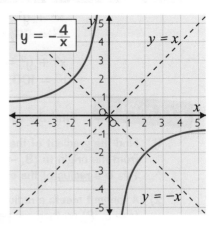

$y = -\dfrac{4}{x}$

Phew — that page could seriously drive you round the k^x...

Remember that you can put numbers into the equations to give you coordinates and find intercepts. This'll come in handy if you forget what a certain graph looks like.

Q1   The increasing population of rats over time (shown on the graph) is modelled by the equation $P = ab^t$, where P = population, t = number of months and a and b are positive constants.

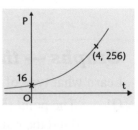

a) Find a and b.   [4 marks] (7)

b) Estimate the population after 7 months.   [2 marks] (7)

Harder Graphs

Before you leave this page, you should be able to close your eyes and picture these three graphs in your head, <u>properly labelled</u> and everything. If you can't, you need to learn them more. I'm not kidding.

Sine 'Waves' and Cos 'Buckets' (8)

1) The underlying shape of the sin and cos graphs is <u>identical</u> — they both bounce between <u>y-limits of exactly +1 and –1</u>.

2) The only difference is that the <u>sin graph</u> is <u>shifted right by 90°</u> compared to the cos graph.

3) <u>For 0° – 360°</u>, the shapes you get are a <u>Sine 'Wave'</u> (one peak, one trough) and a <u>Cos 'Bucket'</u> (starts at the top, dips, and finishes at the top).

4) Sin and cos repeat every 360°. The key to drawing the extended graphs is to first draw the 0° – 360° cycle of either the <u>Sine 'WAVE'</u> or the <u>Cos 'BUCKET'</u> and then you can <u>repeat it</u> forever in <u>both directions</u> as shown above.

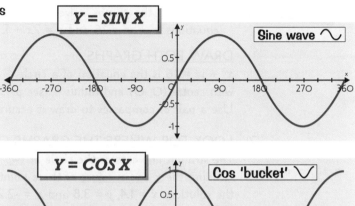

Tan x can be Any Value at all (8)

tan x is <u>different</u> from sin x or cos x — it goes between -∞ and +∞.

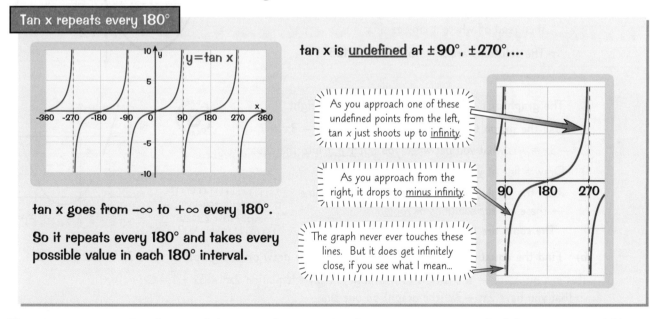

Tan x repeats every 180°

tan x is <u>undefined</u> at ±**90°**, ±**270°**,....

tan x goes from –∞ to +∞ every 180°.

So it repeats every 180° and takes every possible value in each 180° interval.

As you approach one of these undefined points from the left, tan x just shoots up to <u>infinity</u>.

As you approach from the right, it drops to <u>minus infinity</u>.

The graph never ever touches these lines. But it does get infinitely close, if you see what I mean...

The easiest way to <u>sketch</u> any of these graphs is to plot the <u>important points</u> which happen every 90° (e.g. –180°, –90°, 0°, 90°, 180°, 270°, 360°, 450°, 540°...) and then just join the dots up.

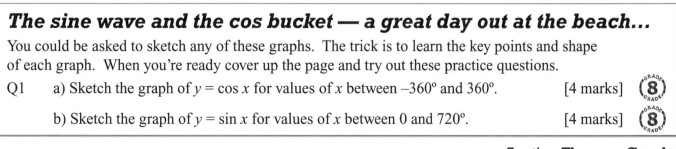

The sine wave and the cos bucket — a great day out at the beach...

You could be asked to sketch any of these graphs. The trick is to learn the key points and shape of each graph. When you're ready cover up the page and try out these practice questions.

Q1   a) Sketch the graph of $y = \cos x$ for values of x between –360° and 360°.   [4 marks] (8)

   b) Sketch the graph of $y = \sin x$ for values of x between 0 and 720°.   [4 marks] (8)

Solving Equations Using Graphs

You can plot graphs to find <u>approximate solutions</u> to simultaneous equations or other awkward equations. Plot the equations you want to solve and the solution lies where the lines <u>intersect</u>.

Plot Both Graphs and See Where They Cross

EXAMPLE: By plotting the graphs, solve the simultaneous equations $x^2 + y^2 = 16$ and $y = 2x + 1$.

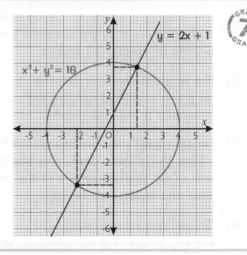

1) <u>DRAW BOTH GRAPHS.</u>
$x^2 + y^2 = 16$ is the equation of a circle with centre (O, O) and radius 4 (see p.49). Use a pair of compasses to draw it accurately.

2) <u>LOOK FOR WHERE THE GRAPHS CROSS.</u>
The straight line crosses the circle at <u>two points</u>. Reading the <u>x and y values</u> of these points gives the solutions $x = 1.4$, $y = 3.8$ and $x = -2.2$, $y = -3.4$ (all to 1 decimal place).

Using Graphs to Solve Harder Equations

EXAMPLES:

1. The graph of $y = \sin x$ is shown to the right. Use the graph to estimate the solutions to $\sin x = 0.7$ between $-180°$ and $180°$

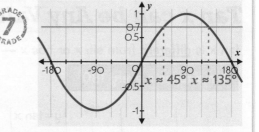

Draw the line $y = 0.7$ on the graph, then read off where it crosses $\sin x$.

The solutions are $x \approx 45°$ and $x \approx 135°$.

2. The graph of $y = 2x^2 - 3x$ is shown on the right.

a) Use the graph to estimate both roots of $2x^2 - 3x = 7$.

$2x^2 - 3x = 7$ is what you get when you put <u>$y = 7$</u> into the equation:

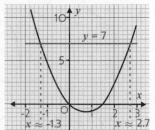

1) <u>Draw</u> a line at $y = 7$.

2) Read the <u>x-values</u> where the curve <u>crosses</u> this line — these are the solutions or <u>roots</u>.

The roots are around $x = -1.3$ and $x = 2.7$.

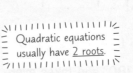
Quadratic equations usually have 2 roots.

b) Find the equation of the line you would need to draw on the graph to solve $2x^2 - 5x + 1 = 0$

This is a bit nasty — the trick is to rearrange the given equation $2x^2 - 5x + 1 = 0$ so that you have $2x^2 - 3x$ (the graph) on one side.

$$2x^2 - 5x + 1 = 0$$

Adding $2x - 1$ to both sides: $\quad 2x^2 - 3x = 2x - 1$

So the line needed is $y = 2x - 1$.

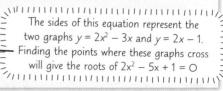
The sides of this equation represent the two graphs $y = 2x^2 - 3x$ and $y = 2x - 1$. Finding the points where these graphs cross will give the roots of $2x^2 - 5x + 1 = 0$

What do you call a giraffe with no eyes? A graph...

Get your graph-plotting pencils ready and have a go at this Practice Question:

Q1   By plotting the graphs, find approximate solutions to the simultaneous equations below.

a) $y = x^2 + 2x - 4$ and $y = 6 - x$ [4 marks]   b) $x^2 + y^2 = 25$ and $y = x + 1$ [4 marks]

Graph Transformations

Don't be put off by <u>function notation</u> involving f(x). It doesn't mean anything complicated, it's just a fancy way of saying "an expression in x". In other words "y = f(x)" just means "y = some totally mundane expression in x, which we won't tell you, we'll just call it f(x) instead to see how many of you get in a flap about it".

Translations on the y-axis: y = f(x) + a (7)

> You must describe this as a 'translation' in the exam — don't just say 'slide'.

This is where the whole graph is <u>slid up or down</u> the y-axis, and is achieved by simply <u>adding a number</u> onto the <u>end</u> of the equation: y = f(x) + a.

EXAMPLE: To the right is the graph of $y = f(x)$.
Write down the coordinates of the minimum point of the graph with equation <u>$y = f(x) + 5$</u>.

The minimum point of $y = f(x)$ has coordinates (2, 2).
$y = f(x) + 5$ is the same shape graph, <u>translated 5 units upwards</u>.
So the minimum point of $y = f(x) + 5$ is at **(2, 7)**.

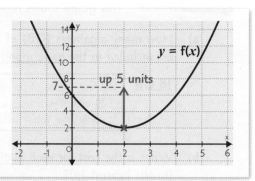

Translations on the x-axis: y = f(x – a) (8)

This is where the whole graph <u>slides to the left or right</u> and it only happens when you replace 'x' everywhere in the equation <u>with 'x – a'</u>. These are tricky because they go 'the wrong way'. If you want to go from y = f(x) to y = f(x – a) you must move the whole graph a distance 'a' in the <u>positive</u> x-direction → (and vice versa).

EXAMPLE: The graph $y = \sin x$ is shown below, for $-360° \le x \le 360$.

a) Sketch the graph of $\sin(x − 60)°$.
$y = \sin(x − 60)°$ is $y = \sin x$
translated 60° in the <u>positive</u> x-direction.

b) Give the coordinates of a point where $y = \sin(x − 60)°$ crosses the x-axis.
$y = \sin x$ crosses the x-axis at (0, 0),
so $y = \sin(x − 60)°$ will cross at (60°, 0)

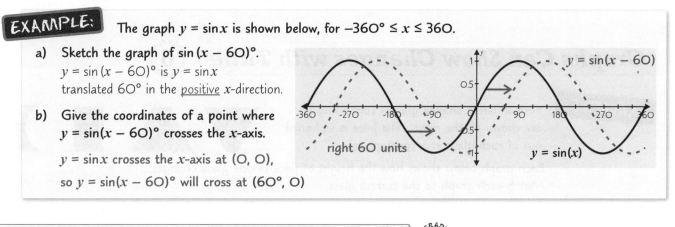

Reflections: y = –f(x) and y = f(–x) (8)

y = –f(x) is the <u>reflection</u> in the <u>x-axis</u> of y = f(x).

Points (–2, 0) and (2, 0) are <u>invariant points</u> — they don't change during the transformation.

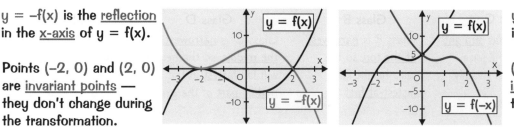

y = f(–x) is the <u>reflection</u> in the <u>y-axis</u> of y = f(x).

(0, 5) is the only <u>invariant point</u> under this reflection.

More sliding and flipping than a martial arts film...

Make sure you learn all the different transformations — then try them out on this Practice Question.

Q1 The coordinates of the maximum point of the graph y = f(x) are (4, 3).
    Give the coordinates of the maximum point of the graph with equation:
    a) $y = f(-x)$ b) $y = f(x) - 4$ c) $y = f(x - 2) + 1$ [3 marks] (8)

Real-Life Graphs

Now and then, graphs mean something more interesting than just $y = x^3 + 4x^2 - 6x + 4...$

Graphs Can Show Billing Structures

GRADE 3 GRADE

Many bills are made up of two charges — a <u>fixed charge</u> and a <u>cost per unit</u>. E.g. You might pay £11 each month for your phone line, and then be charged 3p for each minute of calls you make.

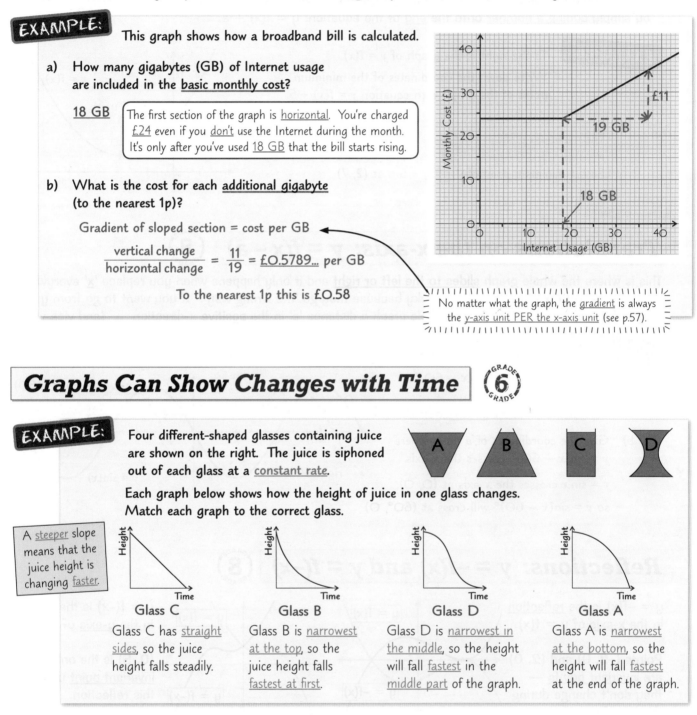

EXAMPLE: This graph shows how a broadband bill is calculated.

a) How many gigabytes (GB) of Internet usage are included in the <u>basic monthly cost</u>?

<u>18 GB</u> The first section of the graph is <u>horizontal</u>. You're charged <u>£24</u> even if you <u>don't</u> use the Internet during the month. It's only after you've used <u>18 GB</u> that the bill starts rising.

b) What is the cost for each <u>additional gigabyte</u> (to the nearest 1p)?

Gradient of sloped section = cost per GB

$\dfrac{\text{vertical change}}{\text{horizontal change}} = \dfrac{11}{19} = £0.5789...$ per GB

To the nearest 1p this is £0.58

No matter what the graph, the <u>gradient</u> is always the <u>y-axis unit PER the x-axis unit</u> (see p.57).

Graphs Can Show Changes with Time

GRADE 6 GRADE

EXAMPLE: Four different-shaped glasses containing juice are shown on the right. The juice is siphoned out of each glass at a <u>constant rate</u>.

Each graph below shows how the height of juice in one glass changes. Match each graph to the correct glass.

A steeper slope means that the juice height is changing <u>faster</u>.

Glass C — Glass C has <u>straight sides</u>, so the juice height falls steadily.

Glass B — Glass B is <u>narrowest at the top</u>, so the juice height falls <u>fastest at first</u>.

Glass D — Glass D is <u>narrowest in the middle</u>, so the height will fall <u>fastest</u> in the <u>middle part</u> of the graph.

Glass A — Glass A is <u>narrowest at the bottom</u>, so the height will fall <u>fastest</u> at the end of the graph.

Exam marks per unit of brainpower...

Distance-time graphs and velocity-time graphs are real-life graphs too — see p.55 and p.56.

Q1 A taxi charges a minimum fare of £4.50, which includes the first three miles.
It then charges 80p for each additional mile.
Draw a graph to show the cost of journeys of up to 10 miles.

[4 marks] GRADE 4 GRADE

Distance-Time Graphs

Ah, what could be better than some nice D/T graphs? OK, so a slap-up meal with Hugh Jackman might be better. Unfortunately this section isn't called 'Tea With The Stars' so a D/T graph will have to do...

Distance-Time Graphs

Distance-time graphs can look a bit awkward at first, but they're not too bad once you get your head around them.

Just remember these 4 important points:

1) At any point, **GRADIENT = SPEED**.
2) The **STEEPER** the graph, the **FASTER** it's going.
3) **FLAT SECTIONS** are where it is **STOPPED**.
4) If the gradient's negative, it's **COMING BACK**.

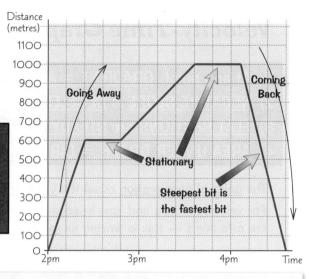

EXAMPLE: Henry went out for a ride on his bike. After a while he got a puncture and stopped to fix it. This graph shows the first part of Henry's journey.

a) **What time did Henry leave home?**

He left home at the point where the line starts. **At 8:15**

b) **How far did Henry cycle before getting a puncture?**

The horizontal part of the graph is where Henry stopped. **12 km**

c) **What was Henry's speed before getting a puncture?**

Using the speed formula is the same as finding the gradient.

$$speed = \frac{distance}{time} = \frac{12\ km}{0.5\ hours}$$
$$= 24\ km/h$$

d) **At 9:30 Henry turns round and cycles home at 24 km/h. Complete the graph to show this.**

You have to work out how long it will take Henry to cycle the 18 km home:

$$time = \frac{distance}{speed} = \frac{18\ km}{24\ km/h} = \underline{0.75\ hours}$$

$$0.75 \times 60\ mins = \underline{45\ mins}$$

Decimal times are yuck, so convert it to minutes.

45 minutes after 9:30 is 10:15, so that's the time Henry gets home. Now you can complete the graph.

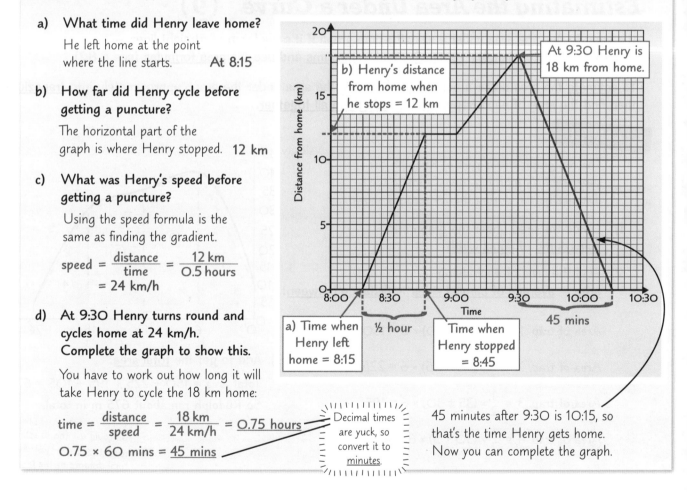

D-T Graphs — filled with highs and lows, an analogy of life...

The only way to get good at distance-time graphs is to practise, practise, practise...

Q1 a) Using the graph above, how long did Henry stop for? [1 mark]

b) What was Henry's speed after he had repaired the puncture, before he turned back home? [2 marks]

Velocity-Time Graphs

Velocity is <u>speed</u> measured in a <u>particular direction</u>. So two objects with velocities of 20 m/s and –20 m/s are moving at the same speed but in opposite directions. For the purpose of these graphs, velocity is just <u>speed</u>.

Velocity-Time Graphs (6)

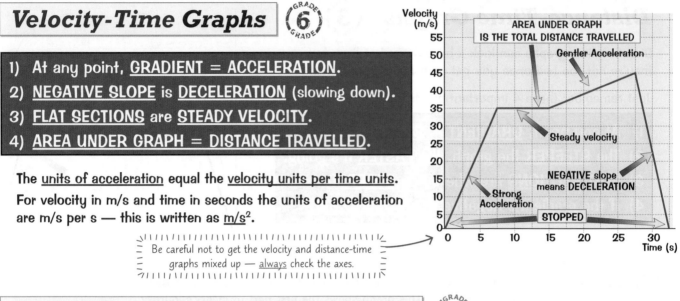

1) At any point, <u>GRADIENT = ACCELERATION</u>.
2) <u>NEGATIVE SLOPE</u> is <u>DECELERATION</u> (slowing down).
3) <u>FLAT SECTIONS</u> are <u>STEADY VELOCITY</u>.
4) <u>AREA UNDER GRAPH = DISTANCE TRAVELLED</u>.

The <u>units of acceleration</u> equal the <u>velocity units per time units</u>.

For velocity in m/s and time in seconds the units of acceleration are m/s per s — this is written as $\underline{m/s^2}$.

Be careful not to get the velocity and distance-time graphs mixed up — <u>always</u> check the axes.

Estimating the Area Under a Curve (9)

It's easy to find the area under a velocity-time graph if it's made up of <u>straight lines</u> — just split it up into <u>triangles</u>, <u>rectangles</u> and <u>trapeziums</u> and use the <u>area formulas</u> (see p.82).

To <u>estimate</u> the area under a curved graph, divide the area under the graph approximately into <u>trapeziums</u>, then find the area of each trapezium and <u>add them all together</u>.

EXAMPLE:

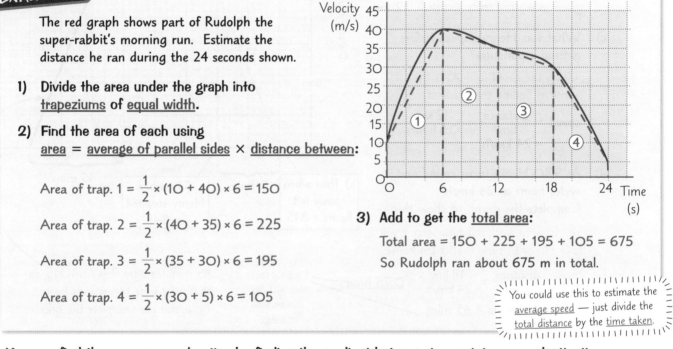

The red graph shows part of Rudolph the super-rabbit's morning run. Estimate the distance he ran during the 24 seconds shown.

1) Divide the area under the graph into <u>trapeziums</u> of <u>equal width</u>.

2) Find the area of each using <u>area = average of parallel sides × distance between</u>:

Area of trap. 1 = $\frac{1}{2}$ × (10 + 40) × 6 = 150

Area of trap. 2 = $\frac{1}{2}$ × (40 + 35) × 6 = 225

Area of trap. 3 = $\frac{1}{2}$ × (35 + 30) × 6 = 195

Area of trap. 4 = $\frac{1}{2}$ × (30 + 5) × 6 = 105

3) Add to get the <u>total area</u>:

Total area = 150 + 225 + 195 + 105 = 675

So Rudolph ran about **675 m** in total.

You could use this to estimate the <u>average speed</u> — just divide the <u>total distance</u> by the <u>time taken</u>.

You can find the <u>average acceleration</u> by finding the gradient between <u>two points</u> on a velocity-time curve, or estimate the acceleration at a <u>specific point</u> by drawing a <u>tangent</u> to the curve (see next page).

Velocity — a bicycle-friendly French town...

Make sure you're happy with gradients and finding the area underneath a velocity-time graph.

Q1   Calculate the total distance travelled in the velocity-time graph at the top of this page. [3 marks] (6)

Gradients of Real-Life Graphs

Gradients are great — they tell you all sorts of stuff, like 'you're accelerating', or 'you need a spirit level'.

The Gradient of a Graph Represents the Rate (5)

No matter what the graph may be,
the meaning of the gradient is always simply:

(y-axis UNITS) PER (x-axis UNITS)

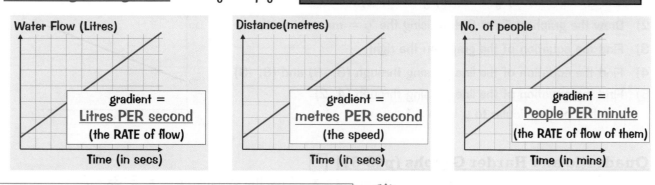

Finding the Average Gradient (7)

You could be asked to find the average gradient between two points on a curve.

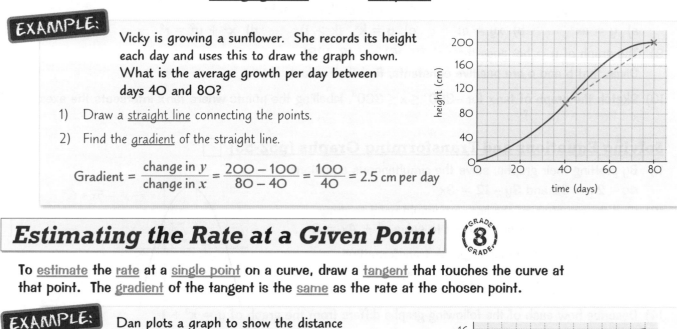

EXAMPLE:

Vicky is growing a sunflower. She records its height each day and uses this to draw the graph shown. What is the average growth per day between days 40 and 80?

1) Draw a straight line connecting the points.
2) Find the gradient of the straight line.

$$\text{Gradient} = \frac{\text{change in } y}{\text{change in } x} = \frac{200 - 100}{80 - 40} = \frac{100}{40} = 2.5 \text{ cm per day}$$

Estimating the Rate at a Given Point (8)

To estimate the rate at a single point on a curve, draw a tangent that touches the curve at that point. The gradient of the tangent is the same as the rate at the chosen point.

EXAMPLE:

Dan plots a graph to show the distance he travelled during a bike race. Estimate Dan's speed after 40 minutes.

1) Draw a tangent to the curve at 40 minutes.
2) Find the gradient of the straight line.

$$\text{Gradient} = \frac{\text{change in } y}{\text{change in } x} = \frac{14 - 10}{55 - 40} = \frac{4}{15} \text{ miles per minute}$$
$$= 16 \text{ miles per hour}$$

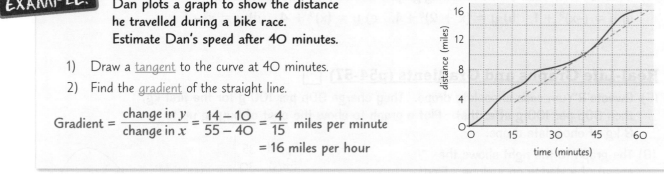

I think I'll have bacon and eggs for tea... wait, no, fish cakes...

Sorry, I was going off on a tangent. Just remember to look at the units and keep a ruler to hand and you'll have no problem with this. Also practise finding the gradient, just to make sure you've got it nailed.

Q1 On the sunflower height graph, estimate the rate of growth on day 20. [2 marks] (8)

Q2 On the cycling graph, calculate the average speed between 25 and 40 minutes. [2 marks] (7)

Revision Questions for Section Three

Well, that wraps up <u>Section Three</u> — time to put yourself to the test and find out <u>how much you really know</u>.
- Try these questions and <u>tick off each one</u> when you <u>get it right</u>.
- When you've done <u>all the questions</u> for a topic and are <u>completely happy</u> with it, tick off the topic.

<u>Straight Lines (p43-47)</u> ☑

1) Sketch the lines a) $y = -x$, b) $y = -4$, c) $x = 2$

2) Draw the graph of $5x = 2 + y$ using the '$y = mx + c$' method.

3) Find the equation of the graph on the right.

4) Find the equation of the line passing through (3, -6) and (6, -3).

5) Find the equation of the line passing through (4, 2) which is perpendicular to $y = 2x - 1$.

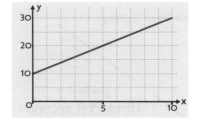

<u>Quadratic and Harder Graphs (p48-51)</u> ☑

6) a) Create and complete a table of values for $-3 \leq x \leq 1$ for the equation $y = x^2 + 3x - 7$

   b) Plot the graph of $y = x^2 + 3x - 7$, labelling the turning point with its exact coordinates.

7) Plot the graph $y = x^2 + 2x - 8$ and use it to estimate the solutions to $-2 = x^2 + 2x - 8$ (to 1 d.p.).

8) Describe <u>in words</u> and with a sketch the forms of these graphs:
   a) $y = ax^3$ b) $xy = a$;   c) $y = k^x$ $(k > 1)$ d) $x^2 + y^2 = r^2$

9) The graph of $y = bc^x$ goes through (2, 16) and (3, 128).
   Given that b and c are positive constants, find their values.

10) Sketch the graph of $\tan x$ for $-360° \leq x \leq 360°$, labelling the points where $\tan x$ intersects the axes.

<u>Solving Equations and Transforming Graphs (p52-53)</u> ☑

11) By plotting their graphs, solve the simultaneous equations
    $4y - 2x = 32$ and $3y - 12 = 3x$

12) Find the equation of the line you would need to draw on the graph shown on the right to solve $x^2 + 4x = 0$

13) What are the three types of graph transformation you need to learn and how does the equation $y = f(x)$ change for each of them?

14) Describe how each of the following graphs differs from the graph of $y = x^3 + 1$
    a) $y = (-x)^3 + 1$,   b) $y = (x + 2)^3 + 1$,   c) $y = (x)^3 + 4$,   d) $y = x^3 - 1$

<u>Real-Life Graphs and Gradients (p54-57)</u> ☑

15) Sweets'R'Yum sells chocolate drops. They charge 90p per 100 g for the first kg, then 60p per 100 g after that. Plot a graph to show the cost of buying up to 3 kg of chocolate drops.

16) The graph to the right shows the speed of a sledge on a slope. Find:
    a) an estimate of the total distance travelled by the sledge.
    b) the average acceleration between 6 and 14 seconds.
    c) the acceleration at 12 seconds.

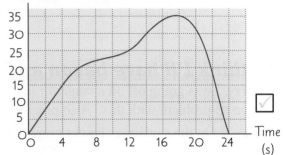

Ratios

Ratios are a pretty important topic — so work your way through the examples on the next three pages, and the whole murky business should become crystal clear...

Writing Ratios as Fractions (3)

You can express ratios as <u>fractions</u> in different ways.

> For example, if a bag of fruit contains apples and oranges in the ratio $2:9$, then there are:
> - $\frac{2}{9}$ as many apples as oranges, or $\frac{9}{2}$ times as many oranges as apples.
> - $2 + 9 = 11$ parts in total. So $\frac{2}{11}$ of the bag are apples and $\frac{9}{11}$ of the bag are oranges.

Reducing Ratios to their Simplest Form (3)

To reduce a ratio to a <u>simpler form</u>, divide <u>all the numbers</u> in the ratio by the <u>same thing</u> (a bit like simplifying a fraction — see p.5). It's in its <u>simplest form</u> when there's nothing left you can divide by.

> **EXAMPLE:** Write the ratio 15:18 in its simplest form.
>
> For the ratio 15:18, both numbers have a <u>factor</u> of 3, so <u>divide them by 3</u>.
>
> We can't reduce this any further. So the simplest form of 15:18 is **5:6**.
>
> $\div 3 \left(\begin{matrix} 15:18 \\ \downarrow \\ = \quad 5:6 \end{matrix} \right) \div 3$

A handy trick for the calculator papers — use the fraction button

If you enter a fraction with the ⊟ or [a b/c] button, the calculator automatically cancels it down when you press ▭.
For the ratio 8:12, enter $\frac{8}{12}$ as a fraction, and it'll simplify to $\frac{2}{3}$. Now you just change it back into a ratio, i.e. <u>2 : 3</u>.

The More Awkward Cases: (3)

1) If the ratio contains <u>decimals</u> or <u>fractions</u> — <u>multiply</u>

> *For fractions, multiply by a number that gets rid of both <u>denominators</u>.*

> **EXAMPLE:** Simplify the ratio 2.4:3.6 as far as possible.
>
> 1) <u>Multiply both sides by 10</u> to get rid of the decimal parts.
> 2) Now <u>divide</u> to reduce the ratio to its simplest form.
>
> $\begin{matrix} & \times 10 \left(\begin{matrix} 2.4:3.6 \\ \downarrow \\ 24:36 \end{matrix} \right) \times 10 \\ = & \div 12 \left(\begin{matrix} \downarrow \\ 2:3 \end{matrix} \right) \div 12 \end{matrix}$

2) If the ratio has <u>mixed units</u> — convert to the <u>smaller unit</u>

> **EXAMPLE:** Reduce the ratio 24 mm:7.2 cm to its simplest form.
>
> 1) <u>Convert</u> 7.2 cm to millimetres.
> 2) <u>Simplify</u> the resulting ratio. Once the units on both sides are the same, <u>get rid of them</u> for the final answer.
>
> $\begin{matrix} & 24 \text{ mm}:7.2 \text{ cm} \\ = & 24 \text{ mm}:72 \text{ mm} \\ = & {}^{\div 24} \searrow 1:3 \swarrow {}^{\div 24} \end{matrix}$

I ain't gettin' on no gosh-darned plane!

Don't be so awkward, case.

3) To get to the form <u>1 : n</u> or <u>n : 1</u> — just <u>divide</u>

> **EXAMPLE:** Reduce 3:56 to the form 1:n.
>
> Divide both sides by 3:
>
> $\begin{matrix} & {}^{\div 3} \left(\begin{matrix} 3:56 \\ \downarrow \\ = \quad 1:\frac{56}{3} \end{matrix} \right) {}^{\div 3} = \quad 1:18\frac{2}{3} \text{ (or } 1:18.\dot{6}) \end{matrix}$
>
> *This form is often the <u>most useful</u>, since it shows the ratio very clearly.*

Ratios

Another page on <u>ratios</u> coming up — it's more <u>interesting</u> than the first but not as exciting as the next one...

Scaling Up Ratios ③

If you know the <u>ratio between parts</u> and the actual size of <u>one part</u>, you can <u>scale the ratio up</u> to find the other parts.

> **EXAMPLE:** Mortar is made from mixing sand and cement in the ratio 7:2. How many buckets of mortar will be made if 21 buckets of sand are used in the mixture?
>
> You need to <u>multiply by 3</u> to go from 7 to 21 on the left-hand side (LHS) — so do that to <u>both sides</u>:
>
> So <u>21 buckets of sand</u> and <u>6 buckets of cement</u> are used.
>
> sand : cement
>
> ×3 (7:2) ×3
> = 21:6
>
> Amount of mortar made = 21 + 6 = 27 buckets

The two parts of a ratio are always in <u>direct proportion</u> (see p.62). So in the example above, sand and cement are in direct proportion, e.g. if the amount of sand <u>doubles</u>, the amount of cement <u>doubles</u>.

Part : Whole Ratios ③

You might come across a ratio where the LHS is <u>included</u> in the RHS — these are called <u>part : whole ratios</u>.

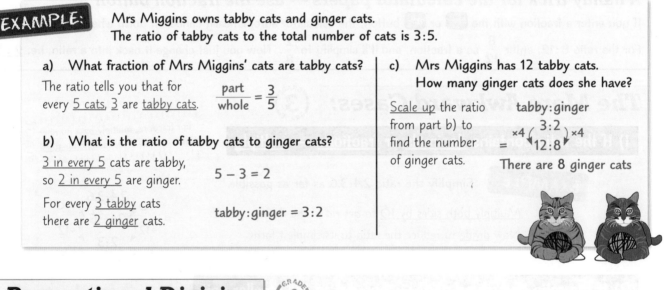

> **EXAMPLE:** Mrs Miggins owns tabby cats and ginger cats. The ratio of tabby cats to the total number of cats is 3:5.
>
> **a)** What fraction of Mrs Miggins' cats are tabby cats?
>
> The ratio tells you that for every <u>5 cats</u>, <u>3</u> are <u>tabby cats</u>.
>
> $$\frac{\text{part}}{\text{whole}} = \frac{3}{5}$$
>
> **b)** What is the ratio of tabby cats to ginger cats?
>
> <u>3 in every 5</u> cats are tabby, so <u>2 in every 5</u> are ginger.
>
> 5 − 3 = 2
>
> For every <u>3 tabby</u> cats there are <u>2 ginger</u> cats.
>
> tabby : ginger = 3:2
>
> **c)** Mrs Miggins has 12 tabby cats. How many ginger cats does she have?
>
> <u>Scale up</u> the ratio from part b) to find the number of ginger cats.
>
> tabby : ginger
>
> ×4 (3:2) ×4
> = 12:8
>
> There are 8 ginger cats

Proportional Division ④

In a <u>proportional division</u> question a <u>TOTAL AMOUNT</u> is split into parts <u>in a certain ratio</u>. The key word here is <u>PARTS</u> — concentrate on 'parts' and it all becomes quite painless:

> **EXAMPLE:** Jess, Mo and Greg share £9100 in the ratio 2:4:7. How much does Mo get?
>
> **1)** <u>ADD UP THE PARTS</u>:
>
> The ratio 2:4:7 means there will be a total of 13 <u>parts</u>:
>
> 2 + 4 + 7 = 13 parts
>
> **2)** <u>DIVIDE TO FIND ONE "PART"</u>:
>
> Just divide the <u>total amount</u> by the number of <u>parts</u>:
>
> £9100 ÷ 13 = £700 (= 1 part)
>
> **3)** <u>MULTIPLY TO FIND THE AMOUNTS</u>:
>
> We want to know <u>Mo's share</u>, which is <u>4 parts</u>:
>
> 4 parts = 4 × £700 = £2800

Ratios

If you were worried I was running out of <u>great stuff</u> to say about ratios then worry no more...

Using the Difference Between Two Parts 4

Sometimes questions give you the <u>difference between two parts</u> instead of the <u>total amount</u>.

EXAMPLE: A baguette is cut into 3 pieces in the ratio 1:2:5. The first piece is 28 cm smaller than the third piece. How long is the second piece?

1) Work out <u>how many parts</u> 28 cm makes up.
   28 cm = 3rd piece − 1st piece
   = 5 parts − 1 part = 4 parts

2) <u>Divide</u> to find <u>one part</u>.
   28 cm ÷ 4 = 7 cm

3) <u>Multiply</u> to find the length of the <u>2nd piece</u>.
   2nd piece = 2 parts = 2 × 7 cm = 14 cm

Changing Ratios 8

You'll need to know how to deal with all sorts of questions where the <u>ratio changes</u>.
Have a look at this example to see how to <u>handle them</u>.

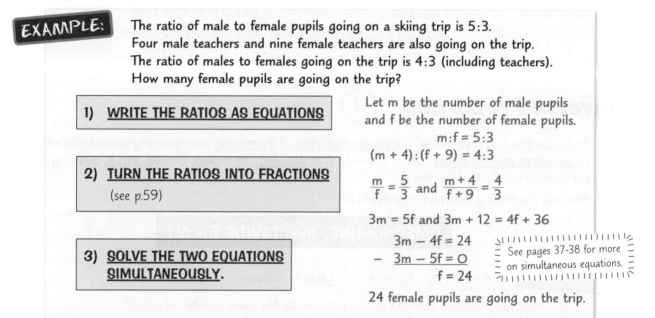

EXAMPLE: The ratio of male to female pupils going on a skiing trip is 5:3.
Four male teachers and nine female teachers are also going on the trip.
The ratio of males to females going on the trip is 4:3 (including teachers).
How many female pupils are going on the trip?

1) **WRITE THE RATIOS AS EQUATIONS**

2) **TURN THE RATIOS INTO FRACTIONS**
   (see p.59)

3) **SOLVE THE TWO EQUATIONS SIMULTANEOUSLY.**

Let m be the number of male pupils and f be the number of female pupils.
$$m:f = 5:3$$
$$(m + 4):(f + 9) = 4:3$$
$$\frac{m}{f} = \frac{5}{3} \text{ and } \frac{m+4}{f+9} = \frac{4}{3}$$
$$3m = 5f \text{ and } 3m + 12 = 4f + 36$$

$$3m - 4f = 24$$
$$- \quad \underline{3m - 5f = 0}$$
$$f = 24$$

See pages 37-38 for more on simultaneous equations.

24 female pupils are going on the trip.

Sorry, 3 pages of ratios was all I could manage. I hope it's enough...

There's loads of stuff to learn about ratios, so have another quick read through the last 3 pages.
Then turn over and write down what you've learned. When you're good and ready, try these questions:

Q1 Simplify: a) $25:35$ b) $3.4:5.1$ c) $\frac{9}{4}:\frac{15}{2}$ [4 marks] 3

Q2 Orange squash is made of water and concentrate in the ratio $11:2$.
a) What fraction of the squash is made up from concentrate? [1 mark] 3
b) How many litres of water are needed to make 1.95 litres of orange squash? [2 marks]

Q3 The ages of Ben, Graham and Pam are in the ratio $3:7:8$.
Pam is 25 years older than Ben. How old is Graham? [2 marks] 5

Q4 A bag contains red and blue balls. If two of each colour ball are removed
from the bag the ratio of red to blue balls is $5:7$. If seven of each colour
ball are added to the original bag, the ratio of red to blue balls is $4:5$.
How many red and blue balls are in the original bag? [6 marks] 8

Direct and Inverse Proportion

There can sometimes be a lot of <u>information</u> packed into proportion questions, but the <u>method</u> of solving them always stays the same — have a look at this page and see what you think.

Direct Proportion

1) Two quantities, A and B, are in <u>direct proportion</u> (or just in <u>proportion</u>) if increasing one increases the other one <u>proportionally</u>. So if quantity A is doubled (or trebled, halved, etc.), so is quantity B.

2) Remember this <u>golden rule</u> for direct proportion questions:

DIVIDE for ONE, then TIMES for ALL

EXAMPLE: Hannah pays £3.60 per 400 g of cheese.
She uses 220 g of cheese to make 4 cheese pasties.
How much would the cheese cost if she wanted to make 50 cheese pasties?

There will often be lots of stages to direct proportion questions — keep track of what you've worked out at each stage.

In <u>1 pasty</u> there is: 220 g ÷ 4 = 55 g of cheese
So in <u>50 pasties</u> there is: 55 g × 50 = 2750 g of cheese

<u>1 g of cheese</u> would cost: £3.60 ÷ 400 = 0.9p
So <u>2750 g of cheese</u> would cost: 0.9 × 2750 = 2475p = £24.75

Inverse Proportion

1) Two quantities, C and D, are in <u>inverse proportion</u> if <u>increasing</u> one quantity causes the other quantity to <u>decrease proportionally</u>. So if quantity C is <u>doubled</u> (or tripled, halved, etc.), quantity D is <u>halved</u> (or divided by 3, doubled etc.).

2) The rule for finding inverse proportions is:

TIMES for ONE, then DIVIDE for ALL

EXAMPLE: 4 bakers can decorate 100 cakes in 5 hours.

a) How long would it take 10 bakers to decorate the same number of cakes?

<u>100 cakes</u> will take <u>1 baker</u>:   5 × 4 = 20 hours

So <u>100 cakes</u> will take <u>10 bakers</u>:   20 ÷ 10 = 2 hours for 10 bakers

b) How long would it take 11 bakers to decorate 220 cakes?

<u>100 cakes</u> will take <u>1 baker</u>:   20 hours

<u>1 cake</u> will take <u>1 baker</u>:   20 ÷ 100 = 0.2 hours

<u>220 cakes</u> will take <u>1 baker</u>:   0.2 × 220 = 44 hours

<u>220 cakes</u> will take <u>11 bakers</u>:   44 ÷ 11 = 4 hours

The number of bakers is <u>inversely proportional</u> to number of hours — but the number of cakes is <u>directly proportional</u> to the number of hours.

Calm down, you're blowing this page all out of proportion...

Q1   It costs £43.20 for 8 people to go on a rollercoaster 6 times.
How much will it cost for 15 people to go on a rollercoaster 5 times?   [4 marks]

Q2   It takes 2 carpenters 4 hours to make 3 bookcases.
How long would it take 5 carpenters to make 10 bookcases?   [4 marks]

Direct and Inverse Proportion

Algebraic proportion questions normally involve two variables (often x and y) which are linked in some way.

Types of Proportion (7)

∝ means 'is proportional to'.

1) The simple proportions are 'y is proportional to x' ($y \propto x$) and 'y is inversely proportional to x' ($y \propto \frac{1}{x}$).

2) You can always turn a proportion statement into an equation by replacing '∝' with '$= k$' like this:

	Proportionality	Equation
'y is proportional to x'	$y \propto x$	$y = kx$
'y is inversely proportional to x'	$y \propto \frac{1}{x}$	$y = \frac{k}{x}$

k is just some constant (unknown number)

3) Trickier proportions involve y varying proportionally or inversely to some function of x, e.g. x^2, x^3, $\sqrt{x}$ etc.

	Proportionality	Equation
'y is proportional to the square of x'	$y \propto x^2$	$y = kx^2$
't is proportional to the square root of h'	$t \propto \sqrt{h}$	$t = k\sqrt{h}$
'V is inversely proportional to r cubed'	$V \propto \frac{1}{r^3}$	$V = \frac{k}{r^3}$

4) Once you've written the proportion statement as an equation you can easily graph it.

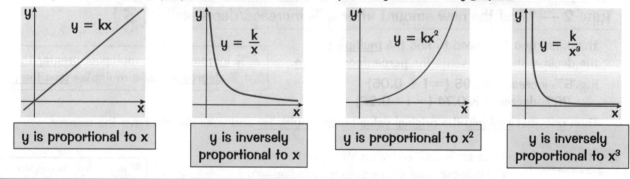

$y = kx$	$y = \frac{k}{x}$	$y = kx^2$	$y = \frac{k}{x^3}$
y is proportional to x	y is inversely proportional to x	y is proportional to x^2	y is inversely proportional to x^3

Handling Algebra Questions on Proportion (7)

1) Write the sentence as a proportionality and replace '∝' with '$= k$' to make an equation (as above).

2) Find a pair of values (x and y) somewhere in the question — substitute them into the equation to find k.

3) Put the value of k into the equation and it's now ready to use, e.g. $y = 3x^2$.

4) Inevitably, they'll ask you to find y, having given you a value for x (or vice versa).

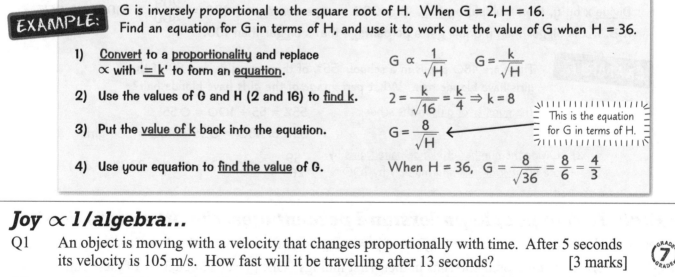

EXAMPLE: G is inversely proportional to the square root of H. When G = 2, H = 16. Find an equation for G in terms of H, and use it to work out the value of G when H = 36.

1) Convert to a proportionality and replace ∝ with '$= k$' to form an equation.
$$G \propto \frac{1}{\sqrt{H}} \qquad G = \frac{k}{\sqrt{H}}$$

2) Use the values of G and H (2 and 16) to find k.
$$2 = \frac{k}{\sqrt{16}} = \frac{k}{4} \Rightarrow k = 8$$

3) Put the value of k back into the equation.
$$G = \frac{8}{\sqrt{H}}$$
This is the equation for G in terms of H.

4) Use your equation to find the value of G.
When H = 36, $G = \frac{8}{\sqrt{36}} = \frac{8}{6} = \frac{4}{3}$

Joy ∝ 1/algebra...

Q1 An object is moving with a velocity that changes proportionally with time. After 5 seconds its velocity is 105 m/s. How fast will it be travelling after 13 seconds? [3 marks] (7)

Q2 P is inversely proportional to the square of Q (P, Q > 0). When P = 3, Q = 4. Find an equation for P in terms of Q and find the exact value of Q when P = 8. [4 marks] (7)

Percentages

'Per cent' means 'out of 100' — remember this and you'll easily be able to convert percentages into fractions and decimals (p.7). Then you're ready to tackle the first three simple types of percentage question.

Three Simple Question Types

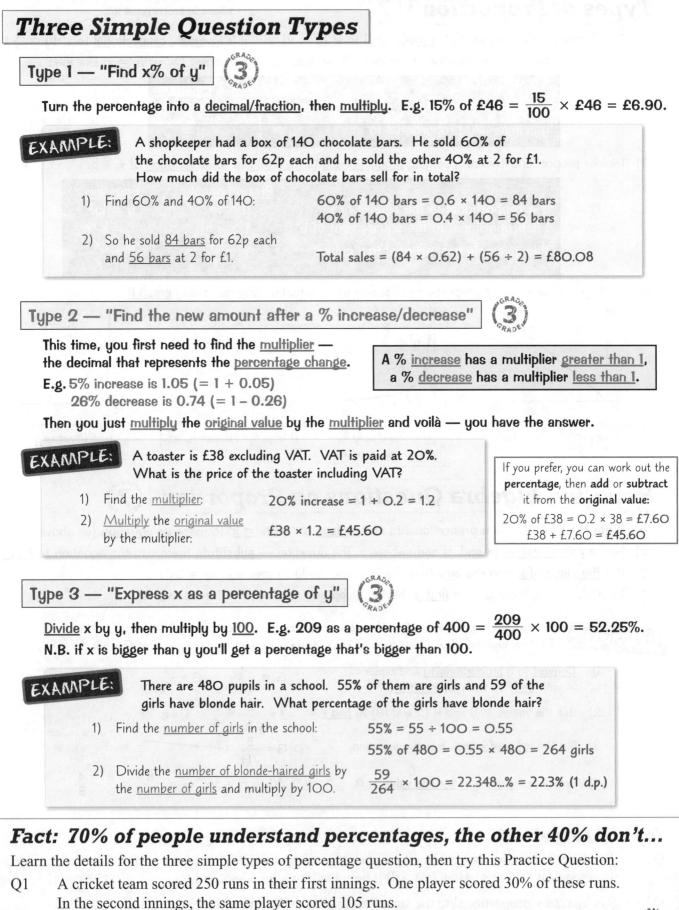

Type 1 — "Find x% of y"

Turn the percentage into a decimal/fraction, then multiply. E.g. 15% of £46 = $\frac{15}{100}$ × £46 = £6.90.

EXAMPLE: A shopkeeper had a box of 140 chocolate bars. He sold 60% of the chocolate bars for 62p each and he sold the other 40% at 2 for £1. How much did the box of chocolate bars sell for in total?

1) Find 60% and 40% of 140:

    60% of 140 bars = 0.6 × 140 = 84 bars
    40% of 140 bars = 0.4 × 140 = 56 bars

2) So he sold 84 bars for 62p each and 56 bars at 2 for £1.

    Total sales = (84 × 0.62) + (56 ÷ 2) = £80.08

Type 2 — "Find the new amount after a % increase/decrease"

This time, you first need to find the multiplier — the decimal that represents the percentage change.

E.g. 5% increase is 1.05 (= 1 + 0.05)
    26% decrease is 0.74 (= 1 − 0.26)

A % increase has a multiplier greater than 1, a % decrease has a multiplier less than 1.

Then you just multiply the original value by the multiplier and voilà — you have the answer.

EXAMPLE: A toaster is £38 excluding VAT. VAT is paid at 20%. What is the price of the toaster including VAT?

1) Find the multiplier:

    20% increase = 1 + 0.2 = 1.2

2) Multiply the original value by the multiplier:

    £38 × 1.2 = £45.60

If you prefer, you can work out the **percentage**, then **add** or **subtract** it from the **original value**:
20% of £38 = 0.2 × 38 = £7.60
£38 + £7.60 = £45.60

Type 3 — "Express x as a percentage of y"

Divide x by y, then multiply by 100. E.g. 209 as a percentage of 400 = $\frac{209}{400}$ × 100 = 52.25%.

N.B. if x is bigger than y you'll get a percentage that's bigger than 100.

EXAMPLE: There are 480 pupils in a school. 55% of them are girls and 59 of the girls have blonde hair. What percentage of the girls have blonde hair?

1) Find the number of girls in the school:

    55% = 55 ÷ 100 = 0.55
    55% of 480 = 0.55 × 480 = 264 girls

2) Divide the number of blonde-haired girls by the number of girls and multiply by 100.

    $\frac{59}{264}$ × 100 = 22.348...% = 22.3% (1 d.p.)

Fact: 70% of people understand percentages, the other 40% don't...

Learn the details for the three simple types of percentage question, then try this Practice Question:

Q1   A cricket team scored 250 runs in their first innings. One player scored 30% of these runs. In the second innings, the same player scored 105 runs. Express his second innings score as a percentage of his first innings score. [3 marks]

Percentages

Watch out for these <u>trickier types</u> of percentage question — they'll often include lots of real-life context. Just make sure you know the <u>proper method</u> for each of them and you'll be fine.

Two Trickier Question Types

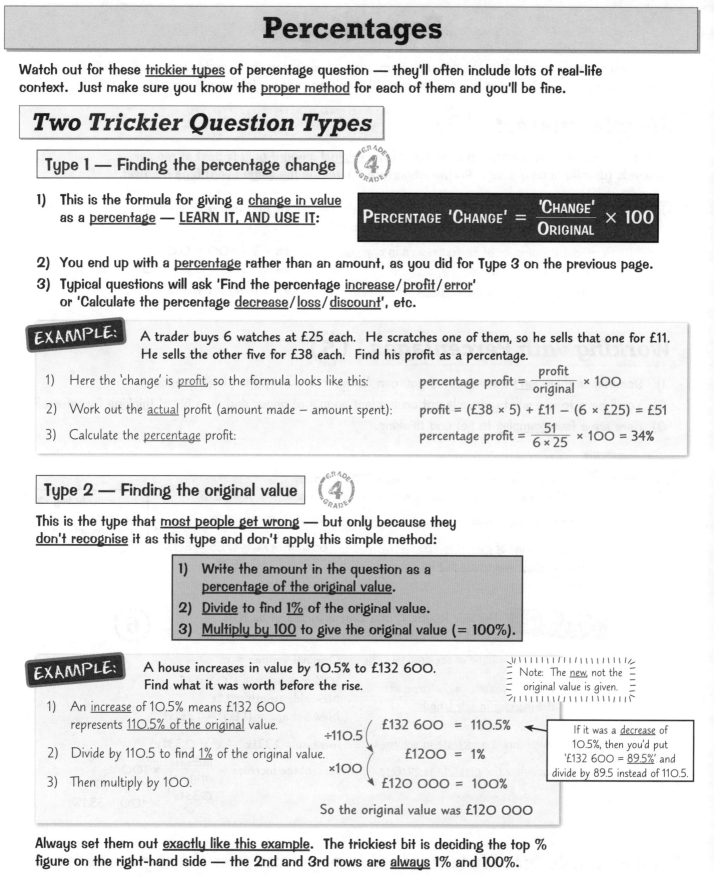

Type 1 — Finding the percentage change

1) This is the formula for giving a <u>change in value</u> as a <u>percentage</u> — <u>LEARN IT, AND USE IT</u>:

$$\text{PERCENTAGE 'CHANGE'} = \frac{\text{'CHANGE'}}{\text{ORIGINAL}} \times 100$$

2) You end up with a <u>percentage</u> rather than an amount, as you did for Type 3 on the previous page.

3) Typical questions will ask 'Find the percentage <u>increase</u>/<u>profit</u>/<u>error</u>' or 'Calculate the percentage <u>decrease</u>/<u>loss</u>/<u>discount</u>', etc.

EXAMPLE: A trader buys 6 watches at £25 each. He scratches one of them, so he sells that one for £11. He sells the other five for £38 each. Find his profit as a percentage.

1) Here the 'change' is <u>profit</u>, so the formula looks like this: $\text{percentage profit} = \frac{\text{profit}}{\text{original}} \times 100$

2) Work out the <u>actual</u> profit (amount made – amount spent): $\text{profit} = (£38 \times 5) + £11 - (6 \times £25) = £51$

3) Calculate the <u>percentage</u> profit: $\text{percentage profit} = \frac{51}{6 \times 25} \times 100 = 34\%$

Type 2 — Finding the original value

This is the type that <u>most people get wrong</u> — but only because they <u>don't recognise</u> it as this type and don't apply this simple method:

1) Write the amount in the question as a <u>percentage of the original value</u>.

2) <u>Divide</u> to find <u>1%</u> of the original value.

3) <u>Multiply by 100</u> to give the original value (= 100%).

EXAMPLE: A house increases in value by 10.5% to £132 600. Find what it was worth before the rise.

> Note: The <u>new</u>, not the original value is given.

1) An <u>increase</u> of 10.5% means £132 600 represents <u>110.5% of the original</u> value.

2) Divide by 110.5 to find <u>1%</u> of the original value.

3) Then multiply by 100.

$÷110.5 \left(\begin{array}{l} £132\ 600 = 110.5\% \\ £1200 = 1\% \\ £120\ 000 = 100\% \end{array} \right. ×100$

> If it was a <u>decrease</u> of 10.5%, then you'd put '£132 600 = <u>89.5%</u>' and divide by 89.5 instead of 110.5.

So the original value was £120 000

Always set them out <u>exactly like this example</u>. The trickiest bit is deciding the top % figure on the right-hand side — the 2nd and 3rd rows are <u>always</u> 1% and 100%.

The % change in my understanding of this topic is 100%...

The methods above are easy to follow but the questions can be a bit tricky. Try these Practice Questions:

Q1 A cereal company has decreased the amount of cereal in a box from 1.2 kg to 900 g. What is the percentage decrease in the amount of cereal per box? [3 marks]

Q2 A shop sells kebabs for a 20% loss. The kebabs sell for £4.88 each. The shop wants to reduce its loss on kebabs to 10%. How much should the shop charge per kebab? [3 marks]

Percentages

Percentages are almost certainly going to come up in your exam, but they could crop up in lots of different topics. Here are some more examples of where you might see them.

Simple Interest (3)

Compound interest is covered on the next page.

Simple interest means a certain percentage of the original amount only is paid at regular intervals (usually once a year). So the amount of interest is the same every time it's paid.

EXAMPLE: Regina invests £380 in an account which pays 3% simple interest each year. How much interest will she earn in 4 years?

1) Work out the amount of interest earned in one year:
   3% = 3 ÷ 100 = 0.03
   3% of £380 = 0.03 × £380 = £11.40

2) Multiply by 4 to get the total interest for 4 years:
   4 × £11.40 = £45.60

Working with Percentages (5)

1) Sometimes there isn't a set method you can follow to answer percentage questions.
2) You'll have to use what you've learnt on the last couple of pages and do a bit of thinking for yourself.
3) Here are a few examples to get you thinking.

EXAMPLE: 80% of the members of a gym are male.
35% of the male members are aged 40 and over.
What percentage of gym members are males under 40 years old?

1) The percentage of male members under 40 is: 100% − 35% = 65%

2) The percentage of gym members that are male and under 40 is:
   65% of 80% = 0.65 × 80%
   = 52%

It's just like finding x% of y — but this time the y is a percentage too.

EXAMPLE: The side length, x, of a cube is increased by 10%. (6)
What is the percentage increase in the volume of the cube?

1) Find the volume of the original cube.
   Original volume = x^3

2) Find the volume of the cube after the increase in side length.
   10% increase = 1 + 0.1 = 1.1
   New side length = $1.1x$
   New volume = $(1.1x)^3 = 1.331x^3$

3) Work out the increase in volume.
   Increase = $1.331x^3 − x^3 = 0.331x^3$

4) Calculate the percentage increase.
   percentage increase = $\dfrac{\text{increase}}{\text{original}} \times 100$
   $= \dfrac{0.331x^3}{x^3} \times 100 = 33.1\%$

Take a simple bit of interest in this page and you'll ace percentages...

You might have to use two or more of the methods you've learnt for finding percentages to answer some of the tougher exam questions. Try the Practice Exam Questions below to see if you've got what it takes...

Q1   Jim invests some money for 5 years in an account at 4% simple interest per annum.
     What is the percentage increase of the investment at the end of the 5 years?   [2 marks] (6)

Q2   At a publishing company 60% of the editors are female.
     30% of the female editors and 20% of the male editors have a maths degree.
     What percentage of all the editors have a maths degree?   [3 marks] (5)

Compound Growth and Decay

One more sneaky % type for you... Unlike <u>simple interest</u>, in <u>compound interest</u> the amount added on (or taken away) <u>changes</u> each time — it's a percentage of the <u>new amount</u>, rather than the <u>original amount</u>.

The Formula

This topic is simple if you <u>LEARN THIS FORMULA</u>. If you don't, it's pretty well impossible:

$$N = N_0 \times (\text{multiplier})^n$$

Amount after n days/hours/years

Number of days/hours/years

Initial amount

Percentage change multiplier
E.g. 5% increase is 1.05 (= 1 + 0.05)
26% decrease is 0.74 (= 1 − 0.26)

3 Examples to show you how EASY it is:

<u>Compound interest</u> is a popular context for these questions — it means the interest is <u>added on each time</u>, and the next lot of interest is calculated using the <u>new total</u> rather than the original amount.

EXAMPLE: Daniel invests £1000 in a savings account which pays 8% compound interest per annum. How much will there be after 6 years?

Use the <u>formula</u>: Amount = $1000(1.08)^6$ = £1586.87

initial amount · 8% increase · 6 years

'Per annum' just means 'each year'.

<u>Depreciation</u> questions are about things (e.g. cars) which <u>decrease in value</u> over time.

EXAMPLE: Susan has just bought a car for £6500.

a) If the car depreciates by 9% each year, how much will it be worth in 3 years' time?

Use the <u>formula</u>: Value = $6500(0.91)^3$ = £4898.21

b) How many complete years will it be before the car is worth less than £3000?

Use the <u>formula</u> again but this time you know don't know <u>n</u>.

Value = $6500(0.91)^n$

Use <u>trial and error</u> to find how many years it will be before the value drops below £3000.

If n = 8, $6500(0.91)^8$ = 3056.6414....
n = 9, $6500(0.91)^9$ = 2781.5437...

It will be 9 years before the car is worth less than £3000.

The compound growth and decay formula can be about <u>population</u> and <u>disease</u> too.

EXAMPLE: The number of bacteria in a sample increases at a rate of 30% each day. After 6 days the number of bacteria is 7500. How many bacteria were there in the original sample?

Put the numbers you know into the formula, then <u>rearrange</u> to find the initial amount, N_0.

$7500 = N_0(1.3)^6$
$N_0 = 7500 \div (1.3)^6$ = 1553.82...

<u>Round</u> the answer to the nearest whole number.

So there were 1554 bacteria originally.

I thought you'd depreciate all the work I've put into this page...

This page is all about the formula really, so make sure you learn it... learn it real good. Oh, and try this:

Q1 Pippa's bank account pays 2.5% compound interest per annum and her balance is £3200.
Kyle has the same bank balance but his account pays simple interest at 3% per annum.
Who will have the most money after 3 years and how much more will they have? [4 marks]

Unit Conversions

A nice easy page for a change — just some <u>facts</u> to learn. Hooray!

Metric and Imperial Units (3)

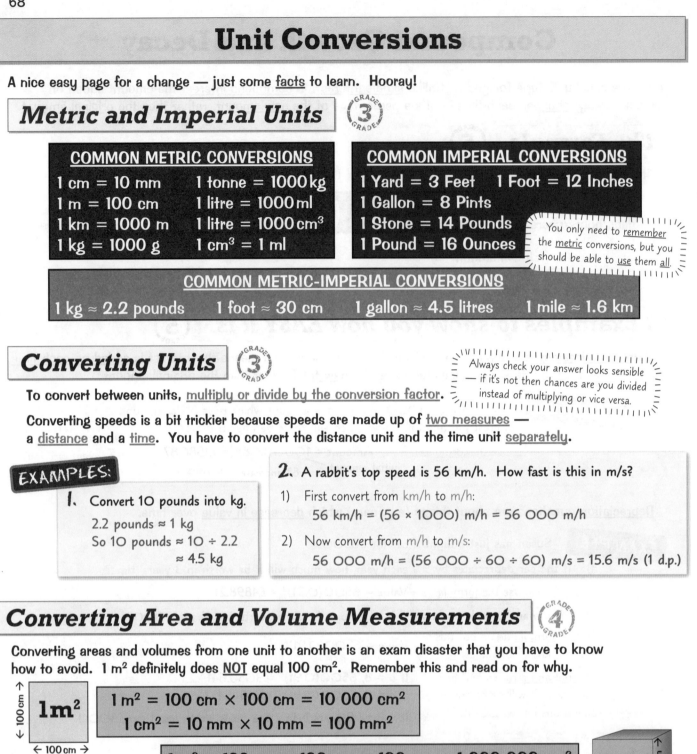

COMMON METRIC CONVERSIONS

1 cm = 10 mm	1 tonne = 1000 kg
1 m = 100 cm	1 litre = 1000 ml
1 km = 1000 m	1 litre = 1000 cm^3
1 kg = 1000 g	1 cm^3 = 1 ml

COMMON IMPERIAL CONVERSIONS

1 Yard = 3 Feet	1 Foot = 12 Inches
1 Gallon = 8 Pints	
1 Stone = 14 Pounds	
1 Pound = 16 Ounces	

You only need to <u>remember</u> the <u>metric</u> conversions, but you should be able to <u>use</u> them <u>all</u>.

COMMON METRIC-IMPERIAL CONVERSIONS

1 kg ≈ 2.2 pounds	1 foot ≈ 30 cm	1 gallon ≈ 4.5 litres	1 mile ≈ 1.6 km

Converting Units (3)

Always check your answer looks sensible — if it's not then chances are you divided instead of multiplying or vice versa.

To convert between units, <u>multiply or divide by the conversion factor</u>.

Converting speeds is a bit trickier because speeds are made up of <u>two measures</u> — a <u>distance</u> and a <u>time</u>. You have to convert the distance unit and the time unit <u>separately</u>.

EXAMPLES:

1. Convert 10 pounds into kg.

2.2 pounds ≈ 1 kg
So 10 pounds ≈ 10 ÷ 2.2
            ≈ 4.5 kg

2. A rabbit's top speed is 56 km/h. How fast is this in m/s?

1) First convert from km/h to m/h:

56 km/h = (56 × 1000) m/h = 56 000 m/h

2) Now convert from m/h to m/s:

56 000 m/h = (56 000 ÷ 60 ÷ 60) m/s = 15.6 m/s (1 d.p.)

Converting Area and Volume Measurements (4)

Converting areas and volumes from one unit to another is an exam disaster that you have to know how to avoid. 1 m^2 definitely does <u>NOT</u> equal 100 cm^2. Remember this and read on for why.

1m^2 (100 cm × 100 cm)

1 m^2 = 100 cm × 100 cm = 10 000 cm^2
1 cm^2 = 10 mm × 10 mm = 100 mm^2

1 m^3 = 100 cm × 100 cm × 100 cm = 1 000 000 cm^3
1 cm^3 = 10 mm × 10 mm × 10 mm = 1000 mm^3

1m^3 (100 cm × 100 cm × 100 cm)

EXAMPLES:

1. Convert 9 m^2 to cm^2.

To change area measurements from m^2 to cm^2 multiply by 100 twice.

9 × 100 × 100 = 90 000 cm^2

2. Convert 60 000 mm^3 to cm^3.

To change volume measurements from mm^3 to cm^3 divide by 10 three times.

60 000 ÷ (10 × 10 × 10) = 60 cm^3

Learn how to convert these questions into marks...

Hmm, I don't know about you, but I quite fancy a conversion-based question after all that.

Q1 Dawn lives 18 km away from work. She drives to work and back 5 days a week.
Her car's fuel consumption is 28 mpg (miles per gallon) and petrol costs £1.39 per litre.
Calculate the weekly cost of petrol for Dawn travelling to and from work. **[5 marks]** (5)

Speed, Density and Pressure

Speed, density and pressure. Just a matter of <u>learning the formulas</u>, bunging the <u>numbers</u> in and watching the <u>units</u>.

Speed = Distance ÷ Time ③

Speed is the <u>distance travelled per unit time</u>, e.g. the number of <u>km per hour</u> or <u>metres per second</u>.

$$\text{SPEED} = \frac{\text{DISTANCE}}{\text{TIME}} \qquad \text{TIME} = \frac{\text{DISTANCE}}{\text{SPEED}} \qquad \text{DISTANCE} = \text{SPEED} \times \text{TIME}$$

<u>Formula triangles</u> are a handy tool for remembering formulas like these. The speed one is shown below.

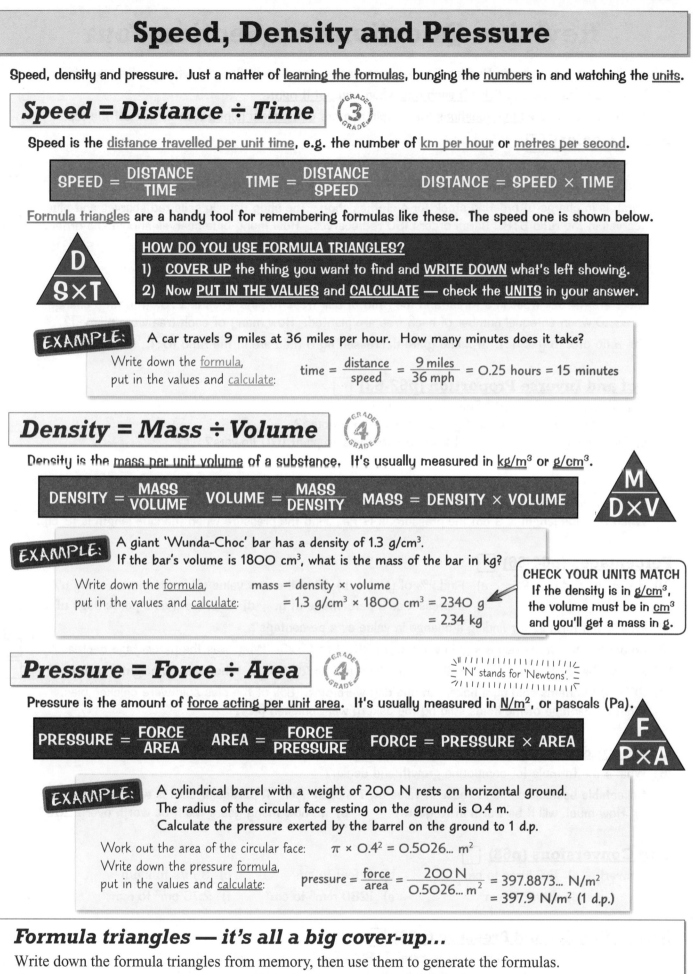

HOW DO YOU USE FORMULA TRIANGLES?
1) **COVER UP** the thing you want to find and **WRITE DOWN** what's left showing.
2) Now **PUT IN THE VALUES** and **CALCULATE** — check the **UNITS** in your answer.

EXAMPLE: A car travels 9 miles at 36 miles per hour. How many minutes does it take?

Write down the <u>formula</u>, put in the values and <u>calculate</u>: $\text{time} = \dfrac{\text{distance}}{\text{speed}} = \dfrac{9 \text{ miles}}{36 \text{ mph}} = 0.25 \text{ hours} = 15 \text{ minutes}$

Density = Mass ÷ Volume ④

Density is the <u>mass per unit volume</u> of a substance. It's usually measured in <u>kg/m³</u> or <u>g/cm³</u>.

$$\text{DENSITY} = \frac{\text{MASS}}{\text{VOLUME}} \qquad \text{VOLUME} = \frac{\text{MASS}}{\text{DENSITY}} \qquad \text{MASS} = \text{DENSITY} \times \text{VOLUME}$$

EXAMPLE: A giant 'Wunda-Choc' bar has a density of 1.3 g/cm³.
If the bar's volume is 1800 cm³, what is the mass of the bar in kg?

Write down the <u>formula</u>, put in the values and <u>calculate</u>:

$\text{mass} = \text{density} \times \text{volume}$
$= 1.3 \text{ g/cm}^3 \times 1800 \text{ cm}^3 = 2340 \text{ g}$
$= 2.34 \text{ kg}$

> **CHECK YOUR UNITS MATCH**
> If the density is in <u>g/cm³</u>, the volume must be in <u>cm³</u> and you'll get a mass in <u>g</u>.

Pressure = Force ÷ Area ④

≡ 'N' stands for 'Newtons'. ≡

Pressure is the amount of <u>force acting per unit area</u>. It's usually measured in <u>N/m²</u>, or pascals (Pa).

$$\text{PRESSURE} = \frac{\text{FORCE}}{\text{AREA}} \qquad \text{AREA} = \frac{\text{FORCE}}{\text{PRESSURE}} \qquad \text{FORCE} = \text{PRESSURE} \times \text{AREA}$$

EXAMPLE: A cylindrical barrel with a weight of 200 N rests on horizontal ground.
The radius of the circular face resting on the ground is 0.4 m.
Calculate the pressure exerted by the barrel on the ground to 1 d.p.

Work out the area of the circular face: $\pi \times 0.4^2 = 0.5026... \text{ m}^2$
Write down the pressure <u>formula</u>, put in the values and <u>calculate</u>:

$\text{pressure} = \dfrac{\text{force}}{\text{area}} = \dfrac{200 \text{ N}}{0.5026... \text{ m}^2} = 397.8873... \text{ N/m}^2$
$= 397.9 \text{ N/m}^2 \text{ (1 d.p.)}$

Formula triangles — it's all a big cover-up...

Write down the formula triangles from memory, then use them to generate the formulas.

Q1 A solid lead cone has a vertical height of 60 cm and a base radius of 20 cm.
If the density of lead is 11.34 g/cm³, find the mass of the cone in kg to 3 s.f. [3 marks] ⑤
(Hint: you'll need to find the volume of the cone — see p85)

Revision Questions for Section Four

Lots of things to remember in <u>Section Four</u> — there's only one way to find out what you've taken in...
- Try these questions and <u>tick off each one</u> when you <u>get it right</u>.
- When you've done <u>all the questions</u> for a topic and are <u>completely happy</u> with it, tick off the topic.

Ratios (p59-61) ☑

1) Pencils and rubbers are in the ratio 13:8. How many times more pencils are there than rubbers? ☑
2) Reduce: a) 1.2:1.6 to its simplest form   b) 49 g:14 g to the form n:1 ☑
3) Sarah is in charge of ordering stock for a clothes shop. The shop usually sells red scarves and blue scarves in the ratio 5:8. Sarah orders 150 red scarves. How many blue scarves should she order? ☑
4) Ryan, Joel and Sam are delivering 800 newspapers. They split the newspapers in the ratio 5:8:12.
   a) What fraction of the newspapers does Ryan deliver?
   b) How many more newspapers does Sam deliver than Joel? ☑
5) There are 44 oak trees in a forest and the ratio of oak trees to pine trees is 2:5. The ratio changes to 9:20 when an equal number of each tree are planted. How many of each tree were planted? ☑
6) The ratio of x to y is 4:1. If x and y are decreased by 6 they are in the ratio 10:1. Find x and y. ☑

Direct and Inverse Proportion (p62-63) ☑

7) 6 gardeners can plant 360 flowers in 3 hours.
   a) How many flowers could 8 gardeners plant in 6 hours?
   b) How many hours would it take for 15 gardeners to plant 1170 flowers? ☑
8) 'y is proportional to the square of x'. a) Write the statement as an equation.
                                          b) Sketch the graph of this proportion for x ≥ 0. ☑
9) The pressure a cube exerts on the ground is inversely proportional to the square of its side length. When the side length is 3 cm the pressure is 17 Pa. Find the pressure when the side length is 13 cm. ☑

Percentages (p64-66) ☑

10) If x = 20 and y = 95:   a) Find x% of y.   b) Find the new value after x is increased by y%.
                            c) Express x as a percentage of y.   d) Express y as a percentage of x. ☑
11) What's the formula for finding a change in value as a percentage? ☑
12) An antique wardrobe decreased in value from £800 to £520. What was the percentage decrease? ☑
13) A tree's height has increased by 15% in the last year to 20.24 m. What was its height a year ago? ☑
14) 25% of the items sold by a bakery in one day were pies. 8% of the pies sold were chicken pies. What percentage of the items sold by the bakery were chicken pies? ☑

Compound Growth and Decay (p67) ☑

15) What's the formula for compound growth and decay? ☑
16) Collectable baseball cards increase in value by 7% each year. A particular card is worth £80.
    a) How much will it be worth in 10 years?   b) In how many years will it be worth over £200? ☑

Unit Conversions (p68) ☑

17) Convert: a) 5.6 litres to cm³   b) 8 feet to cm   c) 3 m/s to km/h
              d) 12 m³ to cm³   e) 1280 mm² to cm²   f) 2.75 cm³ to mm³ ☑

Speed, Density and Pressure (p69) ☑

18) Find the average speed of a car if it travels 63 miles in an hour and a half. ☑
19) Find the volume of a snowman if its density is 0.4 g/cm³ and its mass is 5 kg. ☑
20) Find the area of an object in contact with horizontal ground, if the pressure it exerts on the ground is 120 N/m² and the force acting on the object is 1320 N. ☑

Geometry

If you know <u>all</u> these rules <u>thoroughly</u>, you'll at least have a fighting chance of working out problems with lines and angles. If you don't — you've no chance. Sorry to break it to you like that.

5 Simple Rules — that's all

1) Angles in a triangle add up to 180°.

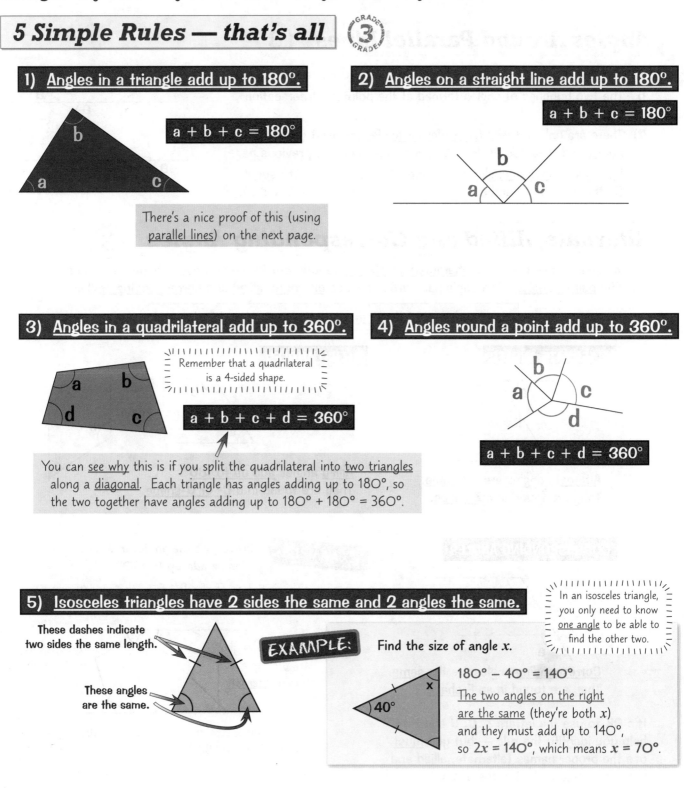

$$a + b + c = 180°$$

There's a nice proof of this (using <u>parallel lines</u>) on the next page.

2) Angles on a straight line add up to 180°.

$$a + b + c = 180°$$

3) Angles in a quadrilateral add up to 360°.

Remember that a quadrilateral is a 4-sided shape.

$$a + b + c + d = 360°$$

You can <u>see why</u> this is if you split the quadrilateral into <u>two triangles</u> along a <u>diagonal</u>. Each triangle has angles adding up to 180°, so the two together have angles adding up to 180° + 180° = 360°.

4) Angles round a point add up to 360°.

$$a + b + c + d = 360°$$

5) Isosceles triangles have 2 sides the same and 2 angles the same.

In an isosceles triangle, you only need to know <u>one angle</u> to be able to find the other two.

These dashes indicate two sides the same length.

These angles are the same.

EXAMPLE: Find the size of angle x.

$$180° - 40° = 140°$$

<u>The two angles on the right are the same</u> (they're both x) and they must add up to 140°, so $2x = 140°$, which means $x = 70°$.

Heaven must be missing an angle...

All the basic facts are pretty easy really, but examiners like to combine them in questions to confuse you. There are some examples of these on p.73, but have a go at this one as a warm-up.

Q1   Find the size of the angle marked x.   [2 marks]

Parallel Lines

Parallel lines are quite straightforward really. (They're also quite straight. And parallel.)
There are a few rules you need to learn — make sure you don't get them mixed up.

Angles Around Parallel Lines

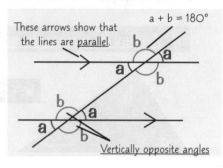

These arrows show that
the lines are parallel.

$a + b = 180°$

Vertically opposite angles

When a line crosses two parallel lines, it forms special sets of angles.

1) The two bunches of angles formed at the points of intersection are the same.

2) There are only actually two different angles involved (labelled a and b here), and they add up to 180° (from rule 2 on the previous page).

3) Vertically opposite angles (ones opposite each other) are equal (in the diagram, a and a are vertically opposite, as are b and b).

Alternate, Allied and Corresponding Angles

The diagram above has some characteristic shapes to look out for — and each shape contains a specific pair of angles. The angle pairs are known as alternate, allied and corresponding angles.

You need to spot the characteristic Z, C, U and F shapes:

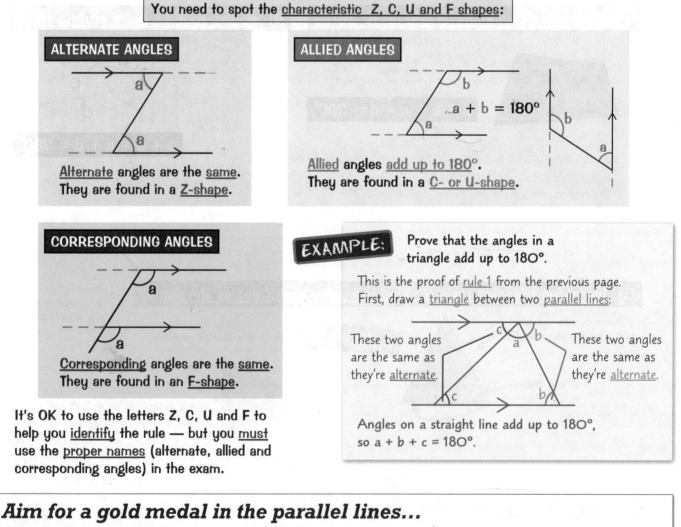

ALTERNATE ANGLES

Alternate angles are the same.
They are found in a Z-shape.

ALLIED ANGLES

$a + b = 180°$

Allied angles add up to 180°.
They are found in a C- or U-shape.

CORRESPONDING ANGLES

Corresponding angles are the same.
They are found in an F-shape.

It's OK to use the letters Z, C, U and F to help you identify the rule — but you must use the proper names (alternate, allied and corresponding angles) in the exam.

EXAMPLE: Prove that the angles in a triangle add up to 180°.

This is the proof of rule 1 from the previous page.
First, draw a triangle between two parallel lines:

These two angles are the same as they're alternate.

These two angles are the same as they're alternate.

Angles on a straight line add up to 180°,
so $a + b + c = 180°$.

Aim for a gold medal in the parallel lines...

Watch out for hidden parallel lines in other geometry questions — the little arrows are a dead giveaway.

Q1   Find the value of x.

$3x + 75°$

$x - 15°$

[3 marks]

Geometry Problems

My biggest geometry problem is that I have to do geometry problems in the first place. *Sigh*
Ah well, best get practising — these problems aren't going to solve themselves.

Try Out All The Rules One By One

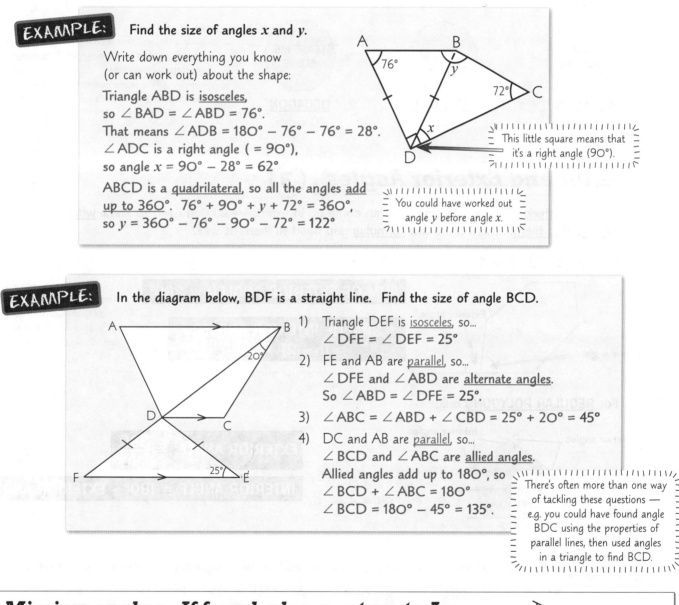

Don't concentrate too much on the angle you have been asked to find.
The best method is to find ALL the angles in whatever order they become obvious.

Before we get going, make sure you're familiar with three-letter angle notation, e.g. $\angle ABC$.
$\angle ABC$, ABC and $A\hat{B}C$ all mean 'the angle formed at B' (it's always the middle letter).
You might even see it written as just $\hat{B}$.

EXAMPLE: Find the size of angles x and y.

Write down everything you know
(or can work out) about the shape:

Triangle ABD is isosceles,
so $\angle BAD = \angle ABD = 76°$.
That means $\angle ADB = 180° - 76° - 76° = 28°$.
$\angle ADC$ is a right angle (= 90°),
so angle $x = 90° - 28° = 62°$

ABCD is a quadrilateral, so all the angles add
up to 360°. $76° + 90° + y + 72° = 360°$,
so $y = 360° - 76° - 90° - 72° = 122°$

This little square means that
it's a right angle (90°).

You could have worked out
angle y before angle x.

EXAMPLE: In the diagram below, BDF is a straight line. Find the size of angle BCD.

1) Triangle DEF is isosceles, so...
   $\angle DFE = \angle DEF = 25°$

2) FE and AB are parallel, so...
   $\angle DFE$ and $\angle ABD$ are alternate angles.
   So $\angle ABD = \angle DFE = 25°$.

3) $\angle ABC = \angle ABD + \angle CBD = 25° + 20° = 45°$

4) DC and AB are parallel, so...
   $\angle BCD$ and $\angle ABC$ are allied angles.
   Allied angles add up to 180°, so
   $\angle BCD + \angle ABC = 180°$
   $\angle BCD = 180° - 45° = 135°$.

There's often more than one way
of tackling these questions —
e.g. you could have found angle
BDC using the properties of
parallel lines, then used angles
in a triangle to find BCD.

Missing: angle x. If found, please return to Amy...

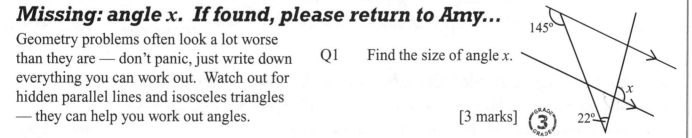

Geometry problems often look a lot worse
than they are — don't panic, just write down
everything you can work out. Watch out for
hidden parallel lines and isosceles triangles
— they can help you work out angles.

Q1 Find the size of angle x.

[3 marks]

Polygons

A <u>polygon</u> is a <u>many-sided shape</u>, and can be <u>regular</u> or <u>irregular</u>. A <u>regular</u> polygon is one where all the <u>sides</u> and <u>angles</u> are the <u>same</u> (in an <u>irregular</u> polygon, the sides and angles are <u>different</u>).

Regular Polygons

Here are the first few <u>regular polygons</u>. Remember that all the <u>sides</u> and <u>angles</u> in a regular polygon are the <u>same</u>.

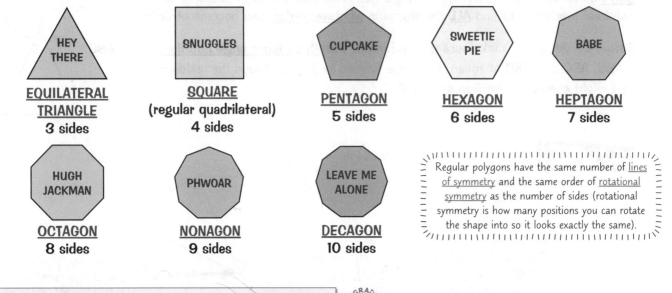

HEY THERE	SNUGGLES	CUPCAKE	SWEETIE PIE	BABE
<u>EQUILATERAL TRIANGLE</u>	<u>SQUARE</u> (regular quadrilateral)	<u>PENTAGON</u>	<u>HEXAGON</u>	<u>HEPTAGON</u>
3 sides	4 sides	5 sides	6 sides	7 sides

HUGH JACKMAN	PHWOAR	LEAVE ME ALONE
<u>OCTAGON</u>	<u>NONAGON</u>	<u>DECAGON</u>
8 sides	9 sides	10 sides

Regular polygons have the same number of <u>lines of symmetry</u> and the same order of <u>rotational symmetry</u> as the number of sides (rotational symmetry is how many positions you can rotate the shape into so it looks exactly the same).

Interior and Exterior Angles

Questions on <u>interior</u> and <u>exterior angles</u> often come up in exams — so you need to know <u>what</u> they are and <u>how to find them</u>. There are a few <u>formulas</u> you need to learn as well.

For <u>ANY POLYGON</u> (regular or irregular):

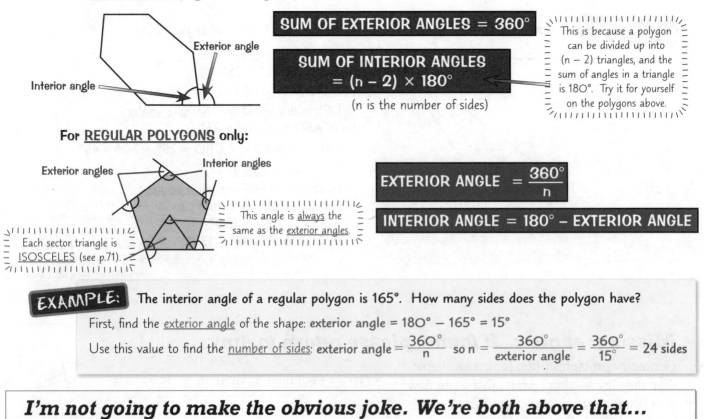

Exterior angle

Interior angle

SUM OF EXTERIOR ANGLES = 360°

SUM OF INTERIOR ANGLES = (n − 2) × 180°

(n is the number of sides)

This is because a polygon can be divided up into (n − 2) triangles, and the sum of angles in a triangle is 180°. Try it for yourself on the polygons above.

For <u>REGULAR POLYGONS</u> only:

Exterior angles

Interior angles

This angle is <u>always</u> the same as the <u>exterior angles</u>.

Each sector triangle is <u>ISOSCELES</u> (see p.71).

EXTERIOR ANGLE = $\dfrac{360°}{n}$

INTERIOR ANGLE = 180° − EXTERIOR ANGLE

> **EXAMPLE:** The interior angle of a regular polygon is 165°. How many sides does the polygon have?
>
> First, find the <u>exterior angle</u> of the shape: exterior angle = 180° − 165° = 15°
>
> Use this value to find the <u>number of sides</u>: exterior angle = $\dfrac{360°}{n}$ so n = $\dfrac{360°}{\text{exterior angle}}$ = $\dfrac{360°}{15°}$ = 24 sides

---

I'm not going to make the obvious joke. We're both above that...

Learn all the formulas on this page, and which ones go with regular and irregular polygons.

Q1 Find the size of the interior angle of a regular decagon. [2 marks]

Aww man, this was gonna be my big break an' everythin'.

Triangles and Quadrilaterals

This page is jam-packed with details about triangles and quadrilaterals — and you need to learn them all.

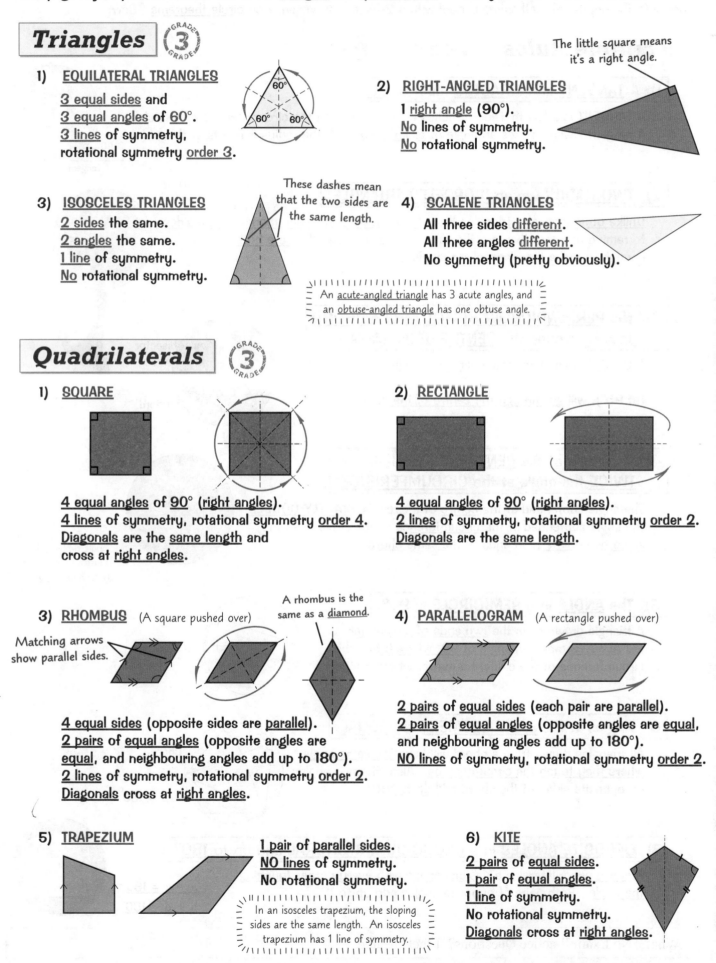

Triangles (GRADE 3)

1) EQUILATERAL TRIANGLES

3 equal sides and
3 equal angles of 60°.
3 lines of symmetry,
rotational symmetry order 3.

60°
60° 60°

The little square means
it's a right angle.

2) RIGHT-ANGLED TRIANGLES

1 right angle (90°).
No lines of symmetry.
No rotational symmetry.

3) ISOSCELES TRIANGLES

2 sides the same.
2 angles the same.
1 line of symmetry.
No rotational symmetry.

These dashes mean
that the two sides are
the same length.

4) SCALENE TRIANGLES

All three sides different.
All three angles different.
No symmetry (pretty obviously).

An acute-angled triangle has 3 acute angles, and
an obtuse-angled triangle has one obtuse angle.

Quadrilaterals (GRADE 3)

1) SQUARE

4 equal angles of 90° (right angles).
4 lines of symmetry, rotational symmetry order 4.
Diagonals are the same length and
cross at right angles.

2) RECTANGLE

4 equal angles of 90° (right angles).
2 lines of symmetry, rotational symmetry order 2.
Diagonals are the same length.

3) RHOMBUS (A square pushed over)

A rhombus is the
same as a diamond.

Matching arrows
show parallel sides.

4 equal sides (opposite sides are parallel).
2 pairs of equal angles (opposite angles are
equal, and neighbouring angles add up to 180°).
2 lines of symmetry, rotational symmetry order 2.
Diagonals cross at right angles.

4) PARALLELOGRAM (A rectangle pushed over)

2 pairs of equal sides (each pair are parallel).
2 pairs of equal angles (opposite angles are equal,
and neighbouring angles add up to 180°).
NO lines of symmetry, rotational symmetry order 2.

5) TRAPEZIUM

1 pair of parallel sides.
NO lines of symmetry.
No rotational symmetry.

In an isosceles trapezium, the sloping
sides are the same length. An isosceles
trapezium has 1 line of symmetry.

6) KITE

2 pairs of equal sides.
1 pair of equal angles.
1 line of symmetry.
No rotational symmetry.
Diagonals cross at right angles.

Section Five — Geometry and Measures

Circle Geometry

After lulling you into a false sense of security with a nice easy page on shapes, it's time to plunge you into the depths of mathematical peril with a 2-page extravaganza on circle theorems. Sorry.

9 ~~Simple~~ Rules to Learn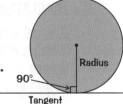

1) A TANGENT and a RADIUS meet at 90°.

A TANGENT is a line that just touches a single point on the circumference of a circle.
A tangent always makes an angle of exactly 90° with the radius it meets at this point.

2) TWO RADII form an ISOSCELES TRIANGLE.

Radii is the plural of radius.

Unlike other isosceles triangles they don't have the little tick marks on the sides to remind you that they are the same — the fact that they are both radii is enough to make it an isosceles triangle.

3) The PERPENDICULAR BISECTOR of a CHORD passes through the CENTRE of the circle.

A CHORD is any line drawn across a circle. And no matter where you draw a chord, the line that cuts it exactly in half (at 90°), will go through the centre of the circle.

4) The angle at the CENTRE of a circle is TWICE the angle at the CIRCUMFERENCE.

The angle subtended at the centre of a circle is EXACTLY DOUBLE the angle subtended at the circumference of the circle from the same two points (two ends of the same chord).

'Angle subtended at' is just a posh way of saying 'angle made at'.

5) The ANGLE in a SEMICIRCLE is 90°.

A triangle drawn from the two ends of a diameter will ALWAYS make an angle of 90° where it hits the circumference of the circle, no matter where it hits.

6) Angles in the SAME SEGMENT are EQUAL.

All triangles drawn from a chord will have the same angle where they touch the circumference. Also, the two angles on opposite sides of the chord add up to 180°.

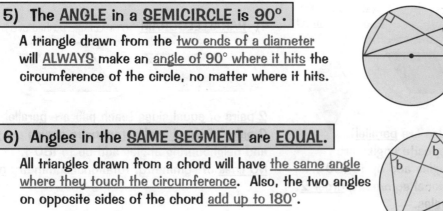

$a+b = 180°$

7) OPPOSITE ANGLES in a CYCLIC QUADRILATERAL add up to 180°.

A cyclic quadrilateral is a 4-sided shape with every corner touching the circle. Both pairs of opposite angles add up to 180°.

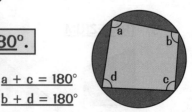

$a + c = 180°$

$b + d = 180°$

What? No Exam Practice Questions? I feel cheated.

Circle Geometry

More circle theorems? But I've had enough. Can't I go home now?

Final 2 Rules to Learn (8)

8) TANGENTS from the SAME POINT are the SAME LENGTH.

Two tangents drawn from an outside point are <u>always equal in length</u>, creating <u>two congruent right-angled triangles</u> as shown.

> There's more about congruence on p.78.

9) The ALTERNATE SEGMENT THEOREM.

The <u>angle between</u> a <u>tangent</u> and a <u>chord</u> is always <u>equal</u> to '<u>the angle in the opposite segment</u>' (i.e. the angle made at the circumference by two lines drawn from ends of the chord).

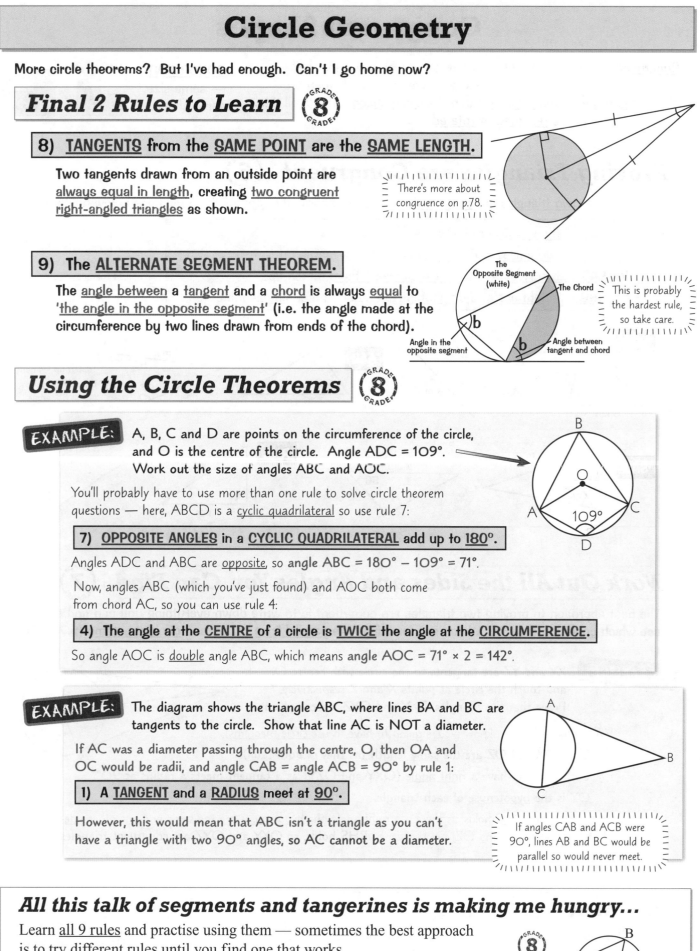

The Opposite Segment (white)

The Chord

> This is probably the hardest rule, so take care.

b

Angle in the opposite segment

b

Angle between tangent and chord

Using the Circle Theorems (8)

EXAMPLE: A, B, C and D are points on the circumference of the circle, and O is the centre of the circle. Angle ADC = 109°. Work out the size of angles ABC and AOC.

You'll probably have to use more than one rule to solve circle theorem questions — here, ABCD is a <u>cyclic quadrilateral</u> so use rule 7:

7) OPPOSITE ANGLES in a CYCLIC QUADRILATERAL add up to 180°.

Angles ADC and ABC are <u>opposite</u>, so angle ABC = 180° − 109° = 71°.

Now, angles ABC (which you've just found) and AOC both come from chord AC, so you can use rule 4:

4) The angle at the CENTRE of a circle is TWICE the angle at the CIRCUMFERENCE.

So angle AOC is <u>double</u> angle ABC, which means **angle AOC = 71° × 2 = 142°.**

EXAMPLE: The diagram shows the triangle ABC, where lines BA and BC are tangents to the circle. Show that line AC is NOT a diameter.

If AC was a diameter passing through the centre, O, then OA and OC would be radii, and angle CAB = angle ACB = 90° by rule 1:

1) A TANGENT and a RADIUS meet at 90°.

However, this would mean that ABC isn't a triangle as you can't have a triangle with two 90° angles, so AC cannot be a diameter.

> If angles CAB and ACB were 90°, lines AB and BC would be parallel so would never meet.

All this talk of segments and tangerines is making me hungry...

Learn <u>all 9 rules</u> and practise using them — sometimes the best approach is to try different rules until you find one that works. (8)

Q1   A, B, C and D are points on the circumference of the circle with centre O. The line EF is a tangent to the circle, and touches the circle at D. Angle ADE is 63°. Find the size of angles ABD and ACD.   [2 marks]

Congruent Shapes

Congruence is another ridiculous maths word which sounds really complicated when it's not. If two shapes are congruent, they are simply <u>the same</u> — the <u>same size</u> and the <u>same shape</u>. That's all it is. They can however be <u>reflected</u> or <u>rotated</u>.

CONGRUENT
— same size, same shape

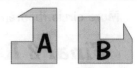

Proving Triangles are Congruent (6)

To prove that <u>two triangles</u> are <u>congruent</u>, you have to show that <u>one</u> of the conditions below holds true:

> 1) **SSS**   <u>three sides</u> are the same
> 2) **AAS**   <u>two angles</u> and a <u>corresponding side</u> match up
> 3) **SAS**   <u>two sides</u> and the <u>angle between them</u> match up
> 4) **RHS**   a <u>right angle</u>, the <u>hypotenuse</u> and one other <u>side</u> all match up

The <u>hypotenuse</u> is the <u>longest side</u> of a right-angled triangle — the one <u>opposite</u> the <u>right angle</u>.

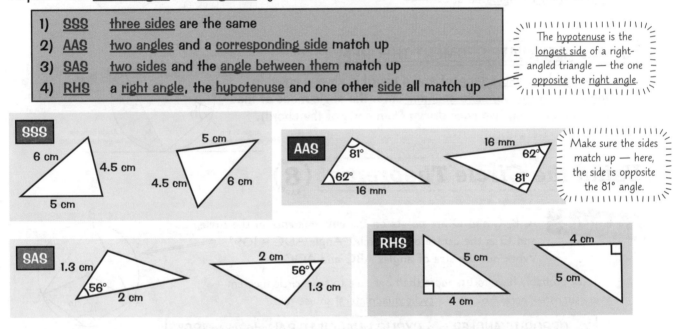

Make sure the sides match up — here, the side is opposite the 81° angle.

Work Out All the Sides and Angles You Can Find (7)

The best approach to proving two triangles are congruent is to <u>write down everything</u> you can find out, then see which <u>condition</u> they fit. Watch out for things like <u>parallel lines</u> (p.72) and <u>circle theorems</u> (p.76-77).

EXAMPLE: XY and YZ are tangents to the circle with centre O, and touch the circle at points X and Z respectively. Prove that the triangles OXY and OYZ are congruent.

Write down what you know (you're going to have to use <u>circle theorems</u>):

- Sides OX and OZ are the <u>same length</u> (as they're both <u>radii</u>).
- Both triangles have a <u>right angle</u> (OXY and OZY) as a <u>tangent</u> meets a <u>radius</u> at 90°.
- OY is the <u>hypotenuse</u> of each triangle.

So the condition <u>RHS</u> holds, as there is a <u>right angle</u>, the <u>hypotenuses</u> are the same and <u>one other side</u> of each triangle (OX and OZ) are the same. RHS holds, so OXY and OYZ are congruent triangles.

SAS? More like SOS...

Learn <u>all 4 conditions</u> and make sure you know how to use them to prove that triangles are congruent. Then have a go at this Exam Practice Question:

Q1   Prove that triangles ABD and BCD are congruent.   [3 marks] (7)

Similar Shapes

Similar shapes are <u>exactly the same shape</u>, but can be <u>different sizes</u> (they can also be <u>rotated</u> or <u>reflected</u>).

SIMILAR — same shape, different size

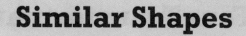

Similar Shapes Have the Same Angles (6)

Generally, for two shapes to be <u>similar</u>, all the <u>angles</u> must match and the <u>sides</u> must be <u>proportional</u>. But for <u>triangles</u>, there are <u>three special conditions</u> — if any one of these is true, you know they're similar.

Two triangles are similar if:

1) All the <u>angles</u> match up   i.e. the angles in one triangle are the same as the other.

2) All three <u>sides</u> are <u>proportional</u> i.e. if <u>one</u> side is twice as long as the corresponding side in the other triangle, <u>all</u> the sides are twice as long as the corresponding sides.

3) Any <u>two sides</u> are <u>proportional</u> and the <u>angle between them</u> is the <u>same</u>.

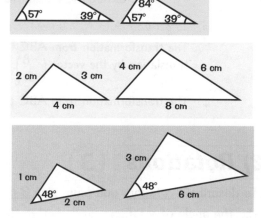

Watch out — if one of the triangles has been rotated or flipped over, it might look as if they're not similar, but don't be fooled.

EXAMPLE: Show that triangles ABC and ADE are similar.

$\angle$ BAC = $\angle$ EAD (vertically opposite angles)

$\angle$ ABC = $\angle$ ADE (alternate angles)

$\angle$ BCA = $\angle$ AED (alternate angles)

See p.72 for more on angles around parallel lines.

The angles in triangle ABC are the same as the angles in triangle ADE, so the triangles are similar.

Use Similarity to Find Missing Lengths (6)

You might have to use the <u>properties</u> of similar shapes to find missing distances, lengths etc. — you'll need to use <u>scale factors</u> (see p.81) to find the lengths of missing sides.

EXAMPLE: Suzanna is swimming in the sea. When she is at point B, she is 20 m from a rock that is 8 m tall at its highest point. There is a lighthouse 50 m away from Suzanna that is directly behind the rock. From her perspective, the top of the lighthouse is in line with the top of the rock. How tall is the lighthouse?

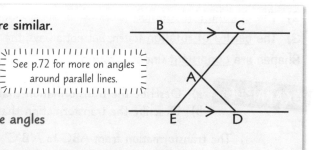

The triangles formed between Suzanna and the rock and Suzanna and the lighthouse are <u>similar</u>, so work out the <u>scale factor</u>:   scale factor = $\frac{50}{20}$ = 2.5

Now <u>use</u> the scale factor to work out the height of the lighthouse: height = 8 × 2.5 = 20 m

Butter and margarine — similar products...

To help remember the difference between similarity and congruence, think '<u>similar siblings</u>, <u>congruent clones</u>' — siblings are alike but not the same, clones are identical.

Q1   Find the length of DB.

[2 marks] (6)

The Four Transformations

There are four <u>transformations</u> you need to know — <u>translation</u>, <u>rotation</u>, <u>reflection</u> and <u>enlargement</u>.

1) Translations (3)

In a <u>translation</u>, the <u>amount</u> the shape moves by is given as a <u>vector</u> (see p.103-104) written $\begin{pmatrix} x \\ y \end{pmatrix}$ — where x is the <u>horizontal movement</u> (i.e. to the <u>right</u>) and y is the <u>vertical movement</u> (i.e. <u>up</u>). If the shape moves <u>left and down</u>, x and y will be <u>negative</u>. Shapes are <u>congruent</u> under translation (see p.78).

EXAMPLE: a) Describe the transformation that maps triangle ABC onto A'B'C'.
b) Describe the transformation that maps triangle ABC onto A"B"C".

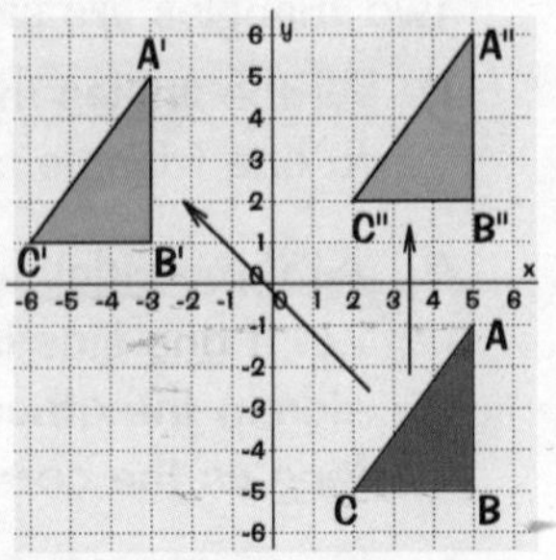

a) To get from A to A', you need to move <u>8 units left</u> and <u>6 units up</u>, so...
The transformation from ABC to A'B'C' is a translation by the vector $\begin{pmatrix} -8 \\ 6 \end{pmatrix}$.

b) The transformation from ABC to A"B"C" is a translation by the vector $\begin{pmatrix} 0 \\ 7 \end{pmatrix}$.

2) Rotations (3)

To describe a <u>rotation</u>, you must give <u>3 details</u>:

1) The <u>angle of rotation</u> (usually 90° or 180°).
2) The <u>direction of rotation</u> (clockwise or anticlockwise).
3) The <u>centre of rotation</u> (often, but not always, the origin).

Shapes are <u>congruent</u> under rotation.

> For a rotation of 180°, it doesn't matter whether you go clockwise or anticlockwise.

EXAMPLE: a) Describe the transformation that maps triangle ABC onto A'B'C'.
b) Describe the transformation that maps triangle ABC onto A"B"C".

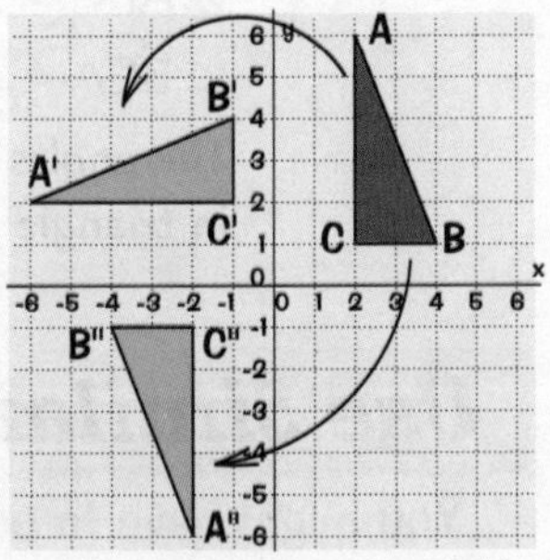

a) The transformation from ABC to A'B'C' is a rotation of <u>90°</u> <u>anticlockwise</u> about the <u>origin</u>.

b) The transformation from ABC to A"B"C" is a rotation of <u>180°</u> clockwise (or anticlockwise) about the <u>origin</u>.

> If it helps, you can use tracing paper to help you find the centre of rotation.

3) Reflections (3)

For a <u>reflection</u>, you must give the <u>equation</u> of the <u>mirror line</u>. Shapes are <u>congruent</u> under reflection as well.

EXAMPLE: a) Describe the transformation that maps shape A onto shape B.
b) Describe the transformation that maps shape A onto shape C.

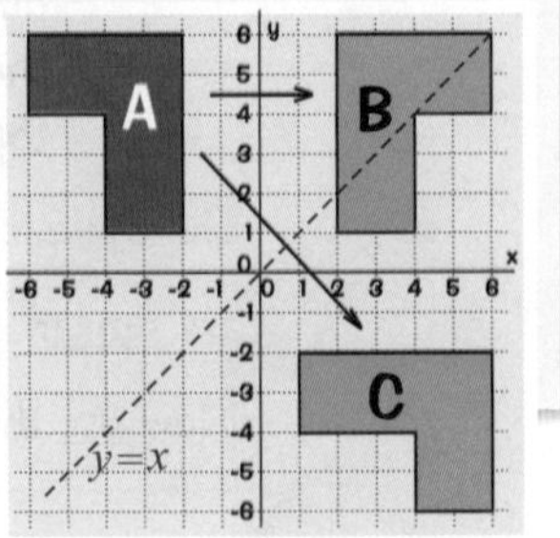

a) The transformation from A to B is a reflection in the y-axis.
b) The transformation from A to C is a reflection in the line $y = x$.

Points are <u>invariant</u> if they remain the same after a transformation — for <u>reflections</u> any point on the <u>mirror line</u> will be invariant.

Moving eet to ze left — a perfect translation...

The reason that shapes are <u>congruent</u> under translation, reflection and rotation is because their <u>size</u> and <u>shape</u> don't change, just their position and orientation. Now have a go at this question:

Q1   On a grid, copy shape A above and rotate it 90° clockwise about the point (–1, –1).   [2 marks] (3)

The Four Transformations

One more transformation coming up — enlargements. They're the trickiest, but also the most fun (honest).

4) Enlargements

For an enlargement, you must specify:

1) The scale factor.
2) The centre of enlargement.

$$\text{scale factor} = \frac{\text{new length}}{\text{old length}}$$

Shapes are similar under enlargement — the position and the size change, but the angles and ratios of the sides don't (see p.79).

EXAMPLE:

a) Describe the transformation that maps triangle A onto triangle B.
b) Describe the transformation that maps triangle B onto triangle A.

a) Use the formula above to find the scale factor (just choose one side):

$$\text{scale factor} = \frac{6}{3} = 2$$

For the centre of enlargement, draw lines that go through corresponding vertices of both shapes and see where they cross.

So the transformation from A to B is an enlargement of scale factor 2, centre (2, 6)

b) Using a similar method, **scale factor** $= \frac{3}{6} = \frac{1}{2}$ and the centre of enlargement is the same as before, **so the transformation from B to A is an enlargement of scale factor $\frac{1}{2}$, centre (2, 6)**

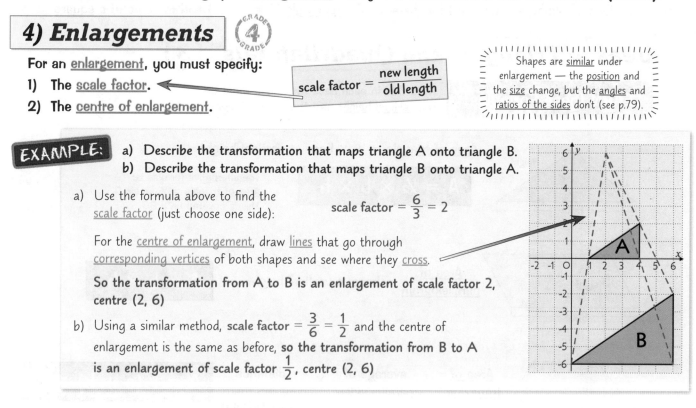

Scale Factors — Four Key Facts

1) If the scale factor is bigger than 1 the shape gets bigger.

2) If the scale factor is smaller than 1 (e.g. ½) it gets smaller.

3) If the scale factor is negative then the shape pops out the other side of the enlargement centre. If the scale factor is –1, it's exactly the same as a rotation of 180°.

4) The scale factor also tells you the relative distance of old points and new points from the centre of enlargement — this is very useful for drawing an enlargement, because you can use it to trace out the positions of the new points.

EXAMPLE: Enlarge shape A below by a scale factor of –3, centre (1, 1). Label the transformed shape B.

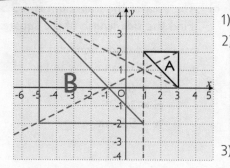

1) First, draw lines going through (1, 1) from each vertex of shape A.

2) Then, multiply the distance from each vertex to the centre of enlargement by 3, and measure this distance coming out the other side of the centre of enlargement.
So on shape A, vertex (3, 2) is 2 right and 1 up from (1, 1) — so the corresponding point on shape B will be 6 left and 3 down from (1, 1). Do this for every point.

3) Join the points you've drawn to form shape B.

Scale factors — they're enough to put the fear of cod into you...

If you have to do more than one transformation, just do them one at a time — here's some practice.

Q1 On a grid, draw triangle A with vertices (2, 1), (4, 1) and (4, 3). Enlarge it by a scale factor of –2 about point (1, 1), then reflect it in the line $x = 0$. [3 marks]

Section Five — Geometry and Measures

Area — Triangles and Quadrilaterals

Be warned — there are lots of <u>area formulas</u> coming up on the next two pages for you to <u>learn</u>. By the way, I'm assuming that you know the formulas for the area of a <u>rectangle</u> (A = l × w) and the area of a <u>square</u> (A = l²).

Areas of Triangles and Quadrilaterals (3)

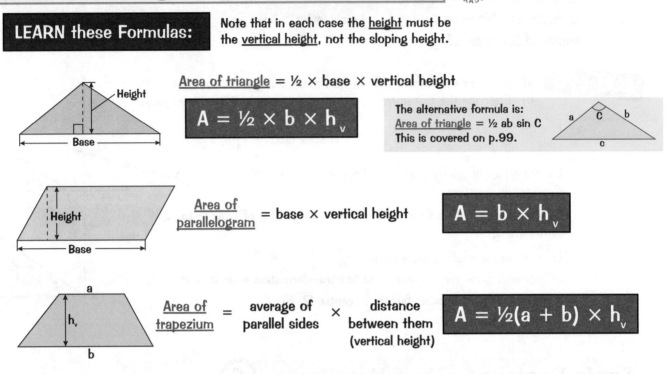

LEARN these Formulas: Note that in each case the <u>height</u> must be the <u>vertical height</u>, not the sloping height.

<u>Area of triangle</u> = ½ × base × vertical height

$$A = ½ × b × h_v$$

The alternative formula is:
<u>Area of triangle</u> = ½ ab sin C
This is covered on p.99.

$$\text{Area of} \atop \underline{\text{parallelogram}} = \text{base × vertical height}$$

$$A = b × h_v$$

$$\underline{\text{Area of} \atop \text{trapezium}} = {\text{average of} \atop \text{parallel sides}} × {\text{distance} \atop \text{between them} \atop \text{(vertical height)}}$$

$$A = ½(a + b) × h_v$$

Use the Formulas to Solve Problems (5)

Examiners like to sneak bits of <u>algebra</u> into area and perimeter questions — you'll often have to <u>set up</u> and then <u>solve an equation</u> to find a missing side length or area of a shape. Meanies.

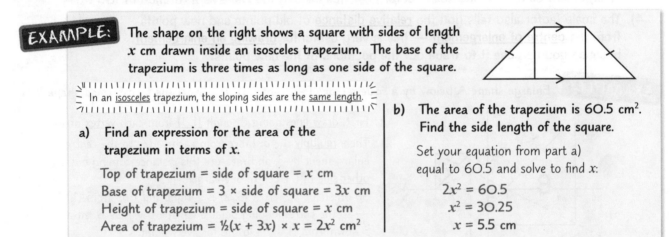

EXAMPLE: The shape on the right shows a square with sides of length *x* cm drawn inside an isosceles trapezium. The base of the trapezium is three times as long as one side of the square.

In an <u>isosceles</u> trapezium, the sloping sides are the <u>same length</u>.

a) Find an expression for the area of the trapezium in terms of *x*.

Top of trapezium = side of square = *x* cm
Base of trapezium = 3 × side of square = 3*x* cm
Height of trapezium = side of square = *x* cm
Area of trapezium = ½(*x* + 3*x*) × *x* = 2*x*² cm²

b) The area of the trapezium is 60.5 cm². Find the side length of the square.

Set your equation from part a) equal to 60.5 and solve to find *x*:

$$2x^2 = 60.5$$
$$x^2 = 30.25$$
$$x = 5.5 \text{ cm}$$

No jokes about my vertical height please...

If you have a composite shape (a shape made up of different shapes stuck together), split it into triangles and quadrilaterals, work out the area of each bit and add them together.

Q1 The triangle and rectangle shown on the right have the same area. Find the value of *x*. [2 marks] (4)

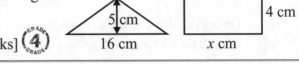

Area — Circles

Yes, I thought I could detect some groaning when you realised that this is another page of formulas. You know the drill...

LEARN these Formulas

Area and Circumference of Circles (3) GRADE

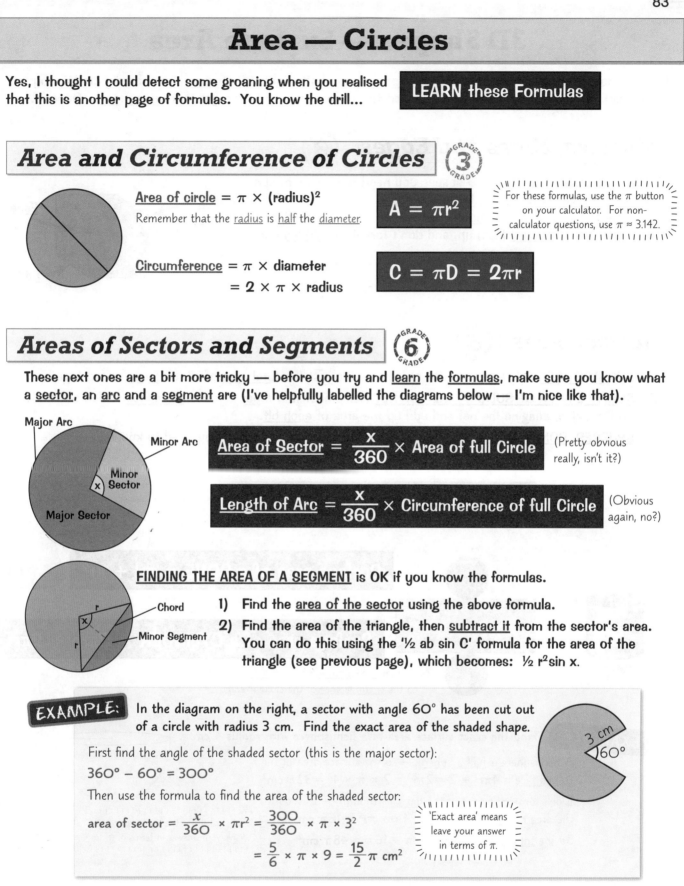

Area of circle = π × (radius)²
Remember that the radius is half the diameter.

$$A = \pi r^2$$

Circumference = π × diameter
= 2 × π × radius

$$C = \pi D = 2\pi r$$

For these formulas, use the π button on your calculator. For non-calculator questions, use π ≈ 3.142.

Areas of Sectors and Segments (6) GRADE

These next ones are a bit more tricky — before you try and learn the formulas, make sure you know what a sector, an arc and a segment are (I've helpfully labelled the diagrams below — I'm nice like that).

Major Arc
Minor Arc
Minor Sector
Major Sector
x

$$\text{Area of Sector} = \frac{x}{360} \times \text{Area of full Circle}$$ (Pretty obvious really, isn't it?)

$$\text{Length of Arc} = \frac{x}{360} \times \text{Circumference of full Circle}$$ (Obvious again, no?)

FINDING THE AREA OF A SEGMENT is OK if you know the formulas.

Chord
x
Minor Segment
r
r

1) Find the **area of the sector** using the above formula.
2) Find the area of the triangle, then **subtract it** from the sector's area. You can do this using the '½ ab sin C' formula for the area of the triangle (see previous page), which becomes: ½ r²sin x.

EXAMPLE: In the diagram on the right, a sector with angle 60° has been cut out of a circle with radius 3 cm. Find the exact area of the shaded shape.

3 cm
60°

First find the angle of the shaded sector (this is the major sector):
360° − 60° = 300°
Then use the formula to find the area of the shaded sector:

area of sector = $\frac{x}{360} \times \pi r^2 = \frac{300}{360} \times \pi \times 3^2$
$= \frac{5}{6} \times \pi \times 9 = \frac{15}{2}\pi$ cm²

'Exact area' means leave your answer in terms of π.

Pi r not square — pi are round. Pi are tasty...

Oo, one more thing — if you're asked to find the perimeter of a semicircle or quarter circle, don't forget to add on the straight edges too. It's an easy mistake to make, and it'll cost you marks.

Q1 For the shape on the right, find to 2 decimal places:
a) the area of the sector   [2 marks]   b) the arc length   [2 marks]
c) the area of the segment   [2 marks]   (6) GRADE

150°
8 cm

3D Shapes — Surface Area

It's time now to move on to the next <u>dimension</u> — yep, that's right, <u>3D shapes</u>. I can hardly contain my excitement. If you do really well on these next few pages, we might even get on to <u>time travel</u>. Ooooooo.

Vertices, Faces and Edges

There are different parts of 3D shapes you need to be able to spot.
These are <u>vertices</u> (corners), <u>faces</u> and <u>edges</u>.
You might be asked for the <u>number</u> of vertices, faces and edges in the exam — just <u>count</u> them up, and don't forget the <u>hidden</u> ones.

Curved faces are sometimes called <u>surfaces</u>.

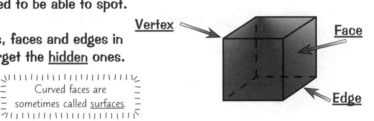

Vertex — Face — Edge

Surface Area

1) <u>SURFACE AREA</u> only applies to 3D objects — it's just the <u>total area</u> of all the <u>faces</u> added together.

2) <u>SURFACE AREA OF SOLID = AREA OF NET</u> (remember that a <u>net</u> is just a <u>3D shape</u> folded out flat). So if it helps, imagine the net and add up the area of <u>each bit</u>.

3) <u>SPHERES, CONES AND CYLINDERS</u> have surface area formulas that you need to know:

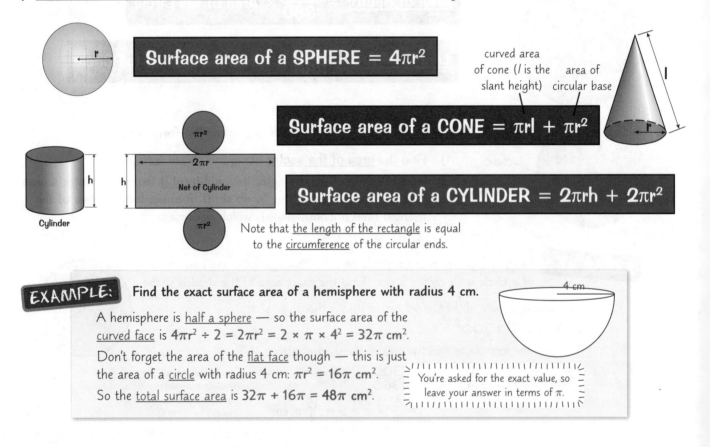

Surface area of a SPHERE = $4\pi r^2$

curved area of cone (*l* is the slant height)   area of circular base

Surface area of a CONE = $\pi rl + \pi r^2$

Net of Cylinder

Surface area of a CYLINDER = $2\pi rh + 2\pi r^2$

Note that <u>the length of the rectangle</u> is equal to the <u>circumference</u> of the circular ends.

EXAMPLE: Find the exact surface area of a hemisphere with radius 4 cm.

A hemisphere is <u>half a sphere</u> — so the surface area of the <u>curved face</u> is $4\pi r^2 \div 2 = 2\pi r^2 = 2 \times \pi \times 4^2 = 32\pi$ cm^2.

Don't forget the area of the <u>flat face</u> though — this is just the area of a <u>circle</u> with radius 4 cm: $\pi r^2 = 16\pi$ cm^2.

So the <u>total surface area</u> is $32\pi + 16\pi = 48\pi$ cm^2.

You're asked for the exact value, so leave your answer in terms of π.

4 cm

Beware of the space-time vertex...

Don't get confused if you're sketching a net — most shapes have more than one net (for example, a cube has about a million. I'm not exaggerating. Well, maybe a little). Anyway, learn all the formulas on this page, then have a go at this lovely Exam Practice Question:

Q1   The surface area of a cone with radius 5 cm is 125π cm^2.
Find the slant height, *l*, of the cone.   [3 marks]

3D Shapes — Volume

Two whole pages on <u>volumes</u> of <u>3D shapes</u> — aren't you lucky? I'm fairly certain that you already know that the volume of a <u>cuboid</u> is length × width × height (and the volume of a <u>cube</u> is length³) — if not, you do now.

Volumes of Prisms

A <u>PRISM</u> is a solid (3D) object which is the same shape all the way through — i.e. it has a <u>CONSTANT AREA OF CROSS-SECTION</u>.

$$\text{VOLUME OF PRISM} = \text{CROSS-SECTIONAL AREA} \times \text{LENGTH}$$

$$V = A \times L$$

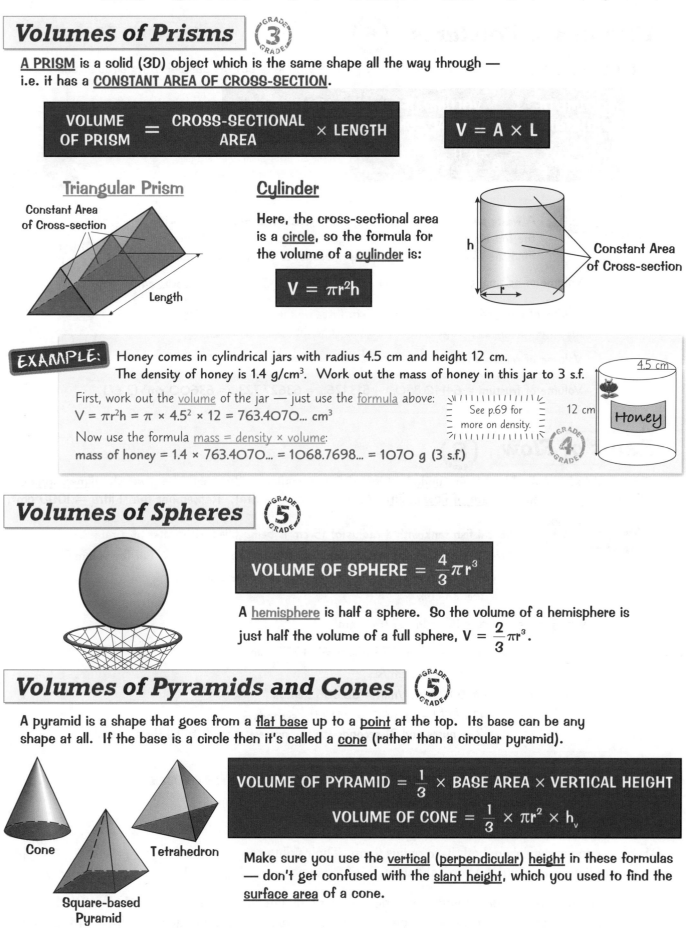

Triangular Prism

Constant Area of Cross-section

Length

Cylinder

Here, the cross-sectional area is a <u>circle</u>, so the formula for the volume of a <u>cylinder</u> is:

$$V = \pi r^2 h$$

Constant Area of Cross-section

EXAMPLE: Honey comes in cylindrical jars with radius 4.5 cm and height 12 cm. The density of honey is 1.4 g/cm³. Work out the mass of honey in this jar to 3 s.f.

First, work out the <u>volume</u> of the jar — just use the <u>formula</u> above:
$$V = \pi r^2 h = \pi \times 4.5^2 \times 12 = 763.4070... \text{ cm}^3$$

See p.69 for more on density.

Now use the formula <u>mass = density × volume</u>:
mass of honey = 1.4 × 763.4070... = 1068.7698... = 1070 g (3 s.f.)

4.5 cm

12 cm

Honey

Volumes of Spheres

$$\text{VOLUME OF SPHERE} = \frac{4}{3}\pi r^3$$

A <u>hemisphere</u> is half a sphere. So the volume of a hemisphere is just half the volume of a full sphere, $V = \frac{2}{3}\pi r^3$.

Volumes of Pyramids and Cones

A pyramid is a shape that goes from a <u>flat base</u> up to a <u>point</u> at the top. Its base can be any shape at all. If the base is a circle then it's called a <u>cone</u> (rather than a circular pyramid).

Cone

Tetrahedron

Square-based Pyramid

$$\text{VOLUME OF PYRAMID} = \frac{1}{3} \times \text{BASE AREA} \times \text{VERTICAL HEIGHT}$$

$$\text{VOLUME OF CONE} = \frac{1}{3} \times \pi r^2 \times h_v$$

Make sure you use the <u>vertical</u> (<u>perpendicular</u>) <u>height</u> in these formulas — don't get confused with the <u>slant height</u>, which you used to find the <u>surface area</u> of a cone.

3D Shapes — Volume

Another page on volumes now, but this is a bit of a weird one.
First up, it's volumes of cones with a bit <u>chopped off</u>, then it's on to <u>rates of flow</u>.

Volumes of Frustums (6)

A <u>frustum of a cone</u> is what's left when the top part of a cone is cut off parallel to its circular base.

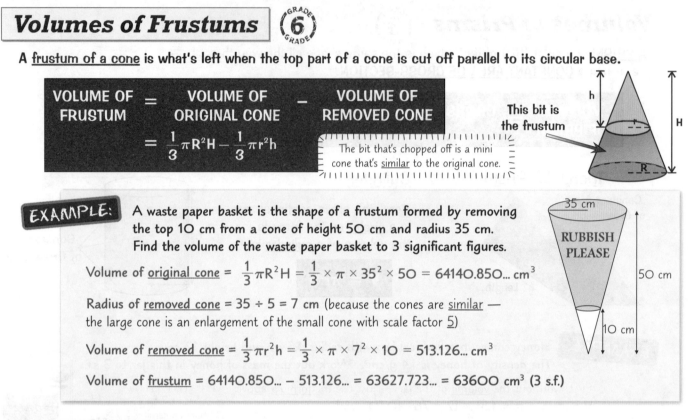

VOLUME OF FRUSTUM	=	VOLUME OF ORIGINAL CONE	−	VOLUME OF REMOVED CONE

$$= \frac{1}{3}\pi R^2 H - \frac{1}{3}\pi r^2 h$$

The bit that's chopped off is a mini cone that's <u>similar</u> to the original cone.

This bit is the frustum

EXAMPLE: A waste paper basket is the shape of a frustum formed by removing the top 10 cm from a cone of height 50 cm and radius 35 cm. Find the volume of the waste paper basket to 3 significant figures.

Volume of <u>original cone</u> = $\frac{1}{3}\pi R^2 H = \frac{1}{3} \times \pi \times 35^2 \times 50 = 64140.850...$ cm^3

Radius of <u>removed cone</u> = 35 ÷ 5 = 7 cm (because the cones are <u>similar</u> — the large cone is an enlargement of the small cone with scale factor <u>5</u>)

Volume of <u>removed cone</u> = $\frac{1}{3}\pi r^2 h = \frac{1}{3} \times \pi \times 7^2 \times 10 = 513.126...$ cm^3

Volume of <u>frustum</u> = 64140.850... − 513.126... = 63627.723... = **63600 cm^3 (3 s.f.)**

35 cm
RUBBISH PLEASE
50 cm
10 cm

Rates of Flow (8)

You need to be really careful with <u>units</u> in rates of flow questions. You might be given the <u>dimensions</u> of a shape in <u>cm</u> or <u>m</u> but the <u>rate of flow</u> in <u>litres</u> (e.g. litres per minute). Remember that 1 litre = 1000 cm^3.

EXAMPLE: A spherical fish tank with a radius of 15 cm is being filled with water at a rate of 4 litres per minute. How long will it take to fill the fish tank $\frac{2}{3}$ full (by volume)? Give your answer in minutes and seconds, to the nearest second.

Find the volume of the fish tank:

$V = \frac{4}{3}\pi r^3 = \frac{4}{3} \times \pi \times 15^3 = 14\,137.166...$ cm^3

So $\frac{2}{3}$ of the fish tank is: $\frac{2}{3} \times 14\,137.166... = 9424.777...$ cm^3

Then convert the rate of flow into cm^3/s:

4 litres per minute = 4000 cm^3/min = 66.666... cm^3/s

So it will take   9424.777... ÷ 66.666... = 141.371... seconds
= 2 minutes and 21 seconds (to the nearest second) to fill the fish tank.

No, a cone isn't 'just as good' — all the other Pharaohs will laugh...

A common misconception is that a frustum is actually called a frustRum
(I thought this until about a year ago. It blew my mind.)

Q1   A cone and a sphere both have radius 9 cm. Their volumes are the same. Find the vertical height, *h*, of the cone.   [4 marks] (8)

9 cm   *h*
9 cm

Q2   A square-based pyramid with base sides of length 60 cm and height 110 cm is being filled with water at a rate of 0.1 litres per second. Does it take longer than 20 minutes to fill?   [4 marks] (8)

More Enlargements and Projections

The two topics on this page aren't really related... but I haven't just shoved them on the same page because I couldn't think of anywhere else to put them. Honest.

How Enlargement Affects Area and Volume   (7)

If a shape is enlarged by a <u>scale factor</u> (see page 81), its <u>area</u>, or <u>surface area</u> and <u>volume</u> (if it's a 3D shape), will change too. However, they <u>don't</u> change by the <u>same value</u> as the scale factor:

For a <u>SCALE FACTOR n</u>:		$n = \dfrac{\text{new length}}{\text{old length}}$ $n^2 = \dfrac{\text{new area}}{\text{old area}}$	Or... AS RATIOS:	
The <u>SIDES</u> are	n times bigger		Lengths	a : b
The <u>AREAS</u> are	n^2 times bigger	$n^3 = \dfrac{\text{new volume}}{\text{old volume}}$	Areas	$a^2 : b^2$
The <u>VOLUMES</u> are	n^3 times bigger		Volumes	$a^3 : b^3$

So if the <u>scale factor</u> is <u>2</u>, the lengths are <u>2 times</u> as long,
the area is $2^2 = \underline{4\ times}$ as big, and the volume is $2^3 = \underline{8\ times}$ as big.
As <u>ratios</u>, these enlargements are <u>1:2</u> (length), $1^2 : 2^2 = \underline{1:4}$ (area) and $1^3 : 2^3 = \underline{1:8}$ (volume).

EXAMPLE: Cylinder A has surface area 6π cm^2, and cylinder B has surface area 54π cm^2. The volume of cylinder A is 2π cm^3. Find the volume of cylinder B, given that B is an enlargement of A.

First, work out the <u>scale factor</u>, n: $n^2 = \dfrac{\text{Area B}}{\text{Area A}} = \dfrac{54\pi}{6\pi} = 9$, so $\underline{n = 3}$

Use this in the <u>volume formula</u>: $n^3 = \dfrac{\text{Volume B}}{\text{Volume A}} \Rightarrow 3^3 = \dfrac{\text{Volume B}}{2\pi}$

$\Rightarrow$ Volume of B $= 2\pi \times 27 = 54\pi$ cm^3

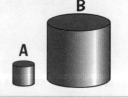

EXAMPLE: The ratio of the surface area of sphere X to the surface area of sphere Y is $16 : 25$. Sphere X has a volume of 448 cm^3. What is the volume of sphere Y?

Work out the <u>ratio of the volumes</u>: $a^2 : b^2 = 16:25$ so $a:b = 4:5$ and $a^3 : b^3 = \underline{64 : 125}$

Use the ratio to find the <u>volume of sphere Y</u>: $448 \div 64 = 7$
so volume of sphere Y $= 125 \times 7 = 875$ cm^3

Projections Show a 3D Shape From Different Viewpoints   (3)

There are three different types of projection — <u>front elevation</u>, <u>side elevation</u> and <u>plan</u>
(elevation is just another word for projection).

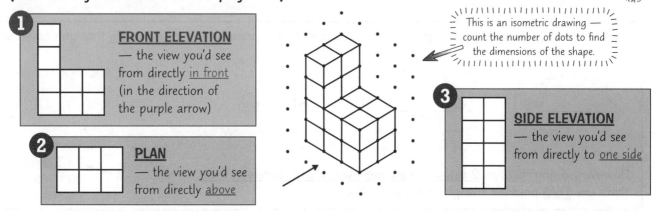

1 **FRONT ELEVATION**
— the view you'd see from directly <u>in front</u> (in the direction of the purple arrow)

2 **PLAN**
— the view you'd see from directly <u>above</u>

This is an isometric drawing — count the number of dots to find the dimensions of the shape.

3 **SIDE ELEVATION**
— the view you'd see from directly to <u>one side</u>

Twice as much learning, 4 times better results, 8 times more fun...

Make sure you don't get the scale factors mixed up — try them out on this Exam Practice Question.

Q1   There are 3 stacking dolls in a set. The dolls are mathematically similar and have heights of 5 cm, 10 cm and 15 cm. The surface area of the middle doll is 80 cm^2, and the volume of the largest doll is 216 cm^3. Find the surface area and volume of the smallest doll.   **(8)**   [4 marks]

There's no room left for time travel. Sorry.

Triangle Construction

How you construct a triangle depends on what <u>info you're given</u> about the triangle...

Three sides — use a Ruler and Compasses (3) GRADE

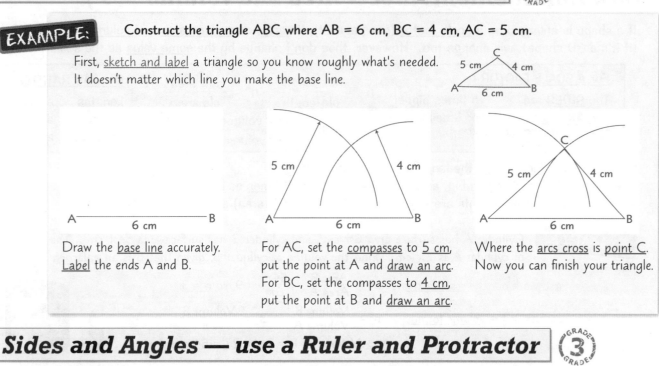

EXAMPLE: Construct the triangle ABC where AB = 6 cm, BC = 4 cm, AC = 5 cm.

First, <u>sketch and label</u> a triangle so you know roughly what's needed. It doesn't matter which line you make the base line.

Draw the <u>base line</u> accurately. <u>Label</u> the ends A and B.

For AC, set the <u>compasses</u> to <u>5 cm</u>, put the point at A and <u>draw an arc</u>. For BC, set the compasses to <u>4 cm</u>, put the point at B and <u>draw an arc</u>.

Where the <u>arcs cross</u> is <u>point C</u>. Now you can finish your triangle.

Sides and Angles — use a Ruler and Protractor (3) GRADE

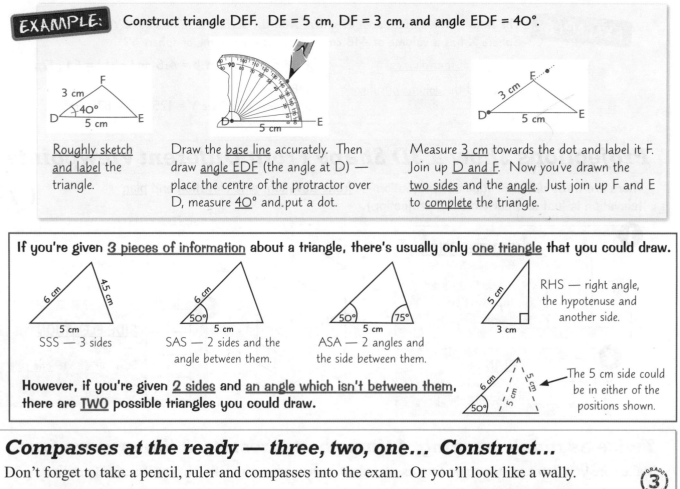

EXAMPLE: Construct triangle DEF. DE = 5 cm, DF = 3 cm, and angle EDF = 40°.

<u>Roughly sketch and label</u> the triangle.

Draw the <u>base line</u> accurately. Then draw <u>angle EDF</u> (the angle at D) — place the centre of the protractor over D, measure <u>40°</u> and put a dot.

Measure <u>3 cm</u> towards the dot and label it F. Join up <u>D and F</u>. Now you've drawn the <u>two sides</u> and the <u>angle</u>. Just join up F and E to <u>complete</u> the triangle.

If you're given <u>3 pieces of information</u> about a triangle, there's usually only <u>one triangle</u> that you could draw.

SSS — 3 sides

SAS — 2 sides and the angle between them.

ASA — 2 angles and the side between them.

RHS — right angle, the hypotenuse and another side.

However, if you're given <u>2 sides</u> and <u>an angle which isn't between them</u>, there are <u>TWO</u> possible triangles you could draw.

The 5 cm side could be in either of the positions shown.

Compasses at the ready — three, two, one... Construct...

Don't forget to take a pencil, ruler and compasses into the exam. Or you'll look like a wally. (3) GRADE

Q1 Construct an equilateral triangle with sides 5 cm. Leave your construction marks visible. [2 marks]

Q2 Construct and label triangle ABC: angle ABC = 45°, angle BCA = 40°, side BC = 7.5 cm. [2 marks]

Loci and Construction

A <u>LOCUS</u> (another ridiculous maths word) is simply:

A LINE or REGION that shows all the points which fit a given rule.

Make sure you learn how to do these <u>PROPERLY</u> using a <u>ruler</u> and <u>compasses</u> as shown on the next few pages.

The Four Different Types of Loci

Loci is just the plural of locus.

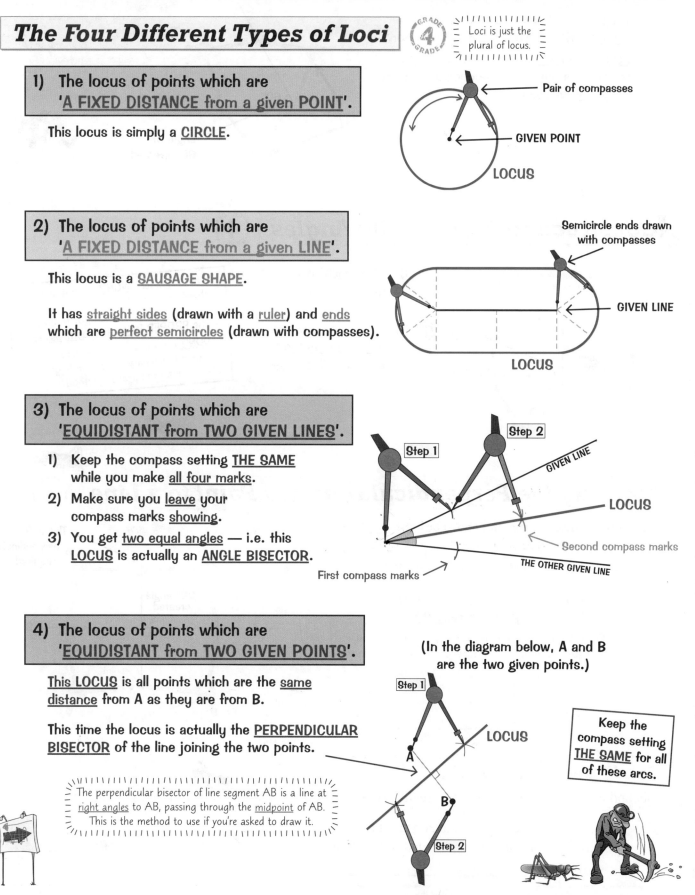

1) The locus of points which are '<u>A FIXED DISTANCE</u> from a given <u>POINT</u>'.

This locus is simply a <u>CIRCLE</u>.

Pair of compasses

GIVEN POINT

LOCUS

2) The locus of points which are '<u>A FIXED DISTANCE</u> from a given <u>LINE</u>'.

This locus is a <u>SAUSAGE SHAPE</u>.

It has <u>straight sides</u> (drawn with a <u>ruler</u>) and <u>ends</u> which are <u>perfect semicircles</u> (drawn with compasses).

Semicircle ends drawn with compasses

GIVEN LINE

LOCUS

3) The locus of points which are '<u>EQUIDISTANT</u> from <u>TWO GIVEN LINES</u>'.

1) Keep the compass setting <u>THE SAME</u> while you make <u>all four marks</u>.
2) Make sure you <u>leave</u> your compass marks <u>showing</u>.
3) You get <u>two equal angles</u> — i.e. this <u>LOCUS</u> is actually an <u>ANGLE BISECTOR</u>.

Step 1

Step 2

GIVEN LINE

LOCUS

Second compass marks

First compass marks

THE OTHER GIVEN LINE

4) The locus of points which are '<u>EQUIDISTANT</u> from <u>TWO GIVEN POINTS</u>'.

This <u>LOCUS</u> is all points which are the <u>same</u> <u>distance</u> from A as they are from B.

This time the locus is actually the <u>PERPENDICULAR</u> <u>BISECTOR</u> of the line joining the two points.

The perpendicular bisector of line segment AB is a line at <u>right angles</u> to AB, passing through the <u>midpoint</u> of AB. This is the method to use if you're asked to draw it.

(In the diagram below, A and B are the two given points.)

Step 1

LOCUS

A

B

Step 2

Keep the compass setting <u>THE SAME</u> for all of these arcs.

Loci and Construction

Don't just read the page through once and hope you'll remember it — get your ruler, compasses and pencil out and have a go. It's the only way of testing whether you really know this stuff.

Constructing Accurate 60° Angles

1) They may well ask you to draw an <u>accurate 60° angle</u> without a protractor.

2) <u>Follow the method</u> shown in this diagram (make sure you leave the compass settings the <u>same</u> for each step).

You can construct 30° angles and 45° angles by <u>bisecting</u> 60° and 90° angles (see previous page).

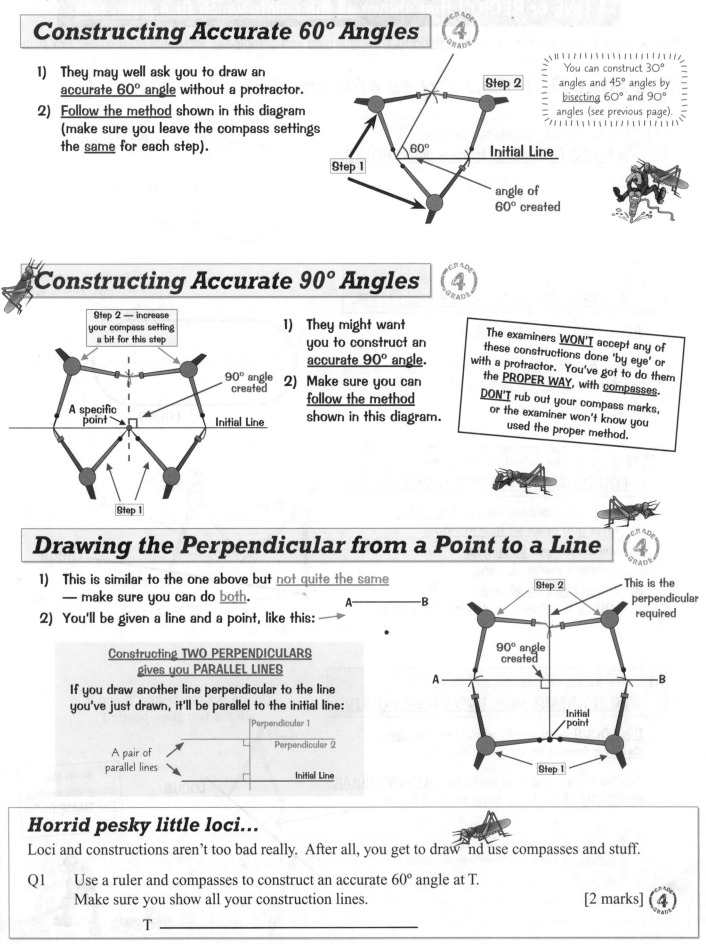

Step 2

Step 1

60°

Initial Line

angle of 60° created

Constructing Accurate 90° Angles

Step 2 — increase your compass setting a bit for this step

90° angle created

A specific point

Step 1

Initial Line

1) They might want you to construct an <u>accurate 90° angle</u>.

2) Make sure you can <u>follow the method</u> shown in this diagram.

The examiners <u>WON'T</u> accept any of these constructions done 'by eye' or with a protractor. You've got to do them the <u>PROPER WAY</u>, with <u>compasses</u>. <u>DON'T</u> rub out your compass marks, or the examiner won't know you used the proper method.

Drawing the Perpendicular from a Point to a Line

1) This is similar to the one above but <u>not quite the same</u> — make sure you can do <u>both</u>.

2) You'll be given a line and a point, like this:

A———B

Step 2

This is the perpendicular required

Constructing TWO PERPENDICULARS gives you PARALLEL LINES

If you draw another line perpendicular to the line you've just drawn, it'll be parallel to the initial line:

A pair of parallel lines

Perpendicular 1

Perpendicular 2

Initial Line

90° angle created

A ————— B

Initial point

Step 1

Horrid pesky little loci...

Loci and constructions aren't too bad really. After all, you get to draw nd use compasses and stuff.

Q1 Use a ruler and compasses to construct an accurate 60° angle at T. Make sure you show all your construction lines. [2 marks]

T _____

Loci and Construction — Worked Examples

Now you know what <u>loci</u> are, and how to do all the <u>constructions</u> you need, it's time to put them all together.

Finding a Locus that Satisfies Lots of Rules

In the exam, you might be given a situation with <u>lots</u> of different <u>conditions</u>, and asked to find the <u>region</u> that satisfies <u>all</u> the conditions. To do this, just draw <u>each locus</u>, then see which bit you want.

EXAMPLE: On the square below, shade the region that is within 3 cm of vertex A and closer to vertex B than vertex D.

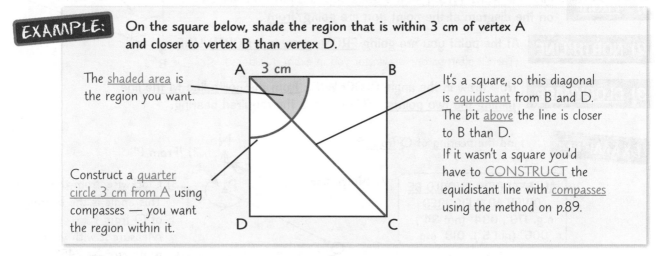

The <u>shaded area</u> is the region you want.

Construct a <u>quarter circle 3 cm from A</u> using compasses — you want the region within it.

It's a square, so this diagonal is <u>equidistant</u> from B and D. The bit <u>above</u> the line is closer to B than D.

If it wasn't a square you'd have to CONSTRUCT the equidistant line with <u>compasses</u> using the method on p.89.

You might be given the information as a <u>wordy problem</u> — work out what you're being asked for and draw it.

EXAMPLE: Tessa is organising a village fete. The fete will take place on a rectangular field, shown in the diagram below. Tessa is deciding where an ice cream van can go. It has to be <u>at least 1 m away from each edge</u> of the field, and <u>closer to side AB than side CD</u>. There is a maypole at M, and the ice cream van must be <u>at least 2 m away from the maypole</u>. The diagram is drawn to a scale of 1 cm = 1 m. Show on it where the ice cream van can go.

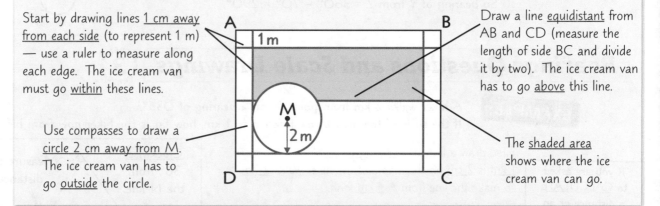

Start by drawing lines <u>1 cm away from each side</u> (to represent 1 m) — use a ruler to measure along each edge. The ice cream van must go <u>within</u> these lines.

Use compasses to draw a <u>circle 2 cm away from M</u>. The ice cream van has to go <u>outside</u> the circle.

Draw a line <u>equidistant</u> from AB and CD (measure the length of side BC and divide it by two). The ice cream van has to go <u>above</u> this line.

The <u>shaded area</u> shows where the ice cream van can go.

In the examples above, the lines were all at <u>right angles</u> to each other, so you could just measure with a <u>ruler</u> rather than do constructions with compasses. If the question says "<u>Leave your construction lines clearly visible</u>", you'll definitely need to <u>get your compasses out</u> and use some of the methods on p.89-90.

Stay at least 3 m away from point C — or I'll release the hounds...

I can't stress this enough — make sure you draw your diagrams ACCURATELY (using a ruler and compasses) — like in this Exam Practice Question:

Q1   The gardens of a stately home are shown on the diagram. The public can visit the gardens, but must stay at least 2 m away from the rectangular pond and at least 2 m away from each of the statues (labelled A and B). Make a copy of this diagram using a scale of 1 cm = 2 m and indicate on it the areas where the public can go.

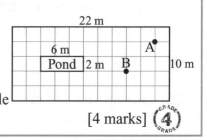

[4 marks]

Bearings

Bearings. They'll be useful next time you're off sailing. Or in your Maths exam.

Bearings (3)

To find or plot a bearing you must remember <u>the three key words</u>:

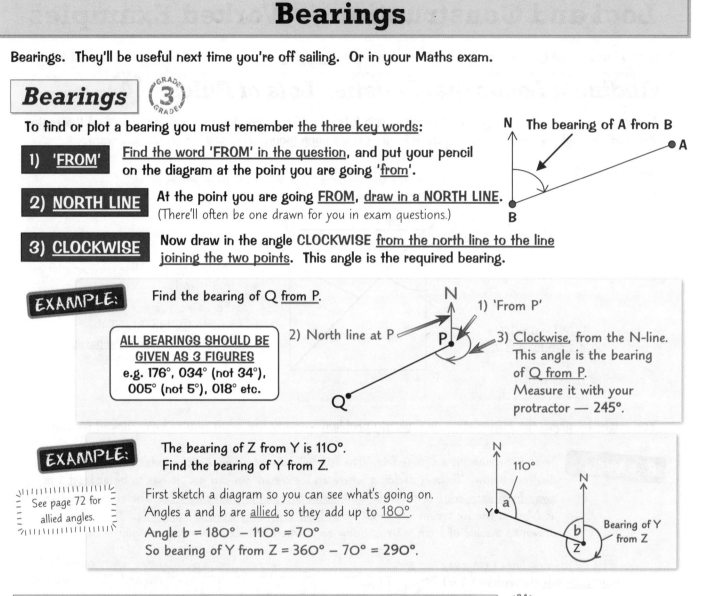

1) 'FROM' <u>Find the word 'FROM' in the question</u>, and put your pencil on the diagram at the point you are going '<u>from</u>'.

2) NORTH LINE At the point you are going **FROM**, <u>draw in a NORTH LINE</u>. (There'll often be one drawn for you in exam questions.)

3) CLOCKWISE Now draw in the angle CLOCKWISE <u>from the north line to the line joining the two points</u>. This angle is the required bearing.

EXAMPLE: Find the bearing of Q <u>from P</u>.

1) 'From P'

2) North line at P

3) <u>Clockwise</u>, from the N-line. This angle is the bearing of <u>Q from P</u>. Measure it with your protractor — 245°.

ALL BEARINGS SHOULD BE GIVEN AS 3 FIGURES e.g. 176°, 034° (not 34°), 005° (not 5°), 018° etc.

EXAMPLE: The bearing of Z from Y is 110°. Find the bearing of Y from Z.

See page 72 for allied angles.

First sketch a diagram so you can see what's going on. Angles a and b are <u>allied</u>, so they add up to <u>180°</u>.

Angle b = 180° − 110° = 70°
So bearing of Y from Z = 360° − 70° = 290°.

Bearings Questions and Scale Drawings (3)

EXAMPLE: A hiker walks 2 km from point A, on a bearing of 036°. If the scale of the map below is 2 cm to 1 km, how far is the hiker now from his car?

If you are asked to <u>CALCULATE</u> a distance or an angle, you'll need to use the <u>cosine or sine rule</u> (see p.99).

First, draw a line at a <u>bearing of 036°</u> from point A. <u>1 km</u> is <u>2 cm</u> on the map and the hiker walks <u>2 km</u>, so make the line from A <u>4 cm</u> long.

You want the distance of the hiker from the car, so use a ruler to measure it on the map, then use the scale to work out the <u>real distance</u> it represents.

Distance to car on map = 3 cm. 2 cm = 1 km, so 1 cm = 0.5 km, therefore 3 cm = 1.5 km.

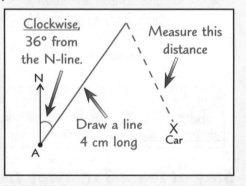

Clockwise, 36° from the N-line.

Measure this distance

Draw a line 4 cm long

X Car

Please bear with me while I figure out where we are...

Learn the three key words above and scribble them out from memory. Now try these practice questions.

Q1 Measure the bearing of T from H. [1 mark] (3)

Q2 A ship sails 12 km on a bearing of 050°, then 20 km on a bearing of 100°. It then sails directly back to its starting position. Calculate this distance to 1 d.p. [5 marks] (8)

Revision Questions for Section Five

There are lots of opportunities to show off your artistic skills here (as long as you use them to answer the questions).

- Try these questions and <u>tick off each one</u> when you <u>get it right</u>.
- When you've done <u>all the questions</u> for a topic and are <u>completely happy</u> with it, tick off the topic.

<u>Angles and Polygons (p71-75)</u> ☑

1) Write down the five simple geometry rules.

2) Find the missing angles in the diagrams below.

a) 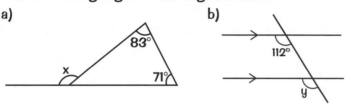   b)   c)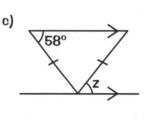

3) Find the exterior angle of a regular hexagon.
   What do the interior angles of a regular hexagon add up to?

4) Write down the number of lines of symmetry and the order of rotational symmetry
   for an equilateral, isosceles and scalene triangle.

5) Name two quadrilaterals that have two pairs of equal angles.

<u>Circle Geometry (p76-77)</u> ☑

6) Write down the nine rules of circle geometry.

7) Find the missing angle in each of the diagrams below.

a) 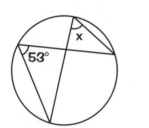   b) 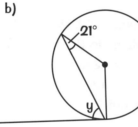   c)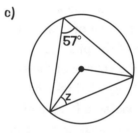

8) Is the quadrilateral on the right cyclic? Explain your answer.

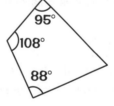

<u>Congruence and Similarity (p78-79)</u> ☑

9) State the four conditions you can use to prove that two triangles are congruent.

10) Prove that triangles ABC and ACD on the right are congruent.

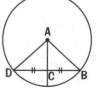

11) The shapes below are similar. What is the length of side x?

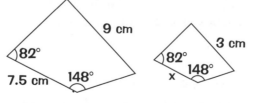

Section Five — Geometry and Measures

Revision Questions for Section Five

Transformations (p80-81) ☑

12) Describe the transformation that maps:
   a) Shape A onto Shape B
   b) Shape A onto Shape C

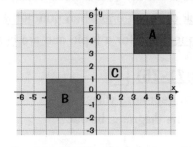

13) Carry out the following transformations on the triangle X, which has vertices (1, 1), (4, 1) and (2, 3):
   a) a rotation of 90° clockwise about (1, 1)   b) a translation by the vector $\binom{-3}{-4}$
   c) an enlargement of scale factor 2, centre (1, 1)

Area and Volume (p82-86) ☑

14) What is the formula for finding the area of a trapezium?
15) Find the area of the shape on the right.
16) A square has an area of 56.25 cm². Find its perimeter.
17) A circle has diameter 16 cm. Find its exact circumference and area.
18) Find the area of the sector with radius 10 cm and angle 45° to 2 d.p.
19) What are the formulas for finding the surface area of a sphere, a cylinder and a cone?
20) The shape on the right is made from a cylinder and a hemisphere. Find its exact surface area.
21) The cross-section of a prism is a regular hexagon with side length 6 cm. The length of the prism is 11 cm. Find its volume to 3 s.f.
22) a) Find the volume of the solid on the right (to 2 d.p.).
   b) How long will it take to fill the solid with water if the water is flowing at 1.5 litres per minute? Give your answer in seconds to 1 d.p.
23) A shape with area 5 cm² is enlarged by a scale factor of 4. What is the area of the enlarged shape?

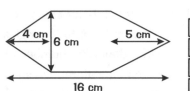

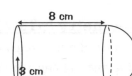

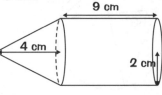

Projections (p87) ☑

24) On squared paper, draw the front elevation, side elevation and plan view of the shape on the right.

Constructions and Loci (p88-91) ☑

25) Construct triangle XYZ, where XY = 5.6 cm, XZ = 7.2 cm and angle YXZ = 55°.
26) Construct two triangles, ABC, with angle A = 40°, AB = 6 cm, BC = 4.5 cm.
27) What shape does the locus of points that are a fixed distance from a given point make?
28) Construct an accurate 45° angle.
29) Draw a line and label it AB. Now construct the perpendicular bisector of AB.
30) Draw a square with sides of length 6 cm and label it ABCD. Shade the region that is nearer to AB than CD and less than 4 cm from vertex A.

Bearings (p92) ☑

31) Describe how to find a bearing from point A to point B.
32) A helicopter flies 25 km on a bearing of 210°, then 20 km on a bearing of 040°. Draw a scale diagram to show this. Use a scale of 1 cm = 5 km.

Pythagoras' Theorem

Pythagoras' theorem sounds hard but it's actually <u>dead simple</u>.
It's also dead important, so make sure you really get your teeth into it.

Pythagoras' Theorem — $a^2 + b^2 = c^2$ (GRADE 4)

1) <u>PYTHAGORAS' THEOREM</u> only works for <u>RIGHT-ANGLED TRIANGLES</u>.

2) Pythagoras uses <u>two sides</u> to find the <u>third side</u>.

3) The <u>BASIC FORMULA</u> for Pythagoras is $a^2 + b^2 = c^2$

4) Make sure you get the numbers in the <u>RIGHT PLACE</u>. c is the <u>longest side</u> (called the hypotenuse) and it's always <u>opposite</u> the right angle.

5) Always <u>CHECK</u> that your answer is <u>SENSIBLE</u>.

$$a^2 + b^2 = c^2$$

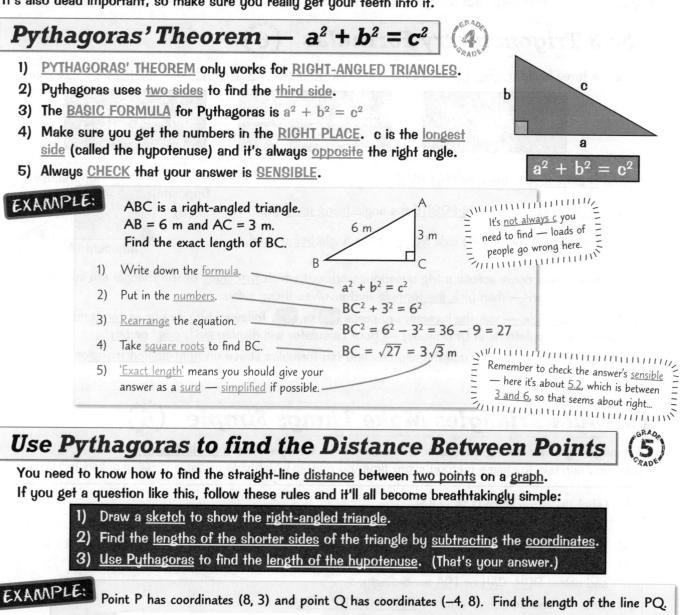

EXAMPLE:

ABC is a right-angled triangle.
AB = 6 m and AC = 3 m.
Find the exact length of BC.

1) Write down the <u>formula</u>.

2) Put in the <u>numbers</u>.

3) <u>Rearrange</u> the equation.

4) Take <u>square roots</u> to find BC.

5) '<u>Exact length</u>' means you should give your answer as a <u>surd</u> — <u>simplified</u> if possible.

$a^2 + b^2 = c^2$

$BC^2 + 3^2 = 6^2$

$BC^2 = 6^2 - 3^2 = 36 - 9 = 27$

$BC = \sqrt{27} = 3\sqrt{3}$ m

It's <u>not always c</u> you need to find — loads of people go wrong here.

Remember to check the answer's <u>sensible</u> — here it's about <u>5.2</u>, which is between <u>3 and 6</u>, so that seems about right…

Use Pythagoras to find the Distance Between Points (GRADE 5)

You need to know how to find the straight-line <u>distance</u> between <u>two points</u> on a <u>graph</u>.
If you get a question like this, follow these rules and it'll all become breathtakingly simple:

1) Draw a <u>sketch</u> to show the <u>right-angled triangle</u>.

2) Find the <u>lengths of the shorter sides</u> of the triangle by <u>subtracting</u> the <u>coordinates</u>.

3) <u>Use Pythagoras</u> to find the <u>length of the hypotenuse</u>. (That's your answer.)

EXAMPLE: Point P has coordinates (8, 3) and point Q has coordinates (−4, 8). Find the length of the line PQ.

① Q (−4, 8)

② Length of <u>side a</u> = 8 − 3 = 5
Length of <u>side b</u> = 8 − −4 = 12

③ Use <u>Pythagoras</u> to find <u>side c</u>:
$c^2 = a^2 + b^2 = 5^2 + 12^2 = 25 + 144 = 169$
So: $c = \sqrt{169} = 13$

Remember, if it's not a right angle, it's a wrong angle…

Once you've learned all the Pythagoras facts on this page, try these Exam Practice Questions.

Q1 Find the length of AC correct to 1 decimal place.

9 m   5 m

[3 marks] (GRADE 4)

Q2 Point A has coordinates (10, 15) and point B has coordinates (6, 12). Find the length of the line AB.

(GRADE 5)

[4 marks]

Q3 A right-angled triangle has a hypotenuse of length $2\sqrt{10}$ cm. Give possible lengths for the other two sides of the triangle, given that the lengths are integers.   [3 marks] (GRADE 7)

Trigonometry — Sin, Cos, Tan

Trigonometry — it's a big scary word. But it's not a big scary topic. An <u>important</u> topic, yes. An <u>always cropping up</u> topic, definitely. But scary? Pur-lease. Takes more than a triangle to scare me. Read on...

The 3 Trigonometry Formulas (6) GRADE

There are three basic <u>trig formulas</u> — each one links <u>two sides and an angle</u> of a <u>right-angled triangle</u>.

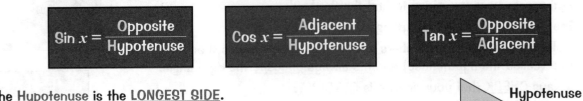

$$\text{Sin } x = \frac{\text{Opposite}}{\text{Hypotenuse}}$$

$$\text{Cos } x = \frac{\text{Adjacent}}{\text{Hypotenuse}}$$

$$\text{Tan } x = \frac{\text{Opposite}}{\text{Adjacent}}$$

- The <u>Hypotenuse</u> is the <u>LONGEST SIDE</u>.

- The <u>Opposite</u> is the side <u>OPPOSITE</u> the angle <u>being used</u> (x).

- The <u>Adjacent</u> is the (other) side <u>NEXT TO</u> the angle <u>being used</u>.

(Triangle diagram labelled: Opposite (O), Hypotenuse (H), Adjacent (A), angle x)

1) Whenever you come across a trig question, work out which <u>two sides</u> of the triangle are involved in that question — then <u>pick the formula</u> that involves those sides.

2) <u>To find the angle — use the inverse</u>, i.e. press [SHIFT] or [2ndF], followed by <u>sin</u>, <u>cos</u> or <u>tan</u> (and make sure your calculator is in DEG mode) — your calculator will display <u>sin⁻¹</u>, <u>cos⁻¹</u> or <u>tan⁻¹</u>.

3) Remember, you can only use the sin, cos and tan formulas above on <u>right-angled triangles</u> — you may have to add lines to the diagram to create one.

There's more about formula triangles on p.69 if you need to jog your memory.

Formula Triangles Make Things Simple (6) GRADE

A handy way to tackle trig questions is to convert the formulas into <u>formula triangles</u>. Then you can use the <u>same method every time</u>, no matter which side or angle is being asked for.

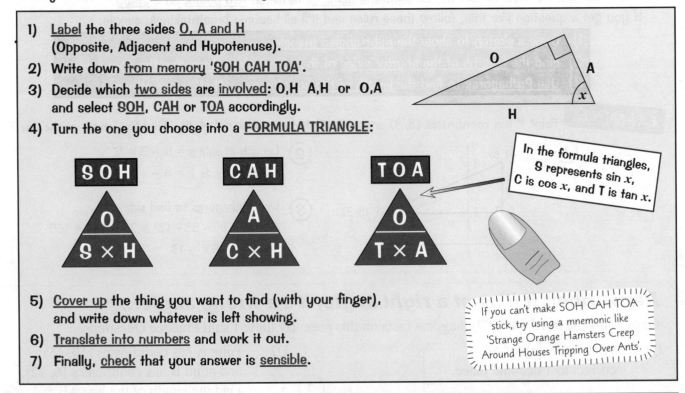

1) <u>Label</u> the three sides <u>O, A and H</u> (Opposite, Adjacent and Hypotenuse).

2) Write down <u>from memory</u> 'SOH CAH TOA'.

3) Decide which <u>two sides</u> are <u>involved</u>: O,H A,H or O,A and select <u>SOH</u>, <u>CAH</u> or <u>TOA</u> accordingly.

4) Turn the one you choose into a <u>FORMULA TRIANGLE</u>:

(Formula triangles shown: SOH with O over S × H; CAH with A over C × H; TOA with O over T × A)

In the formula triangles, S represents sin x, C is cos x, and T is tan x.

5) <u>Cover up</u> the thing you want to find (with your finger), and write down whatever is left showing.

6) <u>Translate into numbers</u> and work it out.

7) Finally, <u>check</u> that your answer is <u>sensible</u>.

If you can't make SOH CAH TOA stick, try using a mnemonic like 'Strange Orange Hamsters Creep Around Houses Tripping Over Ants'.

SOH CAH TOA — the not-so-secret formula for success...

You need to know this stuff off by heart — so go over this page a few times until you've got those formulas firmly lodged and all ready to reel off in the exam. All set? Trigtastic...

Trigonometry — Examples

Here are some lovely examples using the method from p.96 to help you through the trials of trig.

Examples: (GRADE 6)

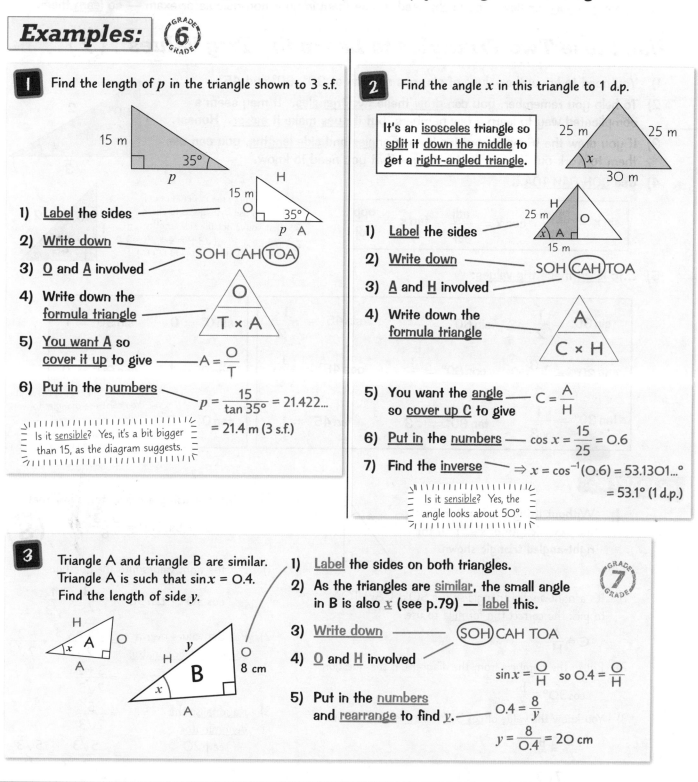

1 Find the length of p in the triangle shown to 3 s.f.

15 m

35°

p

1) **Label** the sides

15 m
O
H
35°
p A

2) **Write down**

3) **O** and **A** involved

SOH CAH (TOA)

4) **Write down the formula triangle**

O / T × A

5) **You want A** so **cover it up** to give — $A = \dfrac{O}{T}$

6) **Put in** the **numbers**

$$p = \frac{15}{\tan 35°} = 21.422...$$
$$= 21.4 \text{ m (3 s.f.)}$$

Is it **sensible**? Yes, it's a bit bigger than 15, as the diagram suggests.

2 Find the angle x in this triangle to 1 d.p.

It's an **isosceles** triangle so **split** it **down the middle** to get a **right-angled triangle**.

25 m   25 m
x
30 m

1) **Label** the sides

25 m
x A
15 m
H
O

2) **Write down**

3) **A** and **H** involved

SOH (CAH) TOA

4) **Write down the formula triangle**

A / C × H

5) **You want the angle** so **cover up C** to give — $C = \dfrac{A}{H}$

6) **Put in** the **numbers** — $\cos x = \dfrac{15}{25} = 0.6$

7) **Find the inverse** $\Rightarrow x = \cos^{-1}(0.6) = 53.1301...°$
$$= 53.1° \text{ (1 d.p.)}$$

Is it **sensible**? Yes, the angle looks about 50°.

3 Triangle A and triangle B are similar. Triangle A is such that $\sin x = 0.4$. Find the length of side y.

H
x A O
A

H
y
x
B
A
O
8 cm

1) **Label** the sides on both triangles.

2) As the triangles are **similar**, the small angle in B is also $\underline{x}$ (see p.79) — **label** this.

3) **Write down** — (SOH) CAH TOA

4) **O** and **H** involved

$\sin x = \dfrac{O}{H}$ so $0.4 = \dfrac{O}{H}$

5) **Put in** the **numbers** and **rearrange** to find y. — $0.4 = \dfrac{8}{y}$

$$y = \frac{8}{0.4} = 20 \text{ cm}$$

(GRADE 7)

I do trigonometry outdoors cos I always get a great sin tan...

If you're really not a fan of formula triangles just use the original formula instead of steps 4 and 5.

Q1 Find the value of x and give your answer to 1 decimal place.

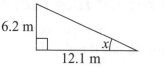

6.2 m

x

12.1 m

[3 marks] (GRADE 6)

Q2 A 3.2 m ladder is leaning against a vertical wall. It is at an angle of 68° to the horizontal ground. How far does the ladder reach up the wall? Give your answer to 3 s.f. [3 marks] (GRADE 6)

Trigonometry — Common Values

Trig questions quite often use the same angles — so it'll make life _easier_ if you know the sin, cos and tan of these _commonly used_ angles. You might need to use them in your non-calculator exam — so _learn_ them.

Use these Two Triangles to Learn the Trig Values

1) You need to know the _values_ of sin, cos and tan at 30°, 60° and 45°.

2) To help you remember, you can _draw_ these _two triangles_. It may seem a complicated way to learn a few numbers, but it _does_ make it _easier_. Honest.

3) If you draw the triangles, putting in their _angles_ and _side lengths_, you can use them to work out the _special trig values_ that you need to know.

4) Use SOH CAH TOA...

$$\sin x = \frac{opp}{hyp} \qquad \cos x = \frac{adj}{hyp} \qquad \tan x = \frac{opp}{adj}$$

You can use Pythagoras to check that you've got the side lengths right, e.g. $1^2 + (\sqrt{3})^2 = 4 = 2^2$

5) ...to _learn_ these _trig values_:

$\sin 30° = \dfrac{1}{2}$	$\sin 60° = \dfrac{\sqrt{3}}{2}$	$\sin 45° = \dfrac{1}{\sqrt{2}}$
$\cos 30° = \dfrac{\sqrt{3}}{2}$	$\cos 60° = \dfrac{1}{2}$	$\cos 45° = \dfrac{1}{\sqrt{2}}$
$\tan 30° = \dfrac{1}{\sqrt{3}}$	$\tan 60° = \sqrt{3}$	$\tan 45° = 1$

$\sin 0° = 0$	$\sin 90° = 1$
$\cos 0° = 1$	$\cos 90° = 0$
$\tan 0° = 0$	

You can't use triangles to work these ones out sadly — you just have to learn them.

EXAMPLES:

1. Without using a calculator, find the exact length of side b in the right-angled triangle shown.

1) It's a right-angled triangle so use SOH CAH TOA to pick the correct _trig formula_ to use.

$$C = \frac{A}{H}$$

2) Put in the _numbers_ from the diagram in the question.

$$\cos 30° = \frac{b}{7}$$

3) You know the _value_ of _cos 30°_, so _substitute_ this in.

$$\frac{\sqrt{3}}{2} = \frac{b}{7}$$

$$b = \frac{7\sqrt{3}}{2} \text{ cm}$$

2. Without using a calculator, show that
$$\cos 30° + \tan 30° = \frac{5\sqrt{3}}{6}$$

1) Put the right values into the question.

$$\cos 30° + \tan 30° = \frac{\sqrt{3}}{2} + \frac{1}{\sqrt{3}}$$

2) Put the values over a _common denominator_.

$$= \frac{\sqrt{3} \times \sqrt{3}}{2\sqrt{3}} + \frac{2}{2\sqrt{3}}$$

$$= \frac{3+2}{2\sqrt{3}}$$

$$= \frac{5}{2\sqrt{3}}$$

3) _Rationalise_ the denominator — see p.20

$$= \frac{5\sqrt{3}}{2\sqrt{3}\sqrt{3}} = \frac{5\sqrt{3}}{6}$$

Tri angles — go on, you might like them...

Use the triangles to learn the trig values — then if you're not sure about a trig value in the exam, you can quickly sketch the triangle to check you've got it right. Have a go at this Exam Practice Question.

Q1　Find the exact area of this triangle.　[4 marks]

5 mm

The Sine and Cosine Rules

Normal trigonometry using SOH CAH TOA etc. can only be applied to <u>right-angled</u> triangles. Which leaves us with the question of what to do with other-angled triangles. Step forward the <u>Sine and Cosine Rules</u>...

Labelling the Triangle

This is very important. You must label the sides and angles properly so that the letters for the sides and angles correspond with each other. Use <u>lower case letters</u> for the <u>sides</u> and <u>capitals</u> for the <u>angles</u>.

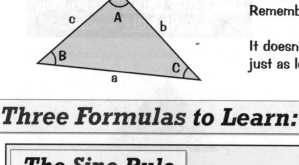

Remember, <u>side 'a' is opposite angle A</u> etc.

It doesn't matter which sides you decide to call a, b, and c, just as long as the angles are then labelled properly.

Three Formulas to Learn:

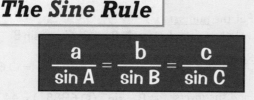

The Sine Rule

$$\frac{a}{\sin A} = \frac{b}{\sin B} = \frac{c}{\sin C}$$

You don't use the whole thing with both '=' signs of course, so it's not half as bad as it looks — you just <u>choose the two bits</u> that you want:

e.g. $\dfrac{b}{\sin B} = \dfrac{c}{\sin C}$ or $\dfrac{a}{\sin A} = \dfrac{b}{\sin B}$

The Cosine Rule

The 'normal' form is...

$$a^2 = b^2 + c^2 - 2bc \cos A$$

...or this form is good for finding an angle (you get it by rearranging the 'normal' version):

$$\text{or} \quad \cos A = \frac{b^2 + c^2 - a^2}{2bc}$$

Area of the Triangle

This formula comes in handy when you know <u>two sides</u> and the <u>angle between them</u>:

$$\underline{\text{Area of triangle}} = \tfrac{1}{2} \, ab \sin C$$

Of course, you already know a <u>simple formula</u> for calculating the area using the <u>base length</u> and <u>height</u> (see p.82). The formula here is for when you don't know those values.

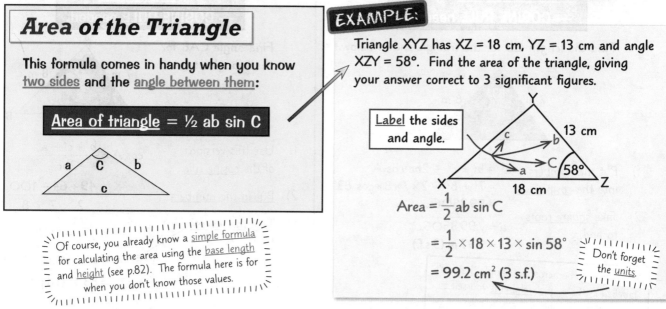

EXAMPLE:

Triangle XYZ has XZ = 18 cm, YZ = 13 cm and angle XZY = 58°. Find the area of the triangle, giving your answer correct to 3 significant figures.

Label the sides and angle.

Area = $\frac{1}{2}$ ab sin C

$= \frac{1}{2} \times 18 \times 13 \times \sin 58°$

$= 99.2 \text{ cm}^2$ (3 s.f.)

Don't forget the <u>units</u>.

...and step back again. Hope you enjoyed a moment in the spotlight...

You need to learn these formulas and make sure you know how to use them.
Here's an area question to have a go at, and fear not, you'll get your chance
to tackle some sine and cosine rule problems on the next page...

Q1 Triangle FGH has FG = 9 cm, FH = 12 cm
and angle GFH = 37°. Find its area, giving
your answer correct to 3 significant figures.

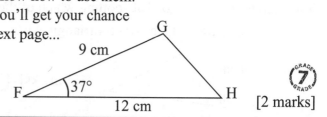

[2 marks]

The Sine and Cosine Rules

There are four main question types where the <u>sine</u> and <u>cosine</u> rules would be applied. So learn the exact details of these four examples and you'll be laughing. WARNING: if you laugh too much people will think you're crazy.

The Four Examples (GRADE 7)

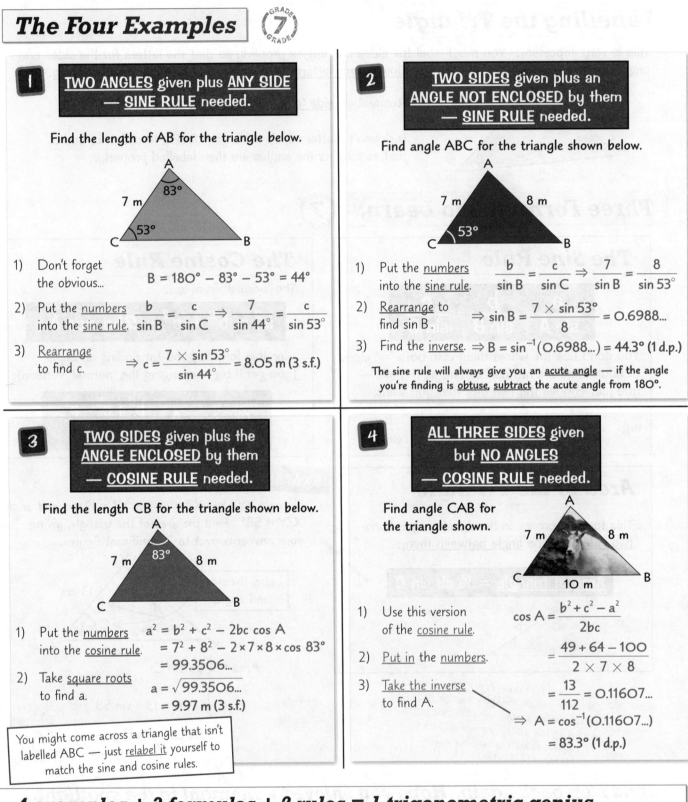

1 | **TWO ANGLES** given plus **ANY SIDE** — **SINE RULE** needed.

Find the length of AB for the triangle below.

(triangle with A at top, angle 83° at A, 7 m on side CA, 53° at C, B at right)

1) Don't forget the obvious... $B = 180° − 83° − 53° = 44°$

2) Put the <u>numbers</u> into the <u>sine rule</u>. $\dfrac{b}{\sin B} = \dfrac{c}{\sin C} \Rightarrow \dfrac{7}{\sin 44°} = \dfrac{c}{\sin 53°}$

3) <u>Rearrange</u> to find c. $\Rightarrow c = \dfrac{7 \times \sin 53°}{\sin 44°} = 8.05 \text{ m (3 s.f.)}$

2 | **TWO SIDES** given plus an **ANGLE NOT ENCLOSED** by them — **SINE RULE** needed.

Find angle ABC for the triangle shown below.

(triangle with A at top, 7 m on CA, 8 m on AB, 53° at C, B at right)

1) Put the <u>numbers</u> into the <u>sine rule</u>. $\dfrac{b}{\sin B} = \dfrac{c}{\sin C} \Rightarrow \dfrac{7}{\sin B} = \dfrac{8}{\sin 53°}$

2) <u>Rearrange</u> to find sin B. $\Rightarrow \sin B = \dfrac{7 \times \sin 53°}{8} = 0.6988...$

3) Find the <u>inverse</u>. $\Rightarrow B = \sin^{-1}(0.6988...) = 44.3° \text{ (1 d.p.)}$

The sine rule will always give you an <u>acute angle</u> — if the angle you're finding is <u>obtuse</u>, <u>subtract</u> the acute angle from 180°.

3 | **TWO SIDES** given plus the **ANGLE ENCLOSED** by them — **COSINE RULE** needed.

Find the length CB for the triangle shown below.

(triangle with A at top, 83° at A, 7 m on CA, 8 m on AB, B at right)

1) Put the <u>numbers</u> into the <u>cosine rule</u>. $a^2 = b^2 + c^2 − 2bc \cos A$
$= 7^2 + 8^2 − 2 \times 7 \times 8 \times \cos 83°$
$= 99.3506...$

2) Take <u>square roots</u> to find a. $a = \sqrt{99.3506...}$
$= 9.97 \text{ m (3 s.f.)}$

You might come across a triangle that isn't labelled ABC — just <u>relabel it</u> yourself to match the sine and cosine rules.

4 | **ALL THREE SIDES** given but **NO ANGLES** — **COSINE RULE** needed.

Find angle CAB for the triangle shown.

(triangle with A at top, 7 m on CA, 8 m on AB, 10 m on CB, C at left, B at right)

1) Use this version of the <u>cosine rule</u>. $\cos A = \dfrac{b^2 + c^2 − a^2}{2bc}$

2) <u>Put in</u> the <u>numbers</u>. $= \dfrac{49 + 64 − 100}{2 \times 7 \times 8}$

3) <u>Take the inverse</u> to find A. $= \dfrac{13}{112} = 0.11607...$
$\Rightarrow A = \cos^{-1}(0.11607...)$
$= 83.3° \text{ (1 d.p.)}$

4 examples + 3 formulas + 2 rules = 1 trigonometric genius...

You need to get really good at spotting which of the four methods to use, so try these practice questions.

Q1 Find the length of side AB for triangle ABC.

(triangle with A at top, 24 cm on AC, 46° at B, 38° at C, B at right)   [3 marks] (GRADE 7)

Q2 Find the size of angle RPQ for triangle PQR.

(triangle with P top-left, 15 m on PR, R top-right, 9 m on PQ, 13 m on QR, Q at bottom)   [3 marks] (GRADE 7)

3D Pythagoras

This is a 3D version of the 2D Pythagoras theorem you saw on page 95.
There's just <u>one simple formula</u> — learn it and the world's your oyster...

3D Pythagoras for Cuboids — $a^2 + b^2 + c^2 = d^2$ (7)

<u>Cuboids</u> have their own formula for calculating
the length of their <u>longest diagonal</u>:

$$a^2 + b^2 + c^2 = d^2$$

In reality it's nothing you haven't seen before
— it's just <u>2D Pythagoras' theorem</u> being used <u>twice</u>:

1) <u>a, b and e</u> make a <u>right-angled triangle</u> so
$$e^2 = a^2 + b^2$$

2) Now look at the <u>right-angled triangle</u>
formed by <u>e, c and d</u>:
$$d^2 = e^2 + c^2 = a^2 + b^2 + c^2$$

EXAMPLE:

Find the exact length of the diagonal BH for the cube in the diagram.

1) Write down the <u>formula</u>.　　$a^2 + b^2 + c^2 = d^2$

2) Put in the <u>numbers</u>.　　$4^2 + 4^2 + 4^2 = BH^2$

3) Take the <u>square root</u> to find BH.　$\Rightarrow BH = \sqrt{48} = 4\sqrt{3}$ cm

The Cuboid Formula can be used in Other 3D Shapes (8)

EXAMPLE:

In the square-based pyramid shown,
M is the midpoint of the base.
Find the vertical height AM.

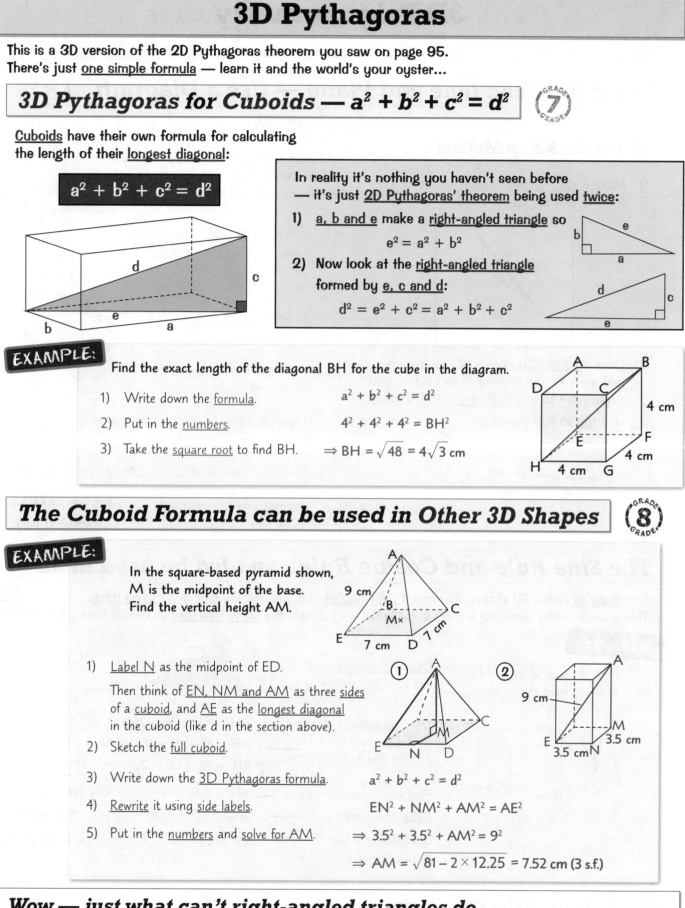

1) <u>Label N</u> as the midpoint of ED.

Then think of <u>EN, NM and AM</u> as three <u>sides</u>
of a <u>cuboid</u>, and <u>AE</u> as the <u>longest diagonal</u>
in the cuboid (like d in the section above).

2) Sketch the <u>full cuboid</u>.

3) Write down the <u>3D Pythagoras formula</u>.　$a^2 + b^2 + c^2 = d^2$

4) <u>Rewrite</u> it using <u>side labels</u>.　$EN^2 + NM^2 + AM^2 = AE^2$

5) Put in the <u>numbers</u> and <u>solve for AM</u>.　$\Rightarrow 3.5^2 + 3.5^2 + AM^2 = 9^2$

$\Rightarrow AM = \sqrt{81 - 2 \times 12.25} = 7.52$ cm (3 s.f.)

Wow — just what can't right-angled triangles do...

You need to be ready to tackle 3D questions in the exam,
so have a go at this Exam Practice Question.

Q1　Find the length AH in the cuboid shown to 3 s.f.

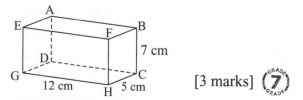

[3 marks] (7)

3D Trigonometry

3D trig may sound tricky, and I suppose it is a bit... but it's actually just using the same old rules.

Angle Between Line and Plane — Use a Diagram (8)

Learn the 3-Step Method

1) Make a right-angled triangle between the line and the plane.

2) Draw a simple 2D sketch of this triangle and mark on the lengths of two sides (you might have to use Pythagoras to find one).

3) Use trig to find the angle.

Have a look at p.95-98 to jog your memory about Pythagoras and trig.

EXAMPLE:

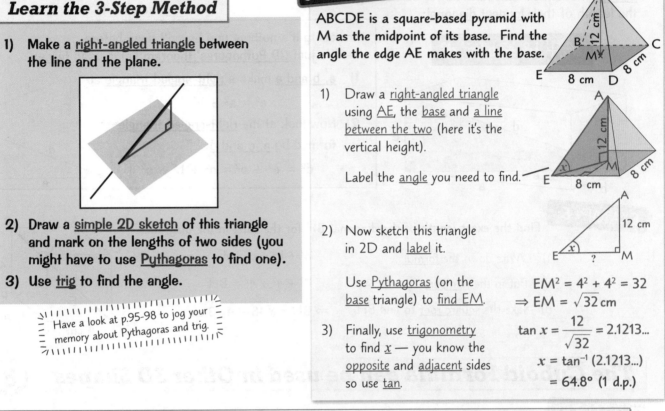

ABCDE is a square-based pyramid with M as the midpoint of its base. Find the angle the edge AE makes with the base.

1) Draw a right-angled triangle using AE, the base and a line between the two (here it's the vertical height).

   Label the angle you need to find.

2) Now sketch this triangle in 2D and label it.

   Use Pythagoras (on the base triangle) to find EM.

   $EM^2 = 4^2 + 4^2 = 32$
   $\Rightarrow EM = \sqrt{32}$ cm

3) Finally, use trigonometry to find x — you know the opposite and adjacent sides so use tan.

   $\tan x = \dfrac{12}{\sqrt{32}} = 2.1213...$

   $x = \tan^{-1}(2.1213...)$
   $= 64.8°$ (1 d.p.)

The Sine Rule and Cosine Rule can also be used in 3D (9)

For triangles inside 3D shapes that aren't right-angled you can use the sine and cosine rules.
This sounds mildly terrifying but it's actually OK — just use the same formulas as before (see p.99-100).

EXAMPLE:

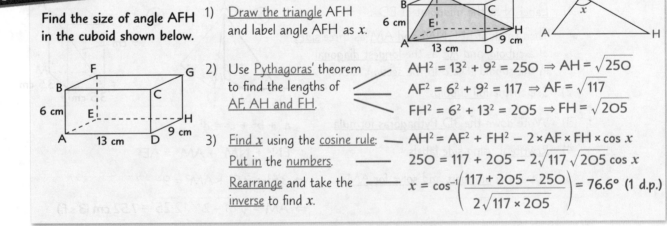

Find the size of angle AFH in the cuboid shown below.

1) Draw the triangle AFH and label angle AFH as x.

2) Use Pythagoras' theorem to find the lengths of AF, AH and FH.

   $AH^2 = 13^2 + 9^2 = 250 \Rightarrow AH = \sqrt{250}$
   $AF^2 = 6^2 + 9^2 = 117 \Rightarrow AF = \sqrt{117}$
   $FH^2 = 6^2 + 13^2 = 205 \Rightarrow FH = \sqrt{205}$

3) Find x using the cosine rule:
   Put in the numbers.
   Rearrange and take the inverse to find x.

   $AH^2 = AF^2 + FH^2 - 2 \times AF \times FH \times \cos x$
   $250 = 117 + 205 - 2\sqrt{117}\sqrt{205} \cos x$
   $x = \cos^{-1}\left(\dfrac{117 + 205 - 250}{2\sqrt{117 \times 205}}\right) = 76.6°$ (1 d.p.)

The Return of the Cosine Rule — out now in 3D...

If you need to find an angle in a 3D question, don't panic — just put those standard trig formulas to work.

Q1   Find the size of the angle between the line PV and the plane PQRS in the cuboid shown.   [4 marks] (8)

4 cm
7 cm
11 cm

Vectors

Vectors represent a movement of a certain <u>size</u> in a certain <u>direction</u>.
They might seem a bit weird at first, but there are really just a few facts to get to grips with...

The Vector Notations (6)

There are several ways to <u>write</u> vectors...

They're represented on a diagram by an <u>arrow</u>.

1) <u>Column</u> vectors: $\begin{pmatrix} 2 \\ -5 \end{pmatrix}$ — 2 units right, 5 units down $\begin{pmatrix} -7 \\ 4 \end{pmatrix}$ — 7 units left, 4 units up

2) **a** —— <u>exam questions</u> use <u>bold</u> like this

3) <u>a</u> or <u>a</u> — <u>you</u> should always <u>underline</u> them

4) $\overrightarrow{AB}$ —— this means the vector <u>from point A to point B</u>

Multiplying a Vector by a Scalar (6)

Multiplying a vector by a <u>positive</u> number <u>changes</u> the vector's <u>size</u> but <u>not its direction</u> — it <u>scales</u> the vector.
If the number's <u>negative</u> then the <u>direction gets switched</u>.

<u>Scalars</u> are just normal numbers (i.e. not vectors).

a   2**a** -1.5**a**

Vectors that are <u>scalar multiples</u> of each other are <u>parallel</u>.

Adding and Subtracting Vectors (6)

You can describe movements between points by <u>adding and subtracting known vectors</u>.
<u>Loads of vector exam questions</u> are based around this.

"<u>a</u> + <u>b</u>" means 'go along <u>a</u> then <u>b</u>'.

"c – d" means 'go along c then backwards along d' (the <u>minus</u> sign means go the <u>opposite</u> way).

In the diagrams, $\overrightarrow{PR} = \underline{a} + \underline{b}$ and $\overrightarrow{XZ} = \underline{c} - \underline{d}$.

When adding <u>column vectors</u>, add the top to the top and the bottom to the bottom. The same goes when subtracting. $\begin{pmatrix} 3 \\ -1 \end{pmatrix} + \begin{pmatrix} 5 \\ 3 \end{pmatrix} = \begin{pmatrix} 8 \\ 2 \end{pmatrix}$

EXAMPLE:

In the diagram below, M is the midpoint of BC.
Find vectors $\overrightarrow{AM}$, $\overrightarrow{OC}$ and $\overrightarrow{AC}$ in terms of **a**, **b** and **m**.

To obtain the <u>unknown vector</u> just '<u>get there</u>' by any route <u>made up of known vectors</u>.

$\overrightarrow{AM} = -\underline{a} + \underline{b} + \underline{m}$ —— A to M via O and B

$\overrightarrow{OC} = \underline{b} + 2\underline{m}$ —— O to C via B and M — M's half-way between B and C so $\overrightarrow{BC} = 2\underline{m}$

$\overrightarrow{AC} = -\underline{a} + \underline{b} + 2\underline{m}$ —— A to C via O, B and M

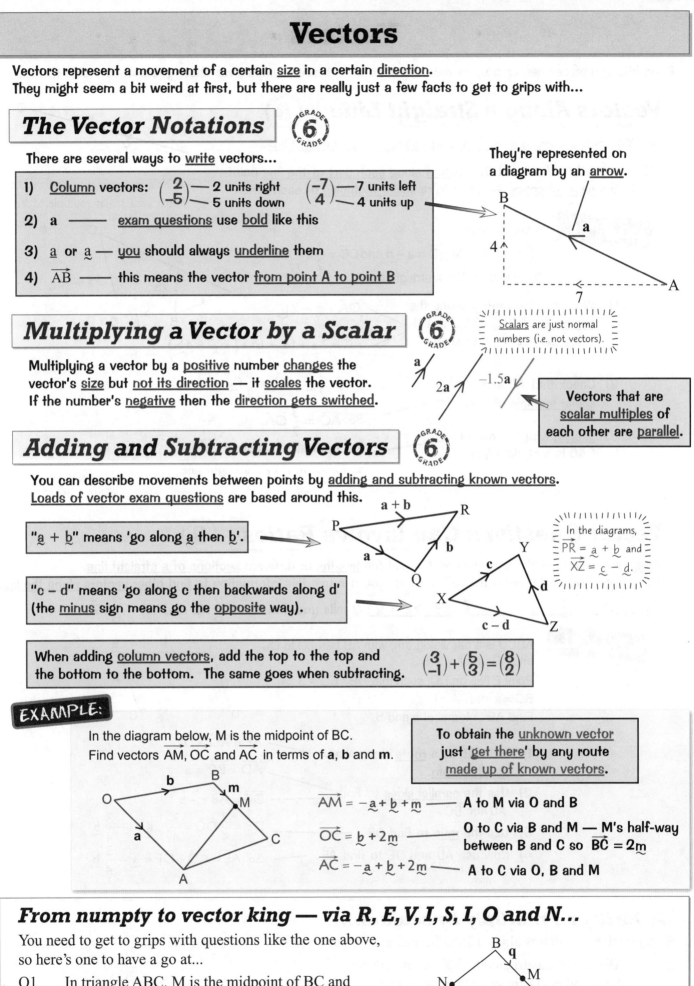

From numpty to vector king — via R, E, V, I, S, I, O and N...

You need to get to grips with questions like the one above, so here's one to have a go at...

Q1   In triangle ABC, M is the midpoint of BC and N is the midpoint of AB. $\overrightarrow{AC} = \mathbf{p}$ and $\overrightarrow{BM} = \mathbf{q}$.
Find $\overrightarrow{AB}$ and $\overrightarrow{NA}$ in terms of **p** and **q**.

[3 marks] (7)

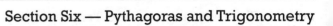

Vectors

Extra bits and pieces can crop up in vector questions — these examples will show you how to tackle them...

Vectors Along a Straight Line (8)

1) You can use <u>vectors</u> to <u>show</u> that <u>points lie on a straight line</u>.

2) You need to show that the <u>vectors</u> along <u>each part of the line</u> point in the <u>same direction</u> — i.e. they're <u>scalar multiples</u> of each other.

If XYZ is a straight line then $\overrightarrow{XY}$ must be a scalar multiple of $\overrightarrow{YZ}$.

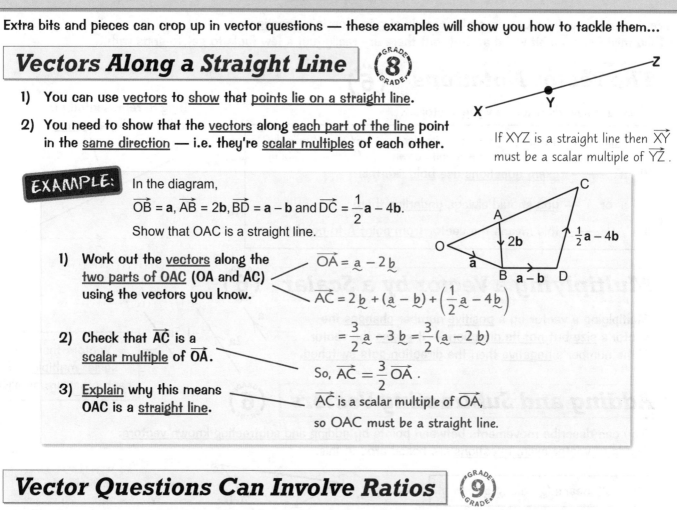

EXAMPLE:

In the diagram,
$\overrightarrow{OB} = \mathbf{a}$, $\overrightarrow{AB} = 2\mathbf{b}$, $\overrightarrow{BD} = \mathbf{a} - \mathbf{b}$ and $\overrightarrow{DC} = \frac{1}{2}\mathbf{a} - 4\mathbf{b}$.

Show that OAC is a straight line.

1) Work out the <u>vectors</u> along the <u>two parts of OAC</u> (OA and AC) using the vectors you know.

$$\overrightarrow{OA} = \underset{\sim}{a} - 2\underset{\sim}{b}$$

$$\overrightarrow{AC} = 2\underset{\sim}{b} + (\underset{\sim}{a} - \underset{\sim}{b}) + \left(\frac{1}{2}\underset{\sim}{a} - 4\underset{\sim}{b}\right)$$

2) Check that $\overrightarrow{AC}$ is a <u>scalar multiple</u> of $\overrightarrow{OA}$.

$$= \frac{3}{2}\underset{\sim}{a} - 3\underset{\sim}{b} = \frac{3}{2}(\underset{\sim}{a} - 2\underset{\sim}{b})$$

So, $\overrightarrow{AC} = \frac{3}{2}\overrightarrow{OA}$.

3) <u>Explain</u> why this means OAC is a <u>straight line</u>.

$\overrightarrow{AC}$ is a scalar multiple of $\overrightarrow{OA}$, so OAC must be a straight line.

Vector Questions Can Involve Ratios (9)

<u>Ratios</u> are used in vector questions to tell you the <u>lengths</u> of different <u>sections of a straight line</u>. If you know the vector along part of that line, you can use this information to <u>find other vectors along the line</u>.

E.g. $\overset{X}{\bullet}$———$\overset{Y}{\bullet}$——————$\overset{Z}{\bullet}$ XY : YZ = 2 : 3 tells you that $\overrightarrow{XY} = \frac{2}{5}\overrightarrow{XZ}$ and $\overrightarrow{YZ} = \frac{3}{5}\overrightarrow{XZ}$.

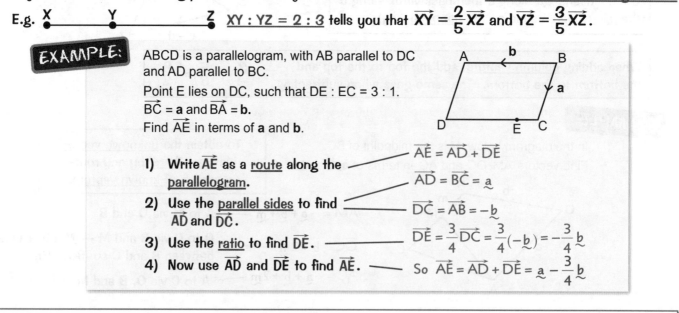

EXAMPLE:

ABCD is a parallelogram, with AB parallel to DC and AD parallel to BC.

Point E lies on DC, such that DE : EC = 3 : 1.
$\overrightarrow{BC} = \mathbf{a}$ and $\overrightarrow{BA} = \mathbf{b}$.
Find $\overrightarrow{AE}$ in terms of $\mathbf{a}$ and $\mathbf{b}$.

1) Write $\overrightarrow{AE}$ as a <u>route</u> along the <u>parallelogram</u>.

$$\overrightarrow{AE} = \overrightarrow{AD} + \overrightarrow{DE}$$

$$\overrightarrow{AD} = \overrightarrow{BC} = \underset{\sim}{a}$$

2) Use the <u>parallel sides</u> to find $\overrightarrow{AD}$ and $\overrightarrow{DC}$.

$$\overrightarrow{DC} = \overrightarrow{AB} = -\underset{\sim}{b}$$

3) Use the <u>ratio</u> to find $\overrightarrow{DE}$.

$$\overrightarrow{DE} = \frac{3}{4}\overrightarrow{DC} = \frac{3}{4}(-\underset{\sim}{b}) = -\frac{3}{4}\underset{\sim}{b}$$

4) Now use $\overrightarrow{AD}$ and $\overrightarrow{DE}$ to find $\overrightarrow{AE}$.

So $\overrightarrow{AE} = \overrightarrow{AD} + \overrightarrow{DE} = \underset{\sim}{a} - \frac{3}{4}\underset{\sim}{b}$

Go forth and multiply by scalars...

So remember — vectors along a straight line or on parallel lines are just scalar multiples of each other.

Q1   ABCD is a quadrilateral. $\overrightarrow{AX} = \mathbf{a}$ and $\overrightarrow{BX} = \mathbf{b}$.
AXC and BXD are straight lines, with AX : XC = BX : XD = 2 : 3.
Find $\overrightarrow{AB}$ and $\overrightarrow{DC}$ in terms of $\mathbf{a}$ and $\mathbf{b}$.
$\overrightarrow{AD}$ and $\overrightarrow{BC}$ are not parallel. What sort of quadrilateral is ABCD?   (9)   [6 marks]

Revision Questions for Section Six

There are a good few facts and formulas in this section, so use this page to check you've got them all sorted.

- Try these questions and <u>tick off each one</u> when you <u>get it right</u>.
- When you've done <u>all the questions</u> for a topic and are <u>completely happy</u> with it, tick off the topic.

Pythagoras' Theorem (p95) ☑

1) What is the formula for Pythagoras' theorem?   What do you use it for?
2) A museum has a flight of stairs up to its front door (see diagram).
   A ramp is to be put over the top of the steps for wheelchair users.
   Calculate the length that the ramp would need to be to 3 s.f.
3) Point P has coordinates (–3, –2) and point Q has coordinates (2, 4).
   Calculate the length of the line PQ to 1 d.p.

Trigonometry — Sin, Cos, Tan (p96-98) ☑

4) Write down the three trigonometry formula triangles.
5) Find the size of angle x in triangle ABC to 1 d.p.
6) Draw two triangles and use them to write down the values
   of sin, cos and tan for 30°, 60° and 45°.
7) Find the exact length of side XZ in triangle XYZ.

The Sine and Cosine Rules (p99-100) ☑

8) Write down the sine and cosine rules and the formula (involving sin) for the area of any triangle.
9) List the 4 different types of sine/cosine rule questions and which rule you need for each.
10) Triangle JKL has side JK = 7 cm, side JL = 11 cm and angle JLK = 32°. Find angle JKL.
11) In triangle FGH side FH = 8 cm, side GH = 9 cm and angle FHG = 47°. Find the length of side FG.
12) Triangle PQR has side PQ = 12 cm, side QR = 9 cm and angle PQR = 63°. Find its area.
13) WXYZ is a quadrilateral.
    a) Find the length of side XY to 3 s.f.
    b) Find the area of the quadrilateral to 3 s.f.

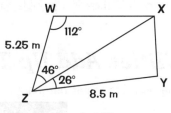

3D Pythagoras (p101) ☑

14) What is the formula for finding the length of the longest diagonal in a cuboid?
15) Find the length of the longest diagonal in the cuboid measuring 5 m × 6 m × 9 m.

3D Trigonometry (p102) ☑

16) Find the angle between the line BH and the plane ABCD in this cuboid.

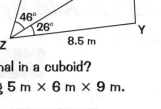

17) Find the size of angle WPU in the cuboid shown to the nearest degree.

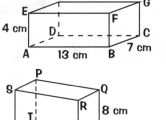

Vectors (p103-104) ☑

18) What is the effect of multiplying a vector by a scalar?
19) $\underset{\sim}{a}$ and $\underset{\sim}{b}$ are column vectors, where $\underset{\sim}{a} = \begin{pmatrix} 4 \\ -2 \end{pmatrix}$ and $\underset{\sim}{b} = \begin{pmatrix} 7 \\ 6 \end{pmatrix}$.
    a) Find $\underset{\sim}{a} - \underset{\sim}{b}$ c) Find $3\underset{\sim}{a} + \underset{\sim}{b}$
    b) Find $5\underset{\sim}{a}$ d) Find $-4\underset{\sim}{a} - 2\underset{\sim}{b}$
20) ABCD is a quadrilateral.
    AXC is a straight line with AX : XC = 1 : 3.
    a) Find $\overrightarrow{AX}$.   b) Find $\overrightarrow{DX}$ and $\overrightarrow{XB}$.
    c) Is DXB a straight line? Explain your answer.

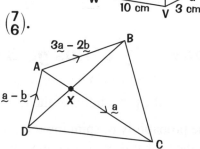

Probability Basics

A lot of people reckon <u>probability</u> is pretty tough. But learn the <u>basics</u> well, and it'll all make sense.

All Probabilities are Between 0 and 1   (GRADE 3)

1) Probabilities are <u>always</u> between 0 and 1. The <u>higher</u> the probability of something, the <u>more likely</u> it is.

2) A probability of <u>ZERO</u> means it will <u>NEVER HAPPEN</u> and a probability of <u>ONE</u> means it <u>DEFINITELY WILL</u>.

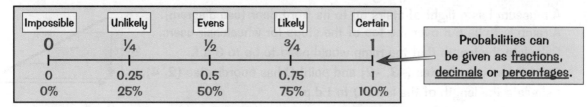

Impossible	Unlikely	Evens	Likely	Certain
0	¼	½	¾	1
0	0.25	0.5	0.75	1
0%	25%	50%	75%	100%

Probabilities can be given as <u>fractions</u>, <u>decimals</u> or <u>percentages</u>.

You Can Find Some Probabilities Using a Formula   (GRADE 3)

<u>Careful</u>... this formula only works if <u>all</u> the possible <u>outcomes</u> (things that could happen) are <u>equally likely</u>.

$$\text{Probability} = \frac{\text{Number of ways for something to happen}}{\text{Total number of possible outcomes}}$$

Words like '<u>fair</u>' and '<u>at random</u>' show possible outcomes are all equally likely. '<u>Biased</u>' and '<u>unfair</u>' mean the opposite.

EXAMPLE: Work out the probability of randomly picking a letter 'P' from the tiles below.

APPLE PIE

1) There are <u>3 P's</u> — so there are <u>3 different ways</u> to 'pick a letter P'.

2) And there are <u>8 tiles</u> altogether — each of these is a <u>possible outcome</u>.

$$\text{Probability} = \frac{\text{number of ways to pick a P}}{\text{total number of possible outcomes}}$$
$$= \frac{3}{8} \text{ (or 0.375)}$$

Probabilities Add Up To 1   (GRADE 3)

1) If <u>only one</u> possible result can happen at a time, then the probabilities of <u>all</u> the results <u>add up to 1</u>.

Probabilities always ADD UP to 1

2) So since something must either <u>happen</u> or <u>not happen</u> (i.e. <u>only one</u> of these can happen at a time):

P(event happens) + P(event doesn't happen) = 1

EXAMPLE: A spinner has different numbers of red, blue and green sections. Work out the value of x and use it to find the probability of spinning red or blue.

Colour	red	blue	green
Probability	$3x$	$2x$	$5x$

1) The probabilities <u>add up to 1</u>. $3x + 2x + 5x = 1$ so $10x = 1$ and so $\underline{x = 0.1}$

2) Spinning red or blue is the same as <u>not spinning green</u>.   P(red or blue) = 1 − P(green)
$$= 1 - (5 \times 0.1) = 0.5$$

'P(result)' just means the probability of that result.

The probability of this getting you marks in the exam = 1...

You need to know the facts in the boxes above. You also need to know how to <u>use</u> them.

Q1   Calculate the probability of the fair spinner on the right landing on 4.   [2 marks] (GRADE 3)

Q2   If the probability of spinning red on a spinner is $1 - 3x$, find the probability of spinning any colour <u>except</u> red.   [1 mark] (GRADE 3)

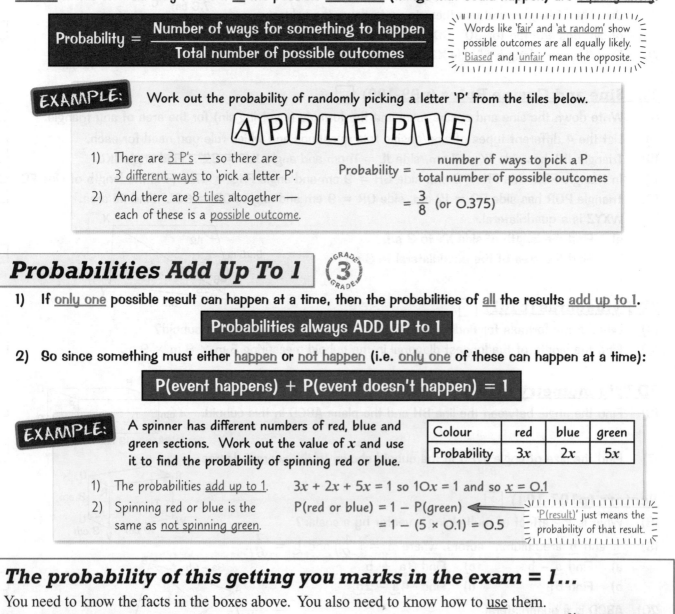

Counting Outcomes

With a lot of probability questions, a good place to start is with a list of all the <u>possible outcomes</u>. Once you've got a <u>list of outcomes</u>, the rest of the question should be straightforward.

Listing All Outcomes

A <u>sample space diagram</u> shows all the possible outcomes. It can be a simple list, but a two-way table works well if there are <u>two activities</u> going on (e.g. two coins being tossed, or a dice being thrown and a spinner being spun).

EXAMPLE: The spinners on the right are spun, and the scores added together.

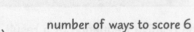

a) Make a sample space diagram showing all the possible outcomes.

1) All the scores from one spinner go <u>along the top</u>. All the scores from the other spinner go <u>down the side</u>.

2) <u>Add</u> the two scores together to get the different possible totals (the <u>outcomes</u>).

+	3	4	5
1	4	5	6
2	5	6	7
3	6	7	8

There are <u>9 outcomes</u> here — even though some of the actual totals are repeated.

b) Find the probability of spinning a total of 6.

There are <u>9 possible outcomes</u> altogether, and <u>3 ways</u> to score 6.

$$P(\text{total} = 6) = \frac{\text{number of ways to score 6}}{\text{total number of possible outcomes}} = \frac{3}{9} = \frac{1}{3}$$

Use the Product Rule to Count Outcomes

1) Sometimes it'll be <u>difficult</u> to list all the outcomes (e.g. if the number of outcomes is <u>large</u> or if there are <u>more than two</u> activities going on).

2) Luckily, you can <u>count</u> outcomes using the <u>product rule</u>.

> The number of ways to carry out a <u>combination</u> of activities equals the number of ways to carry out <u>each activity</u> multiplied together.

EXAMPLE: Jason rolls four fair six-sided dice.

a) How many different ways are there to roll the four dice?
Each dice has <u>6 different ways</u> that it can land (on 1, 2, 3, 4, 5 or 6).
Total number of ways of rolling four dice = 6 × 6 × 6 × 6 = 1296

b) How many different ways are there to only get even numbers when rolling the four dice?
Each dice has <u>3 different ways</u> that it can land on an even number (on 2, 4, or 6).
Number of ways of only rolling even numbers = 3 × 3 × 3 × 3 = 81

c) What is the probability of only getting even numbers when rolling four dice?

$$P(\text{only even numbers}) = \frac{\text{number of ways to only get even numbers}}{\text{total number of ways to roll the dice}} = \frac{81}{1296} = \frac{1}{16}$$

Sample space diagrams — they're out of this world...

When you can draw a sample space diagram, probability questions are easy. If you have to use the product rule things get a bit trickier. Not to worry, have a go at these questions to see if you've got it...

Q1 Three fair coins are tossed: a) List all the possible outcomes. [1 mark]
b) Find the probability of getting exactly 2 heads. [1 mark]

Q2 Ten fair coins are tossed. Find the probability of not getting any heads. [2 marks]

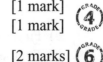

Probability Experiments

Bunsen burners and safety glasses at the ready... it's time for some experiments.

Fair or Biased?

The probability of rolling a three on a normal dice is $\frac{1}{6}$ — you know that each of the 6 numbers on the dice is <u>equally likely</u> to be rolled, and there's <u>only 1 three</u>.

BUT this only works if it's a <u>fair dice</u>. If the dice is a bit <u>wonky</u> (the technical term is '<u>biased</u>') then each number <u>won't</u> have an equal chance of being rolled. This is where <u>relative frequency</u> comes in — you can use it to <u>estimate</u> probabilities when things might be wonky.

Do the Experiment Again and Again and Again...

You need to do an experiment <u>over and over again</u> and count how many times each outcome happens (its <u>frequency</u>). Then you can calculate the <u>relative frequency</u> using this formula:

$$\text{Relative frequency} = \frac{\text{Frequency}}{\text{Number of times you tried the experiment}}$$

An experiment could just mean rolling a dice.

You can use the <u>relative frequency</u> of a result as an <u>estimate</u> of its <u>probability</u>.

EXAMPLE: The spinner on the right was spun 100 times. Use the results in the table below to estimate the probability of getting each of the scores.

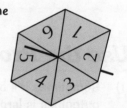

Score	1	2	3	4	5	6
Frequency	3	14	41	20	18	4

<u>Divide</u> each of the frequencies by 100 to find the <u>relative frequencies</u>.

Score	1	2	3	4	5	6
Relative Frequency	$\frac{3}{100}$ = 0.03	$\frac{14}{100}$ = 0.14	$\frac{41}{100}$ = 0.41	$\frac{20}{100}$ = 0.2	$\frac{18}{100}$ = 0.18	$\frac{4}{100}$ = 0.04

The <u>MORE TIMES</u> you do the experiment, the <u>MORE ACCURATE</u> your estimate of the probability should be.

E.g. if you spun the above spinner <u>1000 times</u>, you'd get a <u>better</u> estimate of the probability for each score.

If the relative frequency of a result is <u>far away</u> from what you'd expect, then you can say that the dice/spinner/coin/etc. is probably <u>biased</u>. If not, you can say it's probably <u>not biased</u> or it seems <u>fair</u>.

EXAMPLE: Do the above results suggest that the spinner is biased?

Yes, because the relative frequency of 3 is much higher than you'd expect, while the relative frequencies of 1 and 6 are much lower.

For a <u>fair</u> 6-sided spinner, you'd expect all the relative frequencies to be about 1 ÷ 6 = 0.17(ish).

This topic is tough — make sure you revise it relatively frequently...

If a coin/dice/spinner is <u>fair</u>, then you can tell the probability of each result 'just by looking at it'. But if it's biased, then you have no option but to use relative frequencies to estimate probabilities.

Q1 Sandro rolled a dice 1000 times and got the results shown in the table below.

Score	1	2	3	4	5	6
Frequency	140	137	138	259	161	165

a) Find the relative frequencies for each of the scores 1-6. [2 marks]
b) Do these results suggest that the dice is biased? Give a reason for your answer. [1 mark]

Probability Experiments

Ok, I'll admit it, probability experiments aren't as fun as science experiments but they are <u>useful</u>.

Record Results in Frequency Trees

When an experiment has two or more steps, you can record the results using <u>frequency trees</u>.

EXAMPLE: 120 GCSE maths students were asked if they would go on to do A-level maths.
- 45 of them said they would go on to do A-level maths.
- 30 of the students who said they would do A-level maths actually did.
- 9 of the students who said they wouldn't do A-level maths actually did.

a) Complete the frequency tree below.

b) Use the data to find the relative frequency of each outcome.

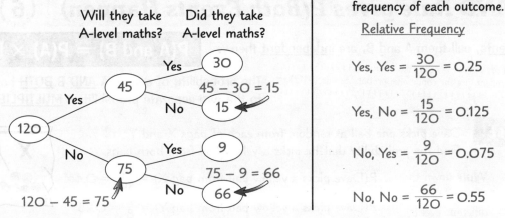

Relative Frequency

Yes, Yes = $\frac{30}{120}$ = 0.25

Yes, No = $\frac{15}{120}$ = 0.125

No, Yes = $\frac{9}{120}$ = 0.075

No, No = $\frac{66}{120}$ = 0.55

Use Probability to Find an "Expected Frequency"

1) You can <u>estimate</u> how many times you'd <u>expect</u> something to happen if you do an experiment <u>n times</u>.

2) This <u>expected frequency</u> is based on the <u>probability</u> of the result happening.

> **Expected frequency of a result = probability × number of trials**

EXAMPLE: A game involves throwing a fair six-sided dice. The player wins if they score either a 5 or a 6. If one person plays the game 180 times, estimate the number of times they will win.

1) First calculate the probability that they win <u>each game</u>.

Probability of winning = $\dfrac{\text{number of ways to win}}{\text{total number of possible outcomes}} = \frac{2}{6} = \frac{1}{3}$

2) Then <u>estimate</u> the number of times they'll win in <u>180</u> separate attempts.

Expected number of wins = probability of winning × number of trials
$= \frac{1}{3} \times 180 = 60$

If you don't know the probability of a result, fear not...
... you can estimate the probability using the <u>relative frequency</u> of the result in <u>past</u> experiments.

I expect you'll be looking back at this page quite frequently...

A relative frequency can be used as an <u>estimated probability</u>. An expected frequency is an <u>estimate</u> for the <u>number of times</u> you'd predict a result to happen in a given number of trials.

Q1 Using the frequency tree above, estimate how many out of 600 GCSE maths students:
   a) You'd expect to say they're going to do A-level maths but then don't. [2 marks]
   b) You'd expect to take A-level maths. [3 marks]

The AND / OR Rules

This page will show you how to find probabilities when <u>more than one</u> thing is happening at a time.

Independent and Dependent Events

1) You need to know the difference between <u>independent</u> and <u>dependent</u> events, if you're going to use the AND / OR rules <u>properly</u>.

2) Two events are <u>independent</u> if one event happening <u>doesn't affect</u> the probability of the other happening. E.g. rolling a 6 both times on two dice rolls or picking a blue ball, <u>replacing it</u>, then picking a red ball.

3) If one event happening <u>does affect</u> the probability of the other happening, the events are <u>dependent</u>. E.g. picking a blue ball then picking a red ball <u>without replacing</u> the blue ball first.

The AND Rule gives P(Both Events Happen)

If <u>two events</u>, call them A and B, are <u>independent</u> then...

$$P(A \text{ and } B) = P(A) \times P(B)$$

If they're <u>dependent</u>, use the conditional probability rule (p.112).

The probability of events A <u>AND</u> B <u>BOTH</u> happening is equal to the two separate probabilities <u>MULTIPLIED together</u>.

EXAMPLE: Dave picks one ball at random from each of bags X and Y. Find the probability that he picks a yellow ball from both bags.

1) Write down the <u>probabilities</u> of the different events.

P(Dave picks a yellow ball from bag X) = $\frac{4}{10}$ = 0.4

P(Dave picks a yellow ball from bag Y) = $\frac{2}{8}$ = 0.25

2) Use the <u>formula</u>.

So P(Dave picks a yellow ball from both bags) = 0.4 × 0.25 = 0.1

The OR Rule gives P(At Least One Event Happens)

For <u>two events</u>, A and B...

$$P(A \text{ or } B) = P(A) + P(B) - P(A \text{ and } B)$$

The probability of <u>EITHER</u> event A <u>OR</u> event B happening is equal to the two separate probabilities <u>ADDED</u> together <u>MINUS</u> the probability of events A <u>AND</u> B <u>BOTH</u> happening.

If the events A and B <u>can't happen together</u> then <u>P(A and B) = 0</u> and the OR rule becomes:

When events can't happen together they're called <u>mutually exclusive</u>.

$$P(A \text{ or } B) = P(A) + P(B)$$

EXAMPLE: A spinner with red, blue, green and yellow sections is spun — the probability of it landing on each colour is shown in the table. Find the probability of spinning either red or green.

Colour	red	blue	yellow	green
Probability	0.25	0.3	0.35	0.1

The spinner <u>can't</u> land on <u>both</u> red and green so use the simpler OR rule. Just put in the <u>probabilities</u>.

P(red or green) = P(red) + P(green)
= 0.25 + 0.1 = 0.35

Learn AND remember this — OR you're in trouble...

When using the AND rule, check whether the events are dependent or independent and when using the OR rule, check if the events can happen together. Remember, you '× with AND' and '+ with OR'.

Q1 Lee rolls 2 fair six-sided dice. Find the probability that he rolls two odd numbers. [2 marks] (6)

Q2 A card is randomly chosen from a pack of 52 playing cards. Find the probability that the card is a black suit or a picture card. [4 marks] (6)

Tree Diagrams

Tree diagrams can really help you work out probabilities when you have a <u>combination of events</u>.

Remember These Four Key Tree Diagram Facts (7)

1) On any set of branches which meet at a point, the probabilities must <u>add up to 1</u>.

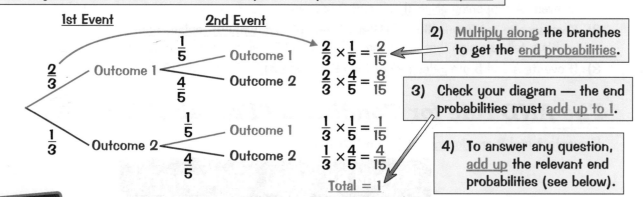

2) <u>Multiply along</u> the branches to get the <u>end probabilities</u>.

3) Check your diagram — the end probabilities must <u>add up to 1</u>.

4) To answer any question, <u>add up</u> the relevant end probabilities (see below).

EXAMPLE:

A box contains 5 red discs and 3 green discs. One disc is taken at random and its colour noted before <u>being replaced</u>. A second disc is then taken. Find the probability that both discs are the same colour.

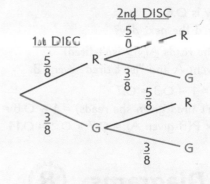

The probabilities for the 1st and 2nd discs are <u>the same</u>. This is because the 1st disc is <u>replaced</u> — so the events are independent.

$$P(\text{both discs are red}) = P(R \text{ and } R) = \frac{5}{8} \times \frac{5}{8} = \frac{25}{64}$$

$$P(\text{both discs are green}) = P(G \text{ and } G) = \frac{3}{8} \times \frac{3}{8} = \frac{9}{64}$$

$$P(\text{both discs are same colour}) = P(R \text{ and } R \underline{\text{ or }} G \text{ and } G)$$
$$= \frac{25}{64} + \frac{9}{64} = \frac{34}{64} = \frac{17}{32}$$

Look Out for 'At Least' Questions (8)

When a question asks for '<u>at least</u>' a certain number of things happening, it's usually easier to work out (<u>1 – probability of 'less than that number of things happening'</u>).

EXAMPLE: I roll 3 fair six-sided dice. Find the probability that I roll at least 1 six.

1) Rewrite this as <u>1 minus</u> a probability.

$$P(\text{at least 1 six}) = 1 - P(\text{less than 1 six})$$
$$= 1 - P(\text{no sixes})$$

2) Work out <u>P(no sixes)</u>. You can use a tree diagram — don't draw the whole thing, just the part you need.

six
not a six — six
$\frac{5}{6}$ not a six — six
$\frac{5}{6}$ not a six
$\frac{5}{6}$

$$P(\text{no sixes}) = \frac{5}{6} \times \frac{5}{6} \times \frac{5}{6} = \frac{125}{216}$$

$$\text{So } P(\text{at least 1 six}) = 1 - \frac{125}{216} = \frac{91}{216}$$

Please don't make a bad tree-based joke. Oak-ay, just this once...

How convenient — answers growing on trees. Learn the routine, and then have a go at this...

Q1 A bag contains 6 red balls and 4 black ones. If two balls are picked at random
(with replacement), find the probability that they're different colours.   [3 marks] (7)

Conditional Probability

Conditional probabilities crop up when you have dependent events — where one event affects another.

Using Conditional Probabilities

1) The conditional probability of A given B is the probability of event A happening given that event B happens.

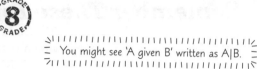 You might see 'A given B' written as A|B.

2) Keep an eye out in questions for items being picked 'without replacement' — it's a tell-tale sign that it's going to be a conditional probability question.

3) If events A and B are independent then P(A given B) = P(A) and P(B given A) = P(B).

The AND rule for Conditional Probabilities

If events A and B are dependent (see p.110) then...

$$P(A \text{ and } B) = P(A) \times P(B \text{ given } A)$$

The probability of events A AND B BOTH happening is equal to the probability of event A happening MULTIPLIED by the probability of event B happening GIVEN that event A happens.

EXAMPLE: Alia either watches TV or reads before bed. The probability she watches TV is 0.3.
If she reads, the probability she is tired the next day is 0.8.
What is the probability that Alia reads and isn't tired the next day?

1) Label the events A and B.

We want to find P(she reads AND isn't tired)
So call "she reads" event A and "isn't tired" event B.

2) Use the information given in the question to work out the probabilities that you'll need to use the formula.

P(A) = P(she reads) = 1 − 0.3 = 0.7
P(B given A) = P(isn't tired given she reads) = 1 − 0.8 = 0.2
P(A and B) = P(A) × P(B given A) = 0.7 × 0.2 = 0.14

Conditional Probabilities on Tree Diagrams

A good way to deal with conditional probability questions is to draw a tree diagram.
The probabilities on a set of branches will change depending on the previous event.

This example was done 'with replacement' on p.111.

EXAMPLE: A box contains 5 red discs and 3 green discs. Two discs are taken at random without replacement. Find the probability that both discs are the same colour.

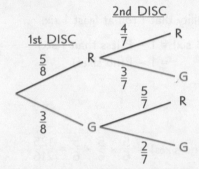

The probabilities for the 2nd pick depend on the colour of the 1st disc picked. This is because the 1st disc is not replaced.

P(both discs are red) = P(R and R) = $\frac{5}{8} \times \frac{4}{7} = \frac{20}{56}$

P(both discs are green) = P(G and G) = $\frac{3}{8} \times \frac{2}{7} = \frac{6}{56}$

P(both discs are same colour) = P(R and R or G and G)
$= \frac{20}{56} + \frac{6}{56} = \frac{26}{56} = \frac{13}{28}$

Find the probability of laughing given that you're reading this...

With probability questions that seem quite hard, drawing a tree diagram is usually a good place to start.
Try it with the (quite hard) Exam Practice Question below...

Q1 There are 21 numbers, 1-21, in a lottery draw. A machine selects the numbers randomly.
Find the probability that out of the first two numbers selected:
a) at least one is even. [3 marks] b) one is odd and one is even [3 marks]

Sets and Venn Diagrams

Venn diagrams are a way of displaying sets in intersecting circles — they're very pretty.

Showing Sets on Venn Diagrams (GRADE 5)

1) Sets are just collections of things (e.g. numbers) — we call these 'things' elements.

2) Sets can be written in different ways but they'll always be in a pair of curly brackets {}.
   E.g. {2, 3, 5, 7}, {prime numbers less than 10}, or {x : x is a prime number less than 10}.

3) n(A) just means 'the number of elements in set A'. E.g. if A = {1, 5, 9, 11}, n(A) = 4.

4) On a Venn diagram, each set is represented by a circle containing
   the elements of the set or the number of elements in the set.

The universal set (ξ), is the group of things that the elements of the sets are selected from.
It's everything inside the rectangle.

The complement of set A, (A'), contains all members of the universal set that aren't in set A.
The complement of set A is the shaded part of this Venn diagram.

The union of sets A and B, (A∪B), contains all the elements in either set A or set B. It's everything inside the circles.

The intersection of sets A and B, (A ∩ B), contains all the elements in both set A and set B. It's where the circles overlap.

Finding Probabilities from Venn Diagrams (GRADE 8)

EXAMPLE: The Venn diagram on the right shows the number of Year 10 pupils going on the History (H) and Geography (G) school trips.

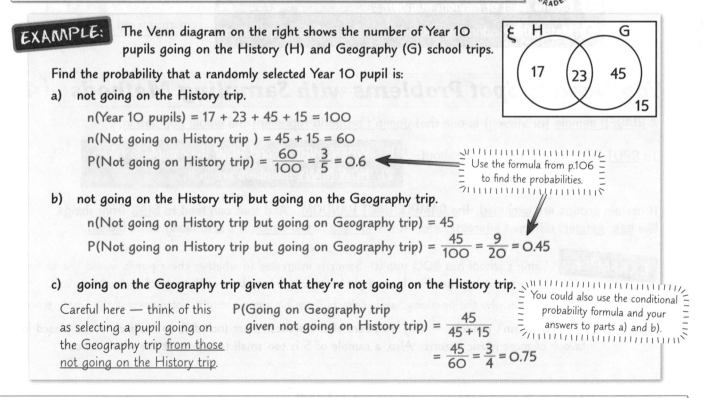

Find the probability that a randomly selected Year 10 pupil is:

a) not going on the History trip.

n(Year 10 pupils) = 17 + 23 + 45 + 15 = 100

n(Not going on History trip) = 45 + 15 = 60

$P(\text{Not going on History trip}) = \frac{60}{100} = \frac{3}{5} = 0.6$

Use the formula from p.106 to find the probabilities.

b) not going on the History trip but going on the Geography trip.

n(Not going on History trip but going on Geography trip) = 45

$P(\text{Not going on History trip but going on Geography trip}) = \frac{45}{100} = \frac{9}{20} = 0.45$

c) going on the Geography trip given that they're not going on the History trip.

Careful here — think of this as selecting a pupil going on the Geography trip from those not going on the History trip.

$P(\text{Going on Geography trip given not going on History trip}) = \frac{45}{45+15}$
$= \frac{45}{60} = \frac{3}{4} = 0.75$

You could also use the conditional probability formula and your answers to parts a) and b).

{Things I love} ∩ {circles} = {Venn diagrams}...

Make sure you can find probabilities from Venn diagrams and are comfortable using sets.

Q1 Out of 80 customers at an ice cream van, 48 had syrup, 28 had sprinkles and 16 had both toppings on their ice cream. Use a Venn diagram to find the probability that a randomly selected customer doesn't have either topping given that they don't have sprinkles. [3 marks] (GRADE 8)

Sampling and Bias

Sampling is about using what you know about smaller groups to tell you about bigger groups. Simple, or is it...

Use a Sample to Find Out About a Population

1) The whole group you want to find out about is called the **POPULATION**. It can be a group of anything — people, plants, penguins, you name it.

2) Often you can't survey the whole population, e.g. because it's too big. So you select a smaller group from the population, called a **SAMPLE**, instead.

3) It's really important that your sample fairly represents the WHOLE population. This allows you to apply any conclusions from your survey to the whole population. E.g. if you find that ¾ of the people in your sample like cheese, you can estimate that ¾ of the people in the whole population like cheese.

For a sample to be representative, it needs to be:

> ❶ A RANDOM SAMPLE
> — which means every member of the population has an equal chance of being in it.
>
> ❷ BIG ENOUGH for the size of the population. The bigger the sample, the more reliable it should be.

Simple Random Sampling — choosing a Random Sample

To SELECT a SIMPLE RANDOM SAMPLE...

❶ Assign a number to every member of the population.

❷ Create a list of random numbers. ⟵

❸ Match the random numbers to members of the population.

E.g. by using a computer, calculator or picking numbers out of a bag.

You Need to Spot Problems with Sampling Methods

A BIASED sample (or survey) is one that doesn't properly represent the whole population.

To SPOT BIAS, you need to think about:

1) WHEN, WHERE and HOW the sample is taken.
2) HOW MANY members are in it.

If certain groups are excluded, the SAMPLE ISN'T RANDOM. And that can lead to BIAS from things like age, gender, different interests, etc. If the sample is too small, it's also likely to be biased.

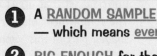

Samir's school has 800 pupils. Samir is interested in whether these pupils would like to have more music lessons. For his sample he selects 5 members of the school orchestra to ask.

Explain why the opinions Samir collects from his sample might not represent the whole school.

The sample isn't random — only members of the orchestra are included, so it's likely to be biased in favour of more music lessons. Also, a sample of 5 is too small to represent the whole school.

When getting a sample — size matters...

Make sure you understand why samples should be representative and how to spot when they're not. Then you'll be ready to take on this Exam Practice Question.

Q1   Tina wants to find out how often people in the UK travel by train. She decides to ask 20 people waiting for trains at her local train station one morning. Comment on whether Tina can use the results of her survey to draw conclusions about the whole population. [2 marks]

Collecting Data

Data you <u>collect yourself</u> is called <u>primary data</u>. If you use data that <u>someone else has collected</u>, e.g. you get it from a website, it's called <u>secondary</u> data. You need to <u>record</u> primary data in a way that's <u>easy to analyse</u> and <u>suitable</u> for the <u>type</u> of data you've got.

There are Different Types of Data

| QUALITATIVE DATA is <u>descriptive</u>. It uses <u>words</u>, not numbers. | E.g. <u>pets' names</u> — Smudge, Snowy, Dave, etc. <u>Favourite flavours of ice cream</u> — 'vanilla', 'chocolate', 'caramel-marshmallow-ripple', etc. |

| QUANTITATIVE DATA measures <u>quantities</u> using <u>numbers</u>. | E.g. <u>heights</u> of people, <u>times taken</u> to finish a race, <u>numbers of goals</u> scored in football matches, and so on. |

There are two types of <u>quantitative</u> data.

| DISCRETE DATA | 1) It's <u>discrete</u> if the numbers can only take certain <u>exact</u> values. |
| | 2) E.g. the number of customers in a shop each day has to be a whole number — you can't have half a person. |

| CONTINUOUS DATA | 1) If the numbers can take <u>any value</u> in a range, it's called <u>continuous</u> data. |
| | 2) E.g. heights and weights are continuous measurements. |

You can Organise your Data into Classes

1) To record data in a <u>table</u>, you often need to <u>group</u> it into <u>classes</u> to make it more manageable. <u>Discrete</u> data classes should have '<u>gaps</u>' between them, e.g. '<u>0-1 goals</u>', '<u>2-3 goals</u>' (jump from 1 to 2 because there are no values in between). <u>Continuous</u> data classes should have <u>no 'gaps'</u>, so are often written using <u>inequalities</u> (see p.118).

2) Whatever the data you have, make sure <u>none of the classes overlap</u> and that they <u>cover all the possible values</u>.

When you <u>group</u> data you <u>lose</u> <u>some accuracy</u> because you don't know the exact values any more.

EXAMPLE: Jonty wants to find out about the ages (in whole years) of people who use his local library. Design a table he could use to collect his data.

Include <u>columns</u> for: the <u>data values</u>, '<u>Tally</u>' to count the data and '<u>Frequency</u>' to show the totals.

Use <u>non-overlapping</u> classes — with <u>gaps</u> because the data's <u>discrete</u>.

Include classes like '<u>...or over</u>', '<u>...or less</u>' or '<u>other</u>' to <u>cover all options</u> in a sensible number of classes.

Age (whole years)	Tally	Frequency
0-19		
20-39		
40-59		
60-79		
80 or over		

Questionnaires should be Designed Carefully

Another way to record data is to ask people to fill in a <u>questionnaire</u>. Your <u>questions</u> should be:

<u>Watch out</u> for <u>response boxes</u> that could be <u>interpreted</u> in <u>different</u> ways, that <u>overlap</u>, or that <u>don't allow</u> for <u>all</u> possible answers.

| 1) <u>Clear</u> and <u>easy to understand</u> |
| 2) <u>Easy</u> to <u>answer</u> |
| 3) <u>Fair</u> — not leading or biased |

<u>Leading</u> questions <u>suggest</u> an answer.

I won't tell you what type of data it is — I'm too discrete...

You need to know what type of data you've got so you can record and display it in a suitable way.

Q1   James asks some students how many times they went to the cinema in the last year. Say whether this data is qualitative, discrete or continuous and design a table to record it in.   [2 marks]

Mean, Median, Mode and Range

Mean, median, mode and range pop up all the time in statistics questions — make sure you know what they are.

The Four Definitions

MODE = MOST common

MEDIAN = MIDDLE value (when values are in order of size)

MEAN = TOTAL of items ÷ NUMBER of items

RANGE = Difference between highest and lowest

REMEMBER:

Mode = most (emphasise the 'mo' in each when you say them)

Median = mid (emphasise the m*d in each when you say them)

Mean is just the average, but it's mean 'cos you have to work it out.

The Golden Rule

There's one vital step for finding the median that lots of people forget:

Always REARRANGE the data in ASCENDING ORDER (and check you have the same number of entries!)

You absolutely must do this when finding the median, but it's also really useful for working out the mode too.

EXAMPLE: Find the median, mode, mean, and range of these numbers:

2, 5, 3, 2, 6, -4, 0, 9, -3, 1, 6, 3, -2, 3

Check that you still have the same number of entries after you've rearranged them.

The MEDIAN is the middle value, so rearrange the numbers in order of size.

When there are two middle numbers, the median is halfway between the two.

-4, -3, -2, 0, 1, 2, (2, 3) 3, 3, 5, 6, 6, 9

← seven numbers this side   seven numbers this side →

Median = 2.5

To find the position of the median of n values, you can use the formula (n + 1) ÷ 2. Here, (14 + 1) ÷ 2 = position 7.5 — that's halfway between the 7th and 8th values.

MODE (or modal value) is the most common value. ⟶ Mode = 3

Data sets can have more than one mode.

$$\text{MEAN} = \frac{\text{total of items}}{\text{number of items}} \longrightarrow \frac{-4-3-2+0+1+2+2+3+3+3+5+6+6+9}{14}$$

$$= 31 \div 14 = 2.214... = 2.21 \text{ (3 s.f.)}$$

RANGE = distance from lowest to highest value, i.e. from -4 up to 9. ⟶ 9 - (-4) = 13

A Trickier Example

EXAMPLE: The heights (to the nearest cm) of 8 penguins at a zoo are 41, 43, 44, 44, 47, 48, 50 and 51. Two of the penguins are moved to a different zoo. If the mean height of the remaining penguins is 44.5 cm, find the heights of the two penguins that moved.

$$\text{Mean} = \frac{\text{total height}}{\text{no. of penguins}}$$

So total height = no. of penguins × mean

Total height of 8 penguins = 368 cm.

Total height of remaining 6 penguins = 6 × 44.5 = 267 cm.

Combined height of penguins that moved = 368 - 267 = 101 cm.

So the heights must be 50 cm and 51 cm.

Strike a pose, there's nothing to it — mode...

Q1 Find the mean, median, mode and range for the set of data below:
1, 3, 14, -5, 6, -12, 18, 7, 23, 10, -5, -14, 0, 25, 8. [4 marks]

Q2 Another value is added to the data in Q1. If the mean is now 5.5, find the new value. [3 marks]

Section Seven — Probability and Statistics

Frequency Tables — Finding Averages

The word FREQUENCY means HOW MANY, so a frequency table is just a 'How many in each category' table. You saw how to find averages and range on p.116 — it's the same ideas here, but with the data in a table.

Find Averages from Frequency Tables

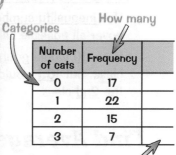

1) The MODE is just the CATEGORY with the MOST ENTRIES.

2) The RANGE is found from the extremes of the first column.

3) The MEDIAN is the CATEGORY containing the middle value.

4) To find the MEAN, you have to WORK OUT A THIRD COLUMN yourself.

The MEAN is then: | 3rd Column Total ÷ 2nd Column Total |

Categories   How many

Number of cats	Frequency	
0	17	
1	22	
2	15	
3	7	

Mysterious 3rd column...

EXAMPLE: Some people were asked how many sisters they have. The table opposite shows the results.

Find the mode, the range, the mean and the median of the data.

Number of sisters	Frequency
0	7
1	15
2	12
3	8
4	4
5	0

1 The MODE is the category with the most entries — i.e. the one with the highest frequency:

The highest frequency is 15 for '1 sister', so MODE = 1

2 The RANGE is the difference between the highest and lowest numbers of sisters — that's 4 sisters (no one has 5 sisters) and no sisters, so:

RANGE = 4 – 0 = 4

3 To find the MEAN, add a 3rd column to the table showing 'number of sisters × frequency'. Add up these values to find the total number of sisters of all the people asked.

You can label the first column x and the frequency column f, then the third column is f × x.

Number of sisters (x)	Frequency (f)	No. of sisters × Frequency (f × x)
0	7	0
1	15	15
2	12	24
3	8	24
4	4	16
5	0	0
Total	46	79

$$\text{MEAN} = \frac{\text{total number of sisters}}{\text{total number of people asked}} = \frac{79}{46} = 1.72 \text{ (3 s.f.)}$$

3rd column total
2nd column total

4 The MEDIAN is the category of the middle value. Work out its position, then count through the 2nd column to find it.

It helps to imagine the data set out in an ordered list:
000000011111111111111122222222222233333333344444
median

The median is in position (n + 1) ÷ 2 = (46 + 1) ÷ 2 = 23.5 — halfway between the 23rd and 24th values. There are a total of (7 + 15) = 22 values in the first two categories, and another 12 in the third category takes you to 34. So the 23rd and 24th values must both be in the category '2 sisters', which means the MEDIAN is 2.

My table has 5 columns, 6 rows and 4 legs...

Learn the four key points about averages, then try this fella.

Q1   50 people were asked how many times a week they play sport. The table opposite shows the results.

     a) Find the median.   [2 marks]

     b) Calculate the mean.   [3 marks]

No. of times sport played	Frequency
0	8
1	15
2	17
3	6
4	4
5 or more	0

Grouped Frequency Tables

Grouped frequency tables group together the data into <u>classes</u>. They look like ordinary frequency tables, but they're a <u>slightly trickier</u> kettle of fish...

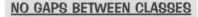

See p.115 for grouped <u>discrete</u> data.

NO GAPS BETWEEN CLASSES
- Use <u>inequality symbols</u> to cover all possible values.
- Here, <u>10</u> would go in the <u>1st</u> class, but <u>10.1</u> would go in the <u>2nd</u> class.

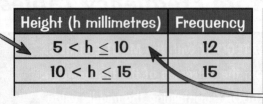

Height (h millimetres)	Frequency
$5 < h \le 10$	12
$10 < h \le 15$	15

To find MID-INTERVAL VALUES:
- Add together the <u>end values</u> of the <u>class</u> and <u>divide by 2</u>.
- E.g. $\dfrac{5+10}{2} = \underline{7.5}$

Find Averages from Grouped Frequency Tables

Unlike with ordinary frequency tables, you <u>don't know the actual data values</u>, only the <u>classes</u> they're in. So you have to <u>ESTIMATE THE MEAN</u>, rather than calculate it exactly. Again, you do this by <u>adding columns</u>:

1) Add a <u>3RD COLUMN</u> and enter the <u>MID-INTERVAL VALUE</u> for each class.

2) Add a <u>4TH COLUMN</u> to show 'FREQUENCY × MID-INTERVAL VALUE' for each class.

You'll be asked to find the <u>MODAL CLASS</u> and the <u>CLASS CONTAINING THE MEDIAN</u>, not exact values. And the <u>RANGE</u> can only be estimated too — using the class boundaries.

EXAMPLE: This table shows information about the weights, in kilograms, of 60 school children.

a) Write down the <u>modal class</u>.
b) Write down the <u>class containing the median</u>.
c) Calculate an <u>estimate for the mean weight</u>.
d) Estimate the <u>range of weights</u>.

Weight (w kg)	Frequency
$30 < w \le 40$	8
$40 < w \le 50$	16
$50 < w \le 60$	18
$60 < w \le 70$	12
$70 < w \le 80$	6

a) | The <u>modal class</u> is the one with the <u>highest frequency</u>.

Modal class is $50 < w \le 60$

b) | Work out the <u>position</u> of the <u>median</u>, then <u>count through</u> the <u>2nd column</u>.

The median is in position $(n + 1) \div 2 = (60 + 1) \div 2 = 30.5$, halfway between the 30th and 31st values. Both these values are in the third class, so the class containing the median is $50 < w \le 60$.

c) | Add extra columns for '<u>mid-interval value</u>' and '<u>frequency × mid-interval value</u>'. Add up the values in the 4th column to estimate the <u>total weight</u> of the 60 children.

Weight (w kg)	Frequency (f)	Mid-interval value (x)	fx
$30 < w \le 40$	8	35	280
$40 < w \le 50$	16	45	720
$50 < w \le 60$	18	55	990
$60 < w \le 70$	12	65	780
$70 < w \le 80$	6	75	450
Total	60	—	3220

Mean $\approx \dfrac{\text{total weight}}{\text{number of children}}$ ⟵ 4th column total / 2nd column total

$= \dfrac{3220}{60} = 53.7$ kg (3 s.f.)

<u>Don't add up</u> the <u>mid-interval values</u>.

d) | Find the <u>difference</u> between the <u>highest</u> and <u>lowest</u> class <u>boundaries</u>.

Estimated range = 80 − 30
= 50 kg

This is the <u>largest possible range</u> — it assumes there are data values on the class boundaries. The actual range is likely to be smaller, but you can't tell without knowing the individual values.

Mid-interval value — cheap ice creams...

Q1 a) Estimate the mean of this data. Give your answer to 3 significant figures. [4 marks]

Length (l cm)	$15.5 \le l < 16.5$	$16.5 \le l < 17.5$	$17.5 \le l < 18.5$	$18.5 \le l < 19.5$
Frequency	12	18	23	8

b) Ana says that 20% of the lengths are below 16.5 cm. Comment on her statement. [2 marks]

Box Plots

The humble <u>box plot</u> might not look very fancy, but it gives you a <u>useful summary</u> of a data set.

Box Plots show the Spread of a Data Set

1) The <u>lower quartile Q_1</u>, the <u>median Q_2</u> and the <u>upper quartile Q_3</u> are the values <u>25%</u> (¼), <u>50%</u> (½) and <u>75%</u> (¾) of the way through an ordered set of data. So if a set of data has <u>n</u> values, you can work out the <u>positions</u> of the <u>quartiles</u> using these formulas:

$$Q_1: (n + 1)/4 \qquad Q_2: (n + 1)/2 \qquad Q_3: 3(n + 1)/4$$

2) The <u>INTERQUARTILE RANGE</u> (IQR) is the <u>difference</u> between the <u>upper quartile</u> and the <u>lower quartile</u> and contains the <u>middle 50%</u> of values.

3) A <u>box plot</u> shows the <u>minimum</u> and <u>maximum</u> values in a data set and the values of the <u>quartiles</u>. But it <u>doesn't</u> tell you the <u>individual</u> data values.

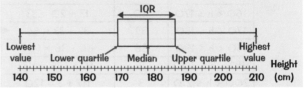

EXAMPLE:

This table gives information about the numbers of rainy days last year in some cities. On the grid below, draw a box plot to show the information.

Number of rainy days

❶ Mark on the <u>quartiles</u> and <u>draw the box</u>.

❷ Draw a <u>line</u> at the <u>median</u>.

❸ Mark on the <u>minimum</u> and <u>maximum</u> points and <u>join them to the box</u> with horizontal lines.

Minimum number	90
Maximum number	195
Lower quartile	130
Median	150
Upper quartile	175

- Box plots show <u>two</u> measures of <u>spread</u> — <u>range</u> (highest – lowest) and <u>interquartile range</u> ($Q_3 - Q_1$).
- The <u>range</u> is based on <u>all</u> of the data values, so it can be <u>affected by outliers</u> — data values that don't fit the general pattern (i.e. that are a long way from the rest of the data).
- The <u>IQR</u> is based on only the <u>middle 50%</u> of the data values, so <u>isn't affected by outliers</u>. This means it can be a <u>more reliable</u> measure of spread than the range.

EXAMPLE: This box plot shows a summary of the heights of a group of gymnasts.

a) Work out the range of the heights.
Range = highest − lowest = 175 − 145 = 30 cm

b) Work out the interquartile range for the heights.
Q_1 = 150 cm and Q_3 = 158 cm, so IQR = 158 − 150 = 8 cm

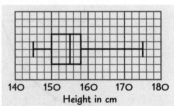
Height in cm

c) Do you think the range or the interquartile range is a more reliable measure of spread for this data? Give a reason for your answer.
The IQR is small and 75% of the values are less than 158 cm, so it's likely that the tallest height of 175 cm is an outlier. The IQR doesn't include the tallest height, so the IQR should be more reliable.

d) Explain whether or not it is possible to work out the number of gymnasts represented by the box plot.
The box plot gives no information about the number of values it represents, so it isn't possible to work out the number of gymnasts.

With my cunning plot, I'll soon control all the world's boxes...

Mwahaha... Make sure you can follow the examples above, then do this Exam Practice Question.

Q1 A large amount of data is analysed and the following conclusions are made: the minimum and maximum values are 5 and 22, 50% of the values are less than 12, 75% of the values are less than 17 and the IQR is 8. Draw a box plot to represent this information. [3 marks]

Cumulative Frequency

Cumulative frequency just means <u>adding it up as you go along</u> — i.e. the <u>total frequency so far</u>.
You need to be able to <u>draw</u> a <u>cumulative frequency graph</u> and <u>make estimates</u> from it.

EXAMPLE: The table below shows information about the heights of a group of people.
a) Draw a <u>cumulative frequency graph</u> for the data.
b) Use your graph to <u>estimate</u> the <u>median</u> and <u>interquartile range</u> of the heights.

Height (h cm)	Frequency	Cumulative Frequency
140 < h ≤ 150	4	4
150 < h ≤ 160	9	4 + 9 = <u>13</u>
160 < h ≤ 170	20	13 + 20 = <u>33</u>
170 < h ≤ 180	33	33 + 33 = <u>66</u>
180 < h ≤ 190	36	66 + 36 = <u>102</u>
190 < h ≤ 200	15	102 + 15 = <u>117</u>
200 < h ≤ 210	3	117 + 3 = <u>120</u>

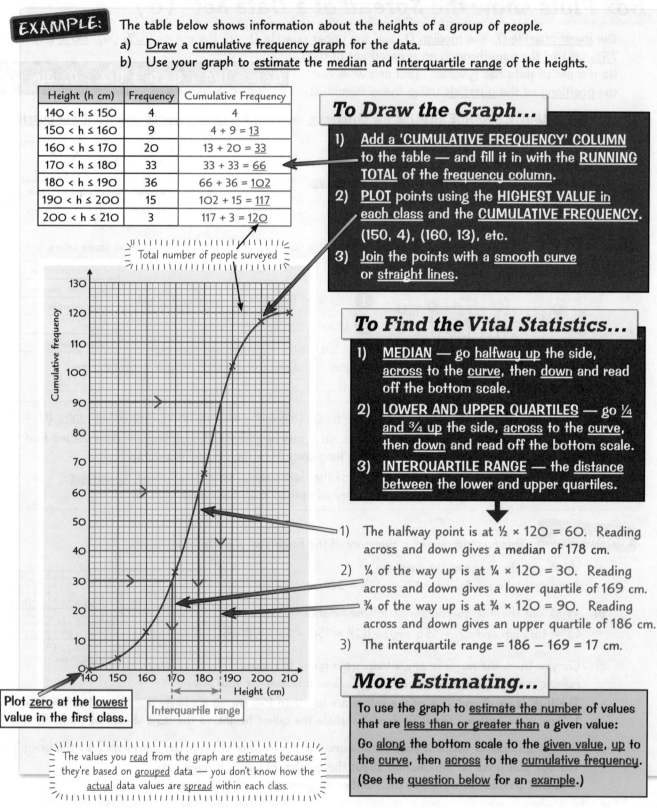

Total number of people surveyed

Plot <u>zero</u> at the <u>lowest</u> value in the first class.

Interquartile range

The values you <u>read</u> from the graph are <u>estimates</u> because they're based on <u>grouped</u> data — you don't know how the <u>actual</u> data values are <u>spread</u> within each class.

To Draw the Graph...

1) Add a 'CUMULATIVE FREQUENCY' COLUMN to the table — and fill it in with the <u>RUNNING TOTAL</u> of the frequency column.

2) <u>PLOT</u> points using the <u>HIGHEST VALUE</u> in each class and the <u>CUMULATIVE FREQUENCY</u>. (150, 4), (160, 13), etc.

3) <u>Join</u> the points with a <u>smooth curve</u> or <u>straight lines</u>.

To Find the Vital Statistics...

1) <u>MEDIAN</u> — go <u>halfway up</u> the side, <u>across</u> to the <u>curve</u>, then <u>down</u> and read off the bottom scale.

2) <u>LOWER AND UPPER QUARTILES</u> — go ¼ and ¾ up the side, <u>across</u> to the <u>curve</u>, then <u>down</u> and read off the bottom scale.

3) <u>INTERQUARTILE RANGE</u> — the <u>distance</u> <u>between</u> the lower and upper quartiles.

1) The halfway point is at ½ × 120 = 60. Reading across and down gives a median of 178 cm.

2) ¼ of the way up is at ¼ × 120 = 30. Reading across and down gives a lower quartile of 169 cm.
¾ of the way up is at ¾ × 120 = 90. Reading across and down gives an upper quartile of 186 cm.

3) The interquartile range = 186 − 169 = 17 cm.

More Estimating...

To use the graph to <u>estimate the number</u> of values that are <u>less than or greater than</u> a given value:

Go <u>along</u> the bottom scale to the <u>given value</u>, <u>up</u> to the <u>curve</u>, then <u>across</u> to the <u>cumulative frequency</u>. (See the <u>question below</u> for an example.)

How do you make a total run...

Time to try another lovely Exam Practice Question.

Q1 a) Draw a cumulative frequency diagram for this data. [3 marks]
   b) Use your diagram to estimate the percentage of fish that are longer than 50 mm. [2 marks]

Length of fish (l mm)	Frequency
0 < l ≤ 20	4
20 < l ≤ 40	11
40 < l ≤ 60	20
60 < l ≤ 80	15
80 < l ≤ 100	6

Histograms and Frequency Density

A <u>histogram</u> is just a bar chart where the bars can be of <u>different widths</u>. This changes them from nice, easy-to-understand diagrams into seemingly incomprehensible monsters.

Histograms Show Frequency Density   GRADE 7

1) The <u>vertical</u> axis on a histogram is always called <u>frequency density</u>. You work it out using this formula:

> Frequency Density = Frequency ÷ Class Width

> Remember... 'frequency' is just another way of saying 'how much' or 'how many'.

2) You can rearrange it to work out <u>how much</u> a bar represents.

> Frequency = Frequency Density × Class Width = AREA of bar

EXAMPLE: This table and histogram show the lengths of beetles found in a garden.

Length (mm)	Frequency
0 < x ≤ 10	32
10 < x ≤ 15	36
15 < x ≤ 18	24
18 < x ≤ 22	28
22 < x ≤ 30	16

a) Use the histogram to find the missing entry in the table.

1) Add a <u>frequency density</u> column to the table and fill in what you can using the formula.

Frequency density
32 ÷ 10 = 3.2
36 ÷ 5 = 7.2
a
28 ÷ 4 = 7
16 ÷ 8 = 2

2) Use the frequency densities to <u>label</u> the <u>vertical axis</u> of the graph.

3) Now use the <u>3rd bar</u> to find the frequency for the class "15 < x ≤ 18".

Frequency density = 8 and class width = 3.

So frequency = frequency density × class width = 8 × 3 = 24

b) Use the table to add the bar for the class "22 < x ≤ 30 " to the histogram.

Frequency density = Frequency ÷ Class Width = $\frac{16}{8}$ = 2

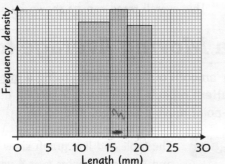

c) Estimate the number of beetles between 7.5 mm and 12.5 mm in length.

Use the formula <u>frequency = frequency density × class width</u> — multiply the frequency density of the <u>class</u> by the <u>width</u> of the <u>part of that class</u> you're interested in.

3.2 × (10 − 7.5) + 7.2 × (12.5 − 10)

= 3.2 × 2.5 + 7.2 × 2.5

= 26

Histograms — horrid foul creatures they are...

Here's a question to make sure you've mastered the methods above...

Q1 a) This table shows information about the lengths of slugs in a garden. Draw a histogram to represent the information.   [4 marks]

b) Estimate the number of slugs that are shorter than 70 mm.   [3 marks]

Length (mm)	Frequency
0 < x ≤ 40	20
40 < x ≤ 60	45
60 < x ≤ 65	15
65 < x ≤ 100	70

GRADE 8

Time Series

A <u>time series</u> is what you get if you measure the <u>same thing</u> at a number of <u>different times</u>.

Line Graphs can show Time Series (6)

1) With <u>time series</u>, a basic pattern often repeats itself — this is called <u>seasonality</u> (though it doesn't have to match the seasons).

   The time series plotted in <u>red</u> has a definite repeating pattern.

2) The time taken for the pattern to repeat itself (measured peak-to-peak or trough-to-trough) is called the <u>period</u>.

   This pattern repeats itself <u>every four points</u>.

3) You can also look at the <u>overall trend</u> — i.e. whether the values are generally getting bigger or generally getting smaller (ignoring any repeating pattern). Look at the <u>peaks and troughs</u> — here they're going up slightly each time, which shows a slight upward trend.

   This overall trend can be shown by a trend line — drawn here in <u>blue</u>.

Use a Moving Average to Smooth Out a Time Series (6)

You can 'smooth out' seasonality using a <u>moving average</u>. This can help you see <u>trends</u> in the data. If the pattern repeats itself every 2 points, use a 2-point moving average, if it repeats every 3 points, use a 3-point moving average, and so on.

EXAMPLE: The table and line graph show how much Jamie spent on heating during Spring/Summer and Autumn/Winter over 4 years. Plot the values for a 2-point moving average and describe the trend in the data.

6-month period	Spr / Sum	Aut / Win	Spr / Sum	Aut / Win	Spr / Sum	Aut / Win	Spr / Sum	Aut / Win
Amount spent (£)	250	350	300	375	290	400	300	425

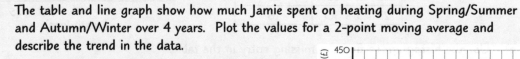

Use a <u>2-point</u> moving average because the seasonal pattern <u>repeats</u> itself every <u>2 points</u>.

To find a 2-point MOVING AVERAGE:

- Find the <u>mean</u> of the <u>1st and 2nd</u> values.
- Then find the <u>mean</u> of the <u>2nd and 3rd</u> values.
- Then find the <u>mean</u> of the <u>3rd and 4th</u> values.
- And so on, until you reach the last pair.

$$\boxed{1} \quad \frac{250 + 350}{2} = £300$$

$$\boxed{2} \quad \frac{350 + 300}{2} = £325$$

$$\boxed{3} \quad \frac{300 + 375}{2} = £337.50$$

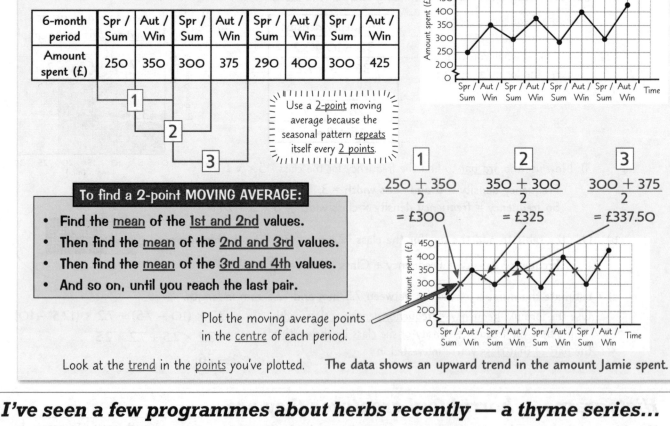

Plot the moving average points in the <u>centre</u> of each period.

Look at the <u>trend</u> in the <u>points</u> you've plotted. The data shows an upward trend in the amount Jamie spent.

I've seen a few programmes about herbs recently — a thyme series...

Quite a lot to take in on this page. Here's a question to check you've got it all.

Q1 This data shows how many times Khalid goes rock-climbing in different quarters over 2 years. (6)

   a) Describe the repeating pattern in the data.   [1 mark]

   b) Find the values of a suitable moving average.   [3 marks]

Quarter	1	2	3	4	1	2	3	4
Climbing	2	4	10	6	1	4	11	7

Scatter Graphs

A <u>scatter graph</u> tells you <u>how closely</u> two things are <u>related</u> — the fancy word is <u>CORRELATION</u>.

Scatter Graphs Show Correlation ③

1) If you can draw a <u>line of best fit</u> pretty close to <u>most</u> of your data points, the two things are <u>correlated</u>. If the points are <u>randomly scattered</u>, and you <u>can't draw</u> a line of best fit, then there's <u>no correlation</u>.

2) <u>Strong correlation</u> is when your points make a <u>fairly straight line</u> — this means the two things are <u>closely related</u> to each other. <u>Weak correlation</u> is when your points <u>don't line up</u> quite so nicely, but you can still draw a line of best fit through them.

3) If the points form a line sloping <u>uphill</u> from left to right, then there is <u>positive correlation</u> — both things increase or decrease <u>together</u>. If the line slopes <u>downhill</u> from left to right, then there is <u>negative correlation</u> — as one thing <u>increases</u> the other <u>decreases</u>.

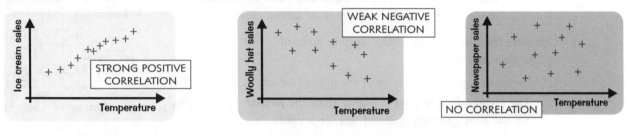

Use a Line of Best Fit to Make Predictions ④

1) You can use a <u>line of best fit</u> to make <u>estimates</u>. Predicting a value <u>within the range</u> of data you have should be <u>fairly reliable</u>, since you can see the <u>pattern</u> within this range. If you extend your line <u>outside</u> the range of data your prediction might be <u>unreliable</u>, since you're just <u>assuming the pattern continues</u>.

2) You also need to watch out for <u>outliers</u> — data points that <u>don't fit the general pattern</u>. These might be errors, but aren't necessarily. Outliers can <u>drag</u> your <u>line of best fit</u> away from the other values, so it's best to <u>ignore</u> them when you're drawing the line.

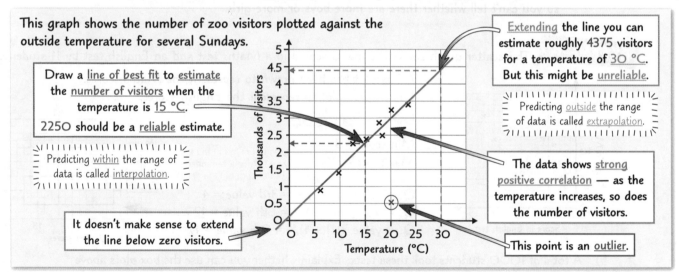

<u>BE CAREFUL</u> with <u>correlation</u> — if two things are correlated it <u>doesn't mean</u> that one causes the other. There could be a third factor affecting both, or it could just be a coincidence.

Relax and take a trip down Correlation Street... ④

Q1 This graph shows Sam's average speed on runs of different lengths.

a) Describe the relationship between length of run and average speed. [1 mark]

b) Circle the point that doesn't follow the trend. [1 mark]

c) Estimate Sam's average speed for an 8-mile run. [1 mark]

d) Comment on the reliability of your estimate in part c). [1 mark]

Comparing Data Sets

You need to be able to <u>compare the distributions</u> of two sets of data represented by <u>graphs and charts</u>. That might mean comparing the <u>shapes</u> of the graphs, or reading off <u>measures of average</u> (mean, median or mode), and <u>spread</u> (range or interquartile range).

Compare Data Sets using Box Plots (6)

For a reminder about box plots, see p.119.

From a box plot you can easily read off the <u>median</u> and work out the <u>range</u> and <u>IQR</u>. Remember to say what these values mean in the <u>context of the data</u>.
A <u>larger spread</u> means the values are <u>less consistent</u> (there is <u>more variation</u> in the data).

EXAMPLE:

An animal park is holding a 'guess the weight of the baby hippo' competition. These box plots summarise the weights guessed by a group of school children.

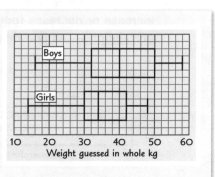

Weight guessed in whole kg

a) Compare the distributions of the weights guessed by the boys and the girls.

   1) Compare <u>averages</u> by looking at the <u>median</u> values.

   The median for the boys is higher than the median for the girls. So the boys generally guessed heavier weights.

   2) Compare the <u>spreads</u> by working out the <u>range</u> and <u>IQR</u>.

   Boys' range = 58 − 16 = 42 and IQR = 50 − 32 = 18.
   Girls' range = 48 − 14 = 34 and IQR = 42 − 30 = 12.

   It's important you give your answers in the context of the data.

   Both the range and the IQR are smaller for the girls' guesses, so there is less variation in the weights guessed by the girls.

b) Can you tell from these box plots whether there are more boys or more girls in this group of children? Explain your answer.

   The box plots don't show information on the numbers of data values, so you can't tell whether there are more boys or more girls.

EXAMPLE:

This scatter graph shows the marks scored in a Maths test and an English test by 11 students.

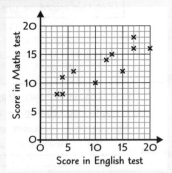

Score in English test

a) A box plot has been drawn to represent the Maths scores. Draw a box plot to represent the English scores.

Using the <u>scatter graph</u>:

Min score = <u>3</u>
Max score = <u>20</u>

See p.119 for a reminder.

Q_1 = value (11 + 1)/4 = 3rd value = <u>4</u>
Q_2 = value (11 + 1)/2 = 6th value = <u>12</u>
Q_3 = value 3(11 + 1)/4 = 9th value = <u>17</u>

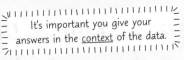

Test scores

b) A total of 1000 students took these tests. Explain whether you can use the box plots above to compare the English and Maths scores of all the students who took the test.

   You can only compare the scores of these 11 students, not all the students, because a sample of 11 isn't big enough to represent the whole population of 1000 students.

Chocolate-peanut-banana butter — not your average spread...

Box plots make it easy to see similarities and differences between data sets. (5)

Q1   This box plot represents the marks scored by the 11 students above in a Science test. Claudia says that these Science scores are more consistent than the English scores. Explain whether Claudia is correct. [2 marks]

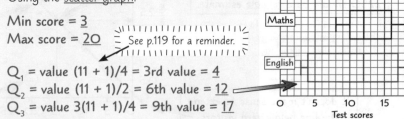

Comparing Data Sets

Compare Data Sets using Histograms

See p.121 for a reminder about histograms.

EXAMPLE: This histogram shows information about the times taken by a large group of children to solve a puzzle.

GRADE 8

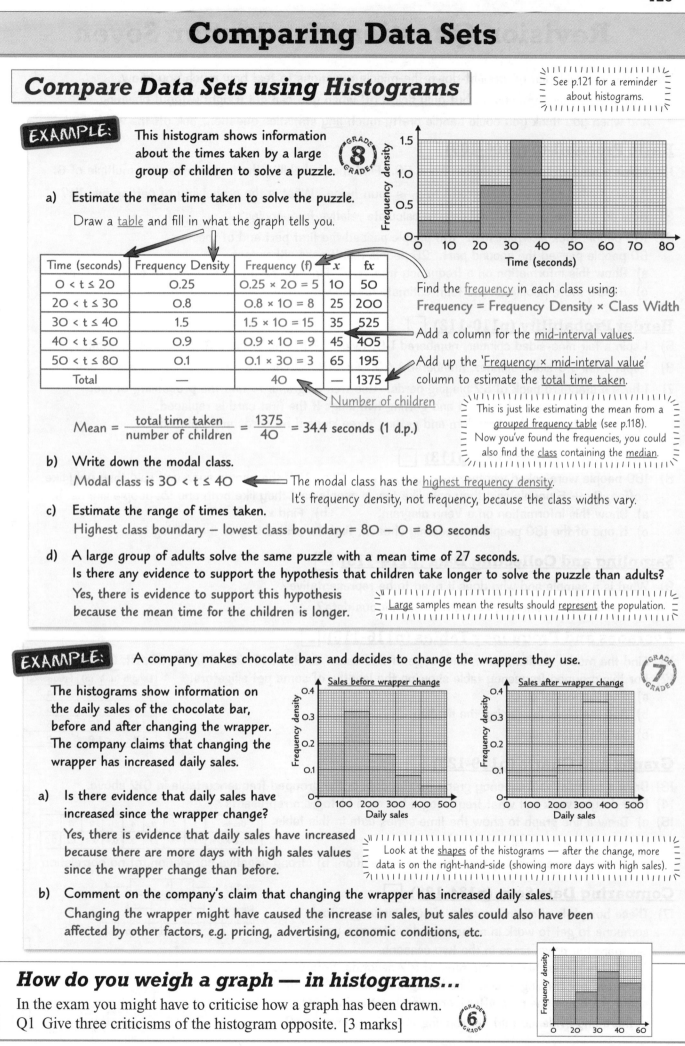

a) Estimate the mean time taken to solve the puzzle.

Draw a **table** and fill in what the graph tells you.

Time (seconds)	Frequency Density	Frequency (f)	x	fx
$0 < t \le 20$	0.25	$0.25 \times 20 = 5$	10	50
$20 < t \le 30$	0.8	$0.8 \times 10 = 8$	25	200
$30 < t \le 40$	1.5	$1.5 \times 10 = 15$	35	525
$40 < t \le 50$	0.9	$0.9 \times 10 = 9$	45	405
$50 < t \le 80$	0.1	$0.1 \times 30 = 3$	65	195
Total	—	40	—	1375

Find the <u>frequency</u> in each class using:
Frequency = Frequency Density × Class Width

Add a column for the <u>mid-interval values</u>.

Add up the '<u>Frequency × mid-interval value</u>' column to estimate the <u>total time taken</u>.

<u>Number of children</u>

$$\text{Mean} = \frac{\text{total time taken}}{\text{number of children}} = \frac{1375}{40} = 34.4 \text{ seconds (1 d.p.)}$$

This is just like estimating the mean from a <u>grouped frequency table</u> (see p.118). Now you've found the frequencies, you could also find the <u>class</u> containing the <u>median</u>.

b) Write down the modal class.

Modal class is $30 < t \le 40$ ⟵ The modal class has the <u>highest frequency density</u>.
It's frequency density, not frequency, because the class widths vary.

c) Estimate the range of times taken.

Highest class boundary − lowest class boundary = 80 − 0 = 80 seconds

d) A large group of adults solve the same puzzle with a mean time of 27 seconds.
Is there any evidence to support the hypothesis that children take longer to solve the puzzle than adults?

Yes, there is evidence to support this hypothesis because the mean time for the children is longer.

<u>Large</u> samples mean the results should <u>represent</u> the population.

EXAMPLE: A company makes chocolate bars and decides to change the wrappers they use.

GRADE 7

The histograms show information on the daily sales of the chocolate bar, before and after changing the wrapper. The company claims that changing the wrapper has increased daily sales.

a) Is there evidence that daily sales have increased since the wrapper change?

Yes, there is evidence that daily sales have increased because there are more days with high sales values since the wrapper change than before.

Look at the <u>shapes</u> of the histograms — after the change, more data is on the right-hand-side (showing more days with high sales).

b) Comment on the company's claim that changing the wrapper has increased daily sales.

Changing the wrapper might have caused the increase in sales, but sales could also have been affected by other factors, e.g. pricing, advertising, economic conditions, etc.

How do you weigh a graph — in histograms...

In the exam you might have to criticise how a graph has been drawn.
Q1 Give three criticisms of the histogram opposite. [3 marks]

GRADE 6

Revision Questions for Section Seven

Here's the inevitable list of straight-down-the-middle questions to test how much you know.

- Have a go at each question... but <u>only tick it off</u> when you can get it right <u>without</u> cheating.
- And when you think you could handle pretty much <u>any</u> statistics question, tick off the whole topic.

Basic Probability (p106-109) ☑

1) I pick a random number between 1 and 50. Find the probability that my number is a multiple of 6. ☑
2) A fair y-sided spinner, numbered 1 to y, is spun twice. What is the probability of getting two 1's? ☑
3) How do you use experimental data to calculate relative frequencies? ☑
4) 160 people took a 2-part test. 105 people passed the first part and of these, 60 people passed the second part. 25 people didn't pass either test.
   a) Show this information on a frequency tree. b) Find the relative frequency of each outcome.
   c) If 300 more people do the test, estimate how many of them would pass both parts. ☑

Harder Probability (p110-112) ☑

5) I spin a fair nine-sided spinner, numbered 1-9, twice. Find P(spinning a 6 then an even number). ☑
6) I spin a fair 20-sided spinner, numbered 1-20. Find P(spinning a factor of 20 or an even number). ☑
7) I have a standard pack of 52 playing cards. Use tree diagrams to find the probability of me:
   a) picking two cards at random and getting two kings if the first card is replaced.
   b) picking three cards at random and getting three kings if no cards are replaced. ☑

Sets and Venn Diagrams (p113) ☑

8) 180 people were asked whether they like tea or coffee. Half the people surveyed said they only like coffee, 2x + 5 people said they only like tea, x people said they like both and 2x people like neither.
   a) Show this information on a Venn diagram. b) Find x.
   c) If one of the 180 people is randomly chosen, find the probability of them liking tea. ☑

Sampling and Collecting Data (p114-115) ☑

9) What is a sample and why does it need to be representative? ☑
10) Is 'eye colour' qualitative, discrete or continuous data? ☑

Averages and Frequency Tables (p116-118) ☑

11) Find the mode, median, mean and range of this data: 2, 8, 11, 15, 22, 24, 27, 30, 31, 31, 41 ☑
12) For this grouped frequency table showing the lengths of some pet alligators:
    a) find the modal class,
    b) find the class containing the median,
    c) estimate the mean. ☑

Length (y, in m)	Frequency
$1.4 \le y < 1.5$	4
$1.5 \le y < 1.6$	8
$1.6 \le y < 1.7$	5
$1.7 \le y < 1.8$	2

Graphs and Charts (p119-123) ☑

13) Draw a cumulative frequency graph for the data in the grouped frequency table in Q12 above. ☑
14) How do you work out what frequency a bar on a histogram represents? ☑
15) a) Draw a line graph to show the time series data in this table.
    b) Describe the overall trend in the data. ☑

Quarter	1	2	3	4	1	2	3	4
Sales (1000's)	1	1.5	1.7	3	0.7	0.9	1.2	2.2

16) Sketch graphs to show: a) weak positive correlation, b) strong negative correlation, c) no correlation ☑

Comparing Data Sets (p124-125) ☑

17) These box plots show information about how long it took someone to get to work in summer and winter one year. Compare the travel times in the two seasons. ☑

18) An 800 m runner had a mean time of 147 seconds, before she increased her training hours. The histogram shows information about the times she runs after increasing her training hours. Is there any evidence that her running times have improved? ☑

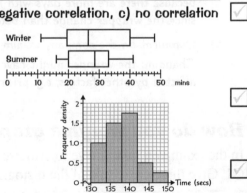

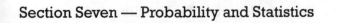

Answers

Get the full versions of these answers online
Step-by-step worked solutions to these questions, with a full mark scheme, are included as a printable PDF with your free Online Edition — you'll find more info about how to get hold of this at the front of this book.

Section One

Page 2 — Types of Number and BODMAS

Q1 55

Page 3 — Multiples, Factors and Prime Factors

Q1 a) $990 = 2 \times 3 \times 3 \times 5 \times 11$
$= 2 \times 3^2 \times 5 \times 11$
b) $160 = 2 \times 2 \times 2 \times 2 \times 2 \times 5$
$= 2^5 \times 5$

Page 4 — LCM and HCF

Q1 a) 36   b) 56
Q2 a) 12   b) 30

Page 6 — Fractions

Q1 a) $\frac{17}{32}$ b) $\frac{2}{3}$
c) $\frac{167}{27} = 6\frac{5}{27}$ d) $-\frac{43}{12} = -3\frac{7}{12}$

Q2 6

Page 7 — Fractions, Decimals and Percentages

Q1 a) $\frac{4}{10} = \frac{2}{5}$ b) $\frac{2}{100} = \frac{1}{50}$
c) $\frac{77}{100}$ d) $\frac{555}{1000} = \frac{111}{200}$
e) $\frac{56}{10} = \frac{28}{5}$

Q2 a) 57%   b) $\frac{6}{25}$ c) 90%

Page 9 — Fractions and Recurring Decimals

Q1 $\frac{14}{111}$
Q2 Let r = 0.0̇7̇.
Then 100r − r = 7.0̇7̇ − 0.0̇7̇
$\Rightarrow$ 99r = 7 $\Rightarrow$ r = $\frac{7}{99}$
Q3 $\frac{5}{111} = \frac{45}{999} = 0.0̇4̇5̇$

Page 11 — Estimating

Q1 a) Answer should be either 5 (if numbers are rounded to 1 s.f.) or 6 (if numbers are rounded to nearest integer).
b) Answer should be in the range 11.6-11.8.
Q2 a) 4000 cm³   b) Bigger

Page 12 — Bounds

Q1 6.2 m/s (1 d.p.)

Page 14 — Standard Form

Q1 8.54×10^5, 1.8×10^{-4}
Q2 a) 2×10^{11} b) 6.47×10^{11}
Q3 2.5×10^{26}

Revision Questions — Section One

Q1 a) Whole numbers — either positive or negative, or zero
b) Numbers that can be written as fractions
c) Numbers which will only divide by themselves or 1 (excluding 1)
Q2 a) 11   b) 0.5   c) 169
Q3 8 packs of buns, 3 packs of cheese slices, 4 packs of hot dogs.
Q4 a) 14   b) 40
Q5 a) $320 = 2 \times 2 \times 2 \times 2 \times 2 \times 2 \times 5$
$= 2^6 \times 5$
$880 = 2 \times 2 \times 2 \times 2 \times 5 \times 11$
$= 2^4 \times 5 \times 11$
b) LCM $= 2^6 \times 5 \times 11 = 3520$
HCF $= 2^4 \times 5 = 80$
Q6 Divide top and bottom by the same number till they won't go any further.
Q7 a) $8\frac{2}{9}$ b) $\frac{33}{7}$
Q8 Multiplying: Multiply top and bottom numbers separately.
Dividing: Turn the second fraction upside down, then multiply.
Adding/subtracting: Put fractions over a common denominator, then add/subtract the numerators.
Q9 a) $\frac{14}{99}$ b) $3\frac{1}{7}$ or $\frac{22}{7}$
c) $\frac{11}{24}$ d) $7\frac{11}{20}$ or $\frac{151}{20}$
Q10 a) 210 kg   b) $\frac{11}{7}$
Q11 $\frac{3}{4} = \frac{30}{40}$, $\frac{5}{8} = \frac{25}{40}$, $\frac{7}{10} = \frac{28}{40}$
So $\frac{7}{10}$ is closer to $\frac{3}{4}$ than $\frac{5}{8}$.
Q12 a) Divide the top by the bottom.
b) Put the digits after the decimal point on the top, and a power of 10 with the same number of zeros as there were decimal places on the bottom.
Q13 a) (i) $\frac{4}{100} = \frac{1}{25}$ (ii) 4%
b) (i) $\frac{65}{100} = \frac{13}{20}$ (ii) 0.65
Q14 orange juice = 12.5 litres, lemonade = 10 litres, cranberry juice = 2.5 litres
Q15 Let r = 0.5̇1̇.
Then 100r − r = 51.5̇1̇ − 0.5̇1̇
$\Rightarrow$ 99r = 51 $\Rightarrow$ r = $\frac{51}{99} = \frac{17}{33}$
Q16 a) 427.96   b) 428.0

---

c) 430   d) 428.0
Q17 Estimates should be around 16-20.
Q18 Estimates should be between 6.6 and 6.8.
Q19 The upper and lower bounds of a rounded measurement are half a unit either side of the rounded value. The upper and lower bounds of a truncated measurement are the truncated value itself and a whole unit above the truncated value.
Q20 2.35 litres $\leq$ V < 2.45 litres
Q21 132.2425 m²
Q22 1. The front number must always be between 1 and 10.
2. The power of 10, n, is how far the decimal point moves.
3. n is positive for big numbers, and negative for small numbers.
Q23 a) 9.7×10^5 b) 3.56×10^9
c) 2.75×10^{-6}
Q24 0.00456, 270 000
Q25 a) 2×10^3 b) 2.739×10^{12}
Q26 2.48×10^9

Section Two

Page 16 — Algebra Basics

Q1 $10x + 6y + 2$ cm

Page 17 — Powers and Roots

Q1 a) e^{11} b) f^4
c) g^3 d) $6h^7j^2$
Q2 a) 125   b) $\frac{1}{5}$ c) 2

Page 18 — Multiplying Out Brackets

Q1 a) $y^2 - y - 20$ b) $4p^2 - 12p + 9$
Q2 a) $2t^2 - 5t\sqrt{2} - 6$
b) $x^3 - 6x^2 + 12x - 8$

Page 19 — Factorising

Q1 $3y(2x + 5y)$
Q2 $(x + 4y)(x - 4y)$
Q3 $(x + \sqrt{11})(x - \sqrt{11})$
Q4 $\frac{6}{x + 7}$

Page 20 — Manipulating Surds

Q1 $13\sqrt{5}$ **Q2** $4 - 2\sqrt{3}$

Page 21 — Solving Equations

Q1 $x = 2$ **Q2** $y = 4$
Q3 $x = 6$

Page 22 — Solving Equations

Q1 $x = \pm 6$ **Q2** $x = 8$

Answers

Page 23 — Rearranging Formulas
Q1 $q = 7p - 14r$
Q2 $v = u + at$

Page 24 — Rearranging Formulas
Q1 a) $y = \pm 2\sqrt{x}$ **b)** $y = \dfrac{xz}{x-1}$

Page 25 — Factorising Quadratics
Q1 $(x + 5)(x - 3)$
Q2 $x = 4$ or $x = 5$

Page 26 — Factorising Quadratics
Q1 $(2x + 3)(x - 4)$
Q2 $x = \dfrac{2}{3}$ or $x = -4$
Q3 $(3x + 2)(x + 10)$
Q4 $x = -\dfrac{2}{5}$ or $x = 3$

Page 27 — The Quadratic Formula
Q1 $x = 0.39$ or $x = -10.39$
Q2 $x = \dfrac{1 \pm \sqrt{3}}{2}$

Page 28 — Completing the Square
Q1 $(x - 6)^2 - 13$
Q2 $(x + 5)^2 - 18 = 0$, so $x = -5 \pm 3\sqrt{2}$

Page 29 — Completing the Square
Q1 a) $2(x + \dfrac{3}{4})^2 - \dfrac{49}{8}$
b) $x = 1, x = -\dfrac{5}{2}$
c) Minimum point $= (-\dfrac{3}{4}, -\dfrac{49}{8})$

Page 30 — Algebraic Fractions
Q1 $\dfrac{x^2 + 2y}{x}$
Q2 $\dfrac{6(x + 2)}{x^2(x + 5)}$
Q3 $\dfrac{5x + 11}{(x - 2)(x + 5)}$

Page 31 — Sequences
Q1 $7n - 5$ **Q2** $2n^2 - 2n + 6$

Page 32 — Sequences
Q1 34, 42 and 50

Page 33 — Inequalities
Q1 a) $x < 3$ **b)** $x \le -3$
Q2 $-2 \le x \le 4$

Page 34 — Inequalities
Q1 a) $-7 < p < 7$
b) $p \le -8$ or $p \ge 8$
Q2 $x = 0, 1, 2, 3, 4$

Page 35 — Graphical Inequalities
Q1

Page 36 — Iterative Methods
Q1 $x = 1.88$

Page 37 — Simultaneous Equations
Q1 One cup of tea costs £1.50 and one slice of cake costs £2
Q2 $x = 3, y = -1$

Page 38 — Simultaneous Equations
Q1 $x = 1, y = -1$ and $x = -4, y = 14$
Q2 $A: (0, 4)$ and B (6, 40)
Length of line AB: $= \sqrt{1332}$ units

Page 39 — Proof
Q1 Take two consecutive even numbers, $2n$ and $2n + 2$, where n is an integer. Then $2n + (2n + 2)$ $= 4n + 2 = 2(2n + 1)$, which is even, as $(2n + 1)$ is an integer.
Q2 $4x + 2 = 3(3a + x)$, so $x = 9a - 2$. If a is odd, then $9a$ is also odd (as odd × odd = odd). $9a - 2$ is always odd (as odd − even = odd), so x cannot be a multiple of 8 as all multiples of 8 are even.

Page 40 — Proof
Q1 Take two consecutive integers, n and $n + 1$, and square them to get n^2 and $n^2 + 2n + 1$. The difference between them is $2n + 1$, which is odd.
Q2 Take two consecutive triangle numbers, $\frac{1}{2}n(n + 1)$ and $\frac{1}{2}(n + 1)(n + 2)$. Their ratio is $\frac{1}{2}n(n + 1) : \frac{1}{2}(n + 1)(n + 2)$, which simplifies to $n : n + 2$.

Page 41 — Functions
Q1 a) 19   **b)** 7
c) $10 - 10x$ **d)** $5x^2 + 14$
e) -16 **f)** $f^{-1}(x) = \dfrac{x + 1}{5}$

Revision Questions — Section Two
Q1 $5x - 4y - 5$
Q2 a) x^9 **b)** y^2 **c)** z^{12}
Q3 a) $6x + 3$ **b)** $x^2 - x - 6$
c) $x^3 + 7x^2 + 7x - 15$

Q4 a) $2(2x + y)(2x - y)$
b) $(7 + 9pq)(7 - 9pq)$
c) $12(x + 2y)(x - 2y)$
Q5 a) $3\sqrt{3}$ **b)** 5
Q6 $3\sqrt{2}$
Q7 a) $x = 2$ **b)** $x = \pm 3$
Q8 a) $p = -\dfrac{4y}{3}$ **b)** $p = \dfrac{qr}{q + r}$
Q9 a) $x = -3$ or $x = -6$
b) $x = 4$ or $x = -\dfrac{3}{5}$
Q10 $x = \dfrac{-b \pm \sqrt{b^2 - 4ac}}{2a}$
Q11 a) $x = 1.56$ or $x = -2.56$
b) $x = 0.27$ or $x = -1.47$
c) $x = 0.44$ or $x = -3.44$
Q12 a) $x = -6 \pm \sqrt{21}$ **b)** $x = 3 \pm \sqrt{11}$
Q13 $y = x^2 - 4x + 9$, so $p = -4, q = 9$
Q14 $\dfrac{3x + 1}{(x + 3)(x - 1)}$
Q15 a) $2n + 5$ **b)** $-3n + 14$
c) $n^2 + n + 3$
Q16 Yes, it's the 5th term.
Q17 a) $x \ge -2$ **b)** $x < -6$ or $x > 6$
Q18

Q19 $x = 3$ gives a value of -6
$x = 4$ gives a value of 5.
There is a sign change so there is a solution between 3 and 4.
Q20 $x = 2, y = 3$
Q21 $x = -2, y = -2$ and $x = -4, y = -8$
Q22 Take an even number, $2p$, and an odd number, $2q + 1$. Their product is $2p \times (2q + 1) = 4pq + 2p$ $= 2(2pq + p)$, which is even as $(2pq + p)$ is an integer (sums and products of integers are also integers).
Q23 a) 6   **b)** 18
c) $16x^2 - 3$ **d)** $f^{-1}(x) = \sqrt{x + 3}$

Section Three

Page 43 — Straight Lines and Gradients
Q1 Gradient is -5

Page 44 — y = mx + c
Q1 $y = \dfrac{2}{3}x + 2$
Q2 $y = \dfrac{1}{2}x + 5$

Answers

Page 45 — Drawing Straight-Line Graphs

Q1

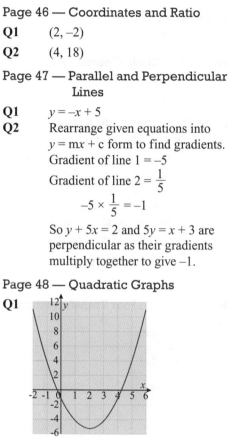

Page 46 — Coordinates and Ratio

Q1 $(2, -2)$

Q2 $(4, 18)$

Page 47 — Parallel and Perpendicular Lines

Q1 $y = -x + 5$

Q2 Rearrange given equations into $y = mx + c$ form to find gradients.

Gradient of line 1 = -5

Gradient of line 2 = $\frac{1}{5}$

$-5 \times \frac{1}{5} = -1$

So $y + 5x = 2$ and $5y = x + 3$ are perpendicular as their gradients multiply together to give -1.

Page 48 — Quadratic Graphs

Q1

Page 49 — Harder Graphs

Q1 Radius = 13

Equation of circle = $x^2 + y^2 = 169$

Page 50 — Harder Graphs

Q1 a) $a = 16$

$b = 2$

b) 2048

Page 51 — Harder Graphs

Q1 a)

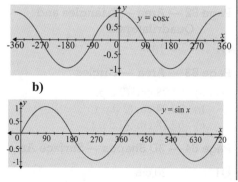

b)

Page 52 — Solving Equations Using Graphs

Q1 a) $x = 2$, $y = 4$ and $x = -5$, $y = 11$

b) $x = -4$, $y = -3$ and $x = 3$, $y = 4$

Page 53 — Graph Transformations

Q1 a) $(-4, 3)$

b) $(4, -1)$

c) $(6, 4)$

Page 54 — Real-life Graphs

Q1

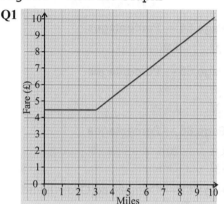

Page 55 — Distance-Time Graphs

Q1 a) 15 minutes

b) 12 km/h

Page 56 — Velocity-time Graphs

Q1 1006.25 m

Page 57 — Gradients of Real-Life Graphs

Q1 2.3 cm per day (allow ±0.3 cm)

Q2 ≈ 0.133 miles per minute
= 8 miles per hour

Revision Questions — Section Three

Q1

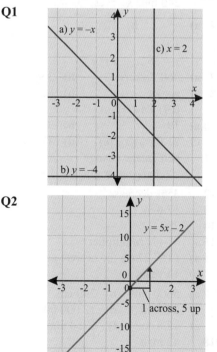

Q2

Q3 $y = 2x + 10$

Q4 $y = x - 9$

Q5 $y = -\frac{1}{2}x + 4$

Q6 a)

x	-3	-2	-1	0	1
y	-7	-9	-9	-7	-3

b)

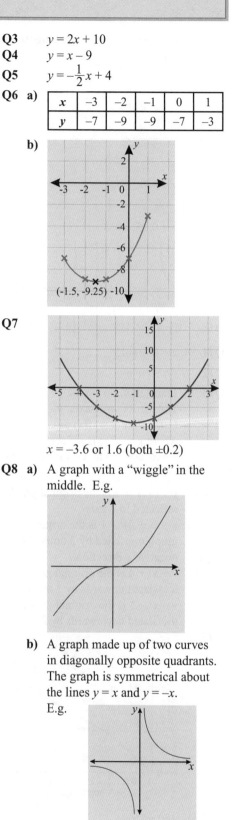

(-1.5, -9.25)

Q7

$x = -3.6$ or 1.6 (both ±0.2)

Q8 a) A graph with a "wiggle" in the middle. E.g.

b) A graph made up of two curves in diagonally opposite quadrants. The graph is symmetrical about the lines $y = x$ and $y = -x$. E.g.

c) A graph which curves rapidly upwards. E.g.

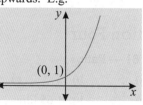

(0, 1)

Answers

d) A circle with radius r, centre (0, 0). E.g.

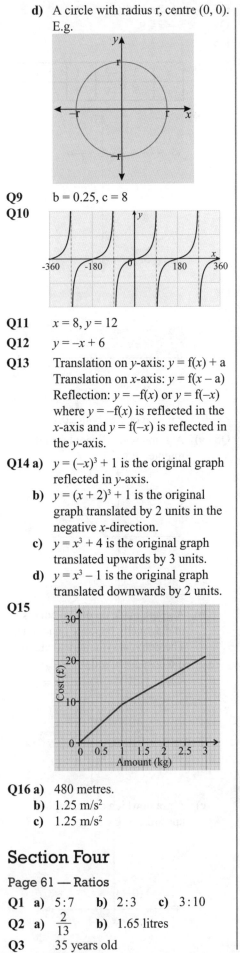

Q9 $b = 0.25, c = 8$

Q10

Q11 $x = 8, y = 12$

Q12 $y = -x + 6$

Q13 Translation on y-axis: $y = f(x) + a$
Translation on x-axis: $y = f(x - a)$
Reflection: $y = -f(x)$ or $y = f(-x)$
where $y = -f(x)$ is reflected in the x-axis and $y = f(-x)$ is reflected in the y-axis.

Q14 a) $y = (-x)^3 + 1$ is the original graph reflected in y-axis.

b) $y = (x + 2)^3 + 1$ is the original graph translated by 2 units in the negative x-direction.

c) $y = x^3 + 4$ is the original graph translated upwards by 3 units.

d) $y = x^3 - 1$ is the original graph translated downwards by 2 units.

Q15

Q16 a) 480 metres.
b) 1.25 m/s²
c) 1.25 m/s²

Section Four

Page 61 — Ratios

Q1 a) 5:7 **b)** 2:3 **c)** 3:10

Q2 a) $\frac{2}{13}$ **b)** 1.65 litres

Q3 35 years old

Q4 17 red balls and 23 blue balls

Page 62 — Direct and Inverse Proportion

Q1 £67.50
Q2 5 hours 20 mins

Page 63 — Direct and Inverse Proportion

Q1 273 m/s

Q2 $P = \dfrac{48}{Q^2}$
When $P = 8$, $Q = \sqrt{6}$

Page 64 — Percentages

Q1 140%

Page 65 — Percentages

Q1 25%
Q2 £5.49

Page 66 — Percentages

Q1 20%
Q2 26%

Page 67 — Compound Growth and Decay

Q1 Kyle will have £41.95 more.

Page 68 — Unit Conversions

Q1 £25 (2 s.f.)

Page 69 — Speed, Density and Pressure

Q1 285 kg (3 s.f.)

Revision Questions — Section Four

Q1 $\dfrac{13}{8}$ or 1.625

Q2 a) 3:4 **b)** 3.5:1

Q3 240 blue scarves

Q4 a) $\dfrac{1}{5}$ **b)** 128

Q5 10

Q6 $x = 36$ $y = 9$

Q7 a) 960 flowers **b)** 3.9 hours

Q8 a) $y = kx^2$ **b)** See p.63

Q9 0.91 Pa (2 d.p.)

Q10 a) 19 **b)** 39
c) 21.05% (2 d.p.) **d)** 475%

Q11 percentage change
= (change ÷ original) × 100

Q12 35% decrease

Q13 17.6 m

Q14 2%

Q15 $N = N_0(\text{multiplier})^n$

Q16 a) £157.37 (to the nearest penny)
b) 14 years

Q17 a) 5600 cm³ **b)** 240 cm
c) 10.8 km/h **d)** 12 000 000 cm³
e) 12.8 cm² **f)** 2750 mm³

Q18 42 mph

Q19 12 500 cm³

Q20 11 m²

Section Five

Page 71 — Geometry

Q1 $x = 108°$

Page 72 — Parallel Lines

Q1 $x = 30°$

Page 73 — Geometry Problems

Q1 $x = 123°$

Page 74 — Polygons

Q1 144°

Page 77 — Circle Geometry

Q1 angle ABD = 63°
angle ACD = 63°

Page 78 — Congruent Shapes

Q1 E.g. Angles ABD and BDC are the same (alternate angles). Angles ADB and DBC are the same (alternate angles). Side BD is the same in each shape. So triangles ABD and BCD are congruent as the condition AAS holds.

Page 79 — Similar Shapes

Q1 BD = 10 cm

Page 80 — The Four Transformations

Q1

Page 81 — The Four Transformations

Q1

Page 82 — Area — Triangles and Quadrilaterals

Q1 $x = 10$

Page 83 — Area — Circles

Q1 a) 83.78 cm² (2 d.p.)
b) 20.94 cm (2 d.p.)
c) 67.78 cm² (2 d.p.)

Page 84 — 3D Shapes — Surface Area

Q1 $l = 20$ cm

Page 86 — 3D Shapes — Volume
Q1 $h = 36$ cm
Q2 Volume of pyramid = 132 000 cm³
Time taken to fill = 1320 s
= 22 mins so yes, it takes longer
than 20 mins to fill.

Page 87 — More Enlargements and Projections
Q1 Surface area = 20 cm²
Volume = 8 cm³

Page 88 — Triangle Construction
Q1

Q2

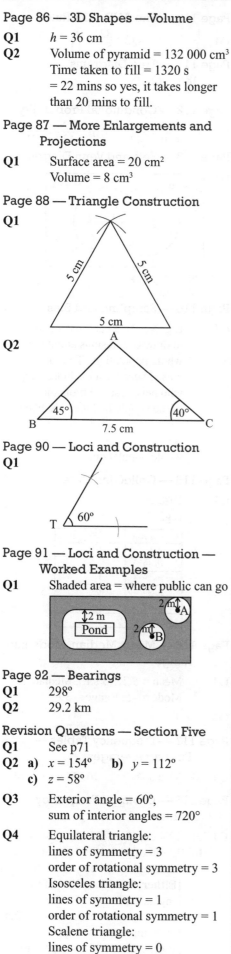

Page 90 — Loci and Construction
Q1

Page 91 — Loci and Construction — Worked Examples
Q1 Shaded area = where public can go

Page 92 — Bearings
Q1 298°
Q2 29.2 km

Revision Questions — Section Five
Q1 See p71
Q2 a) $x = 154°$ **b)** $y = 112°$
 c) $z = 58°$

Q3 Exterior angle = 60°,
sum of interior angles = 720°

Q4 Equilateral triangle:
lines of symmetry = 3
order of rotational symmetry = 3
Isosceles triangle:
lines of symmetry = 1
order of rotational symmetry = 1
Scalene triangle:
lines of symmetry = 0
order of rotational symmetry = 1

Q5 E.g. rhombus and parallelogram
Q6 See p76-77
Q7 a) $x = 53°$
 b) $y = 69°$
 c) $z = 33°$
Q8 No — opposite angles in a cyclic
quadrilateral add up to 180°, but
88° + 95° = 183° ≠ 180°.
Q9 SSS, AAS, SAS, RHS
Q10 E.g. angles ACB and ACD
are right angles (as it's a
perpendicular bisector of a chord)
AB = AD (they're both radii)
CB = CD (as the chord is bisected)
So the condition RHS holds and
the triangles are congruent.
Q11 $x = 2.5$ cm
Q12 a) Translation by vector $\begin{pmatrix} -7 \\ -5 \end{pmatrix}$ OR
rotation 180° about point (1, 2).
 b) Enlargement of scale factor $\frac{1}{3}$
and centre of enlargement (0, 0).
Q13

Q14 $A = ½(a + b) \times h_v$
Q15 69 cm²
Q16 30 cm
Q17 Circumference = 16π cm,
area = 64π cm²
Q18 39.27 cm²
Q19 S. A. of a sphere = $4\pi r^2$
S. A. of a cylinder = $2\pi rh + 2\pi r^2$
S. A. of a cone = $\pi rl + \pi r^2$
Q20 75π cm²
Q21 1030 cm³ (3 s.f.)
Q22 a) 129.85 cm³ (2 d.p.)
 b) 5.2 s (1 d.p.)
Q23 80 cm²
Q24

Front	Side	Plan

Q25

Q26

Q27 A circle
Q28

Q29 See p89
Q30

Q31 Put your pencil on the diagram
at the point you're going FROM.
Draw a north line at this point.
Draw in the angle clockwise from
the north line — this is the bearing
you want.

Q32

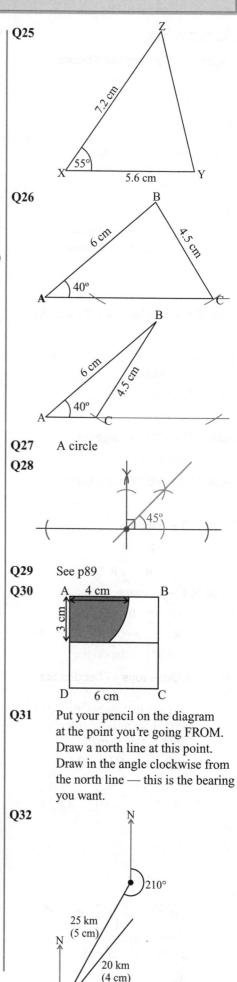

Answers

Section Six

Page 95 — Pythagoras' Theorem

Q1   10.3 m

Q2   5

Q3   2 cm and 6 cm

Page 97 — Trigonometry — Examples

Q1   27.1°

Q2   2.97 m

Page 98 — Trigonometry — Common Values

Q1 $\dfrac{25\sqrt{3}}{6}$ mm^2

Page 99 — The Sine and Cosine Rules

Q1   32.5 cm^2

Page 100 — The Sine and Cosine Rules

Q1   20.5 cm (3 s.f.)

Q2   59.5° (3 s.f.)

Page 101 — 3D Pythagoras

Q1   14.8 cm (3 s.f.)

Page 102 — 3D Trigonometry

Q1   17.1° (3 s.f.)

Page 103 — Vectors

Q1 $\overrightarrow{AB} = \mathbf{p} - 2\mathbf{q}$

      $\overrightarrow{NA} = \mathbf{q} - \dfrac{1}{2}\mathbf{p}$

Page 104 — Vectors

Q1 $\overrightarrow{AB} = \mathbf{a} - \mathbf{b}$

      $\overrightarrow{DC} = \dfrac{3}{2}\mathbf{a} - \dfrac{3}{2}\mathbf{b} = \dfrac{3}{2}(\mathbf{a} - \mathbf{b})$

      ABCD is a trapezium.

Revision Questions — Section Six

Q1 $a^2 + b^2 = c^2$

      You use Pythagoras' theorem to find the missing side of a right-angled triangle.

Q2   4.72 m   **Q3**   7.8

Q4

Q5   33.4°

Q6   See p98

Q7 $4\sqrt{3}$ cm

Q8   Sine rule:

      $\dfrac{a}{\sin A} = \dfrac{b}{\sin B} = \dfrac{c}{\sin C}$

      Cosine rule:

      $a^2 = b^2 + c^2 - 2bc \cos A$

      Area $= \dfrac{1}{2}ab \sin C$

Q9   Two angles given plus any side — sine rule.
Two sides given plus an angle not enclosed by them — sine rule.
Two sides given plus the angle enclosed by them — cosine rule.
All three sides given but no angles — cosine rule.

Q10   56.4° (3 s.f.)

Q11   6.84 cm (3 s.f.)

Q12   48.1 cm^2 (3 s.f.)

Q13 a)   6.52 m   **b)**   48.7 m^2

Q14 $a^2 + b^2 + c^2 = d^2$

Q15   11.9 m (3 s.f.)

Q16   15.2° (3 s.f.)

Q17   54°

Q18   Multiplying by a scalar changes the size of a vector but not its direction.

Q19 a) $\begin{pmatrix} -3 \\ -8 \end{pmatrix}$ **b)** $\begin{pmatrix} 20 \\ -10 \end{pmatrix}$

     c) $\begin{pmatrix} 19 \\ 0 \end{pmatrix}$ **d)** $\begin{pmatrix} -30 \\ -4 \end{pmatrix}$

Q20 a) $\overrightarrow{AX} = \dfrac{1}{3}\mathbf{a}$

     b) $\overrightarrow{DX} = \dfrac{4}{3}\mathbf{a} - \mathbf{b}$

        $\overrightarrow{XB} = \dfrac{8}{3}\mathbf{a} - 2\mathbf{b}$

     c) $\overrightarrow{XB} = 2\,\overrightarrow{DX}$, so DXB is a straight line.

Section Seven

Page 106 — Probability Basics

Q1 $\dfrac{3}{10}$ or 0.3

Q2 $3x$

Page 107 — Counting Outcomes

Q1 a)   HHH, HHT, HTH, THH, THT, HTT, TTT

     b) $\dfrac{3}{8}$ or 0.375

Q2 $\dfrac{1}{1024}$

Page 108 — Probability Experiments

Q1 a)

Score	Relative frequency
1	0.14
2	0.137
3	0.138
4	0.259
5	0.161
6	0.165

     b)   Yes, because the relative frequency for 4 is much higher than you'd expect from a fair dice (which is $1 \div 6 = 0.166...$).

Page 109 — Probability Experiments

Q1 a)   75   **b)**   195

Page 110 — The AND / OR Rules

Q1 $\dfrac{1}{4}$ **Q2** $\dfrac{32}{52} = \dfrac{8}{13}$

Page 111 — Tree Diagrams

Q1 $\dfrac{48}{100} = \dfrac{12}{25}$

Page 112 — Conditional Probability

Q1 a) $\dfrac{310}{420} = \dfrac{31}{42}$ **b)** $\dfrac{220}{420} = \dfrac{11}{21}$

Page 113 — Sets and Venn Diagrams

Q1

     $\dfrac{20}{52} = \dfrac{5}{13}$

Page 114 — Sampling and Bias

Q1   E.g. No, Tina can't use her results to draw conclusions about the whole population. The sample is biased because it excludes people who never use the train and most of the people included are likely to use the train regularly. The sample is also too small to represent the whole population.

Page 115 — Collecting Data

Q1   Discrete data
E.g.

Cinema visits	Tally	Frequency
0-9		
10-19		
20-29		
30-39		
40-49		
50 or over		

Page 116 — Mean, Median, Mode and Range

Q1   Mean = 5.27 (3 s.f.), Median = 6
Mode = -5, Range = 39

Q2   9

Page 117 — Frequency Tables — Finding Averages

Q1 a)   Median = 2   **b)**   Mean = 1.66

Page 118 — Grouped Frequency Tables

Q1 a)   17.4 cm (3 s.f.)

     b)   12 out of 61 = 19.67...% of the lengths are below 16.5 cm.
[Either] Less than 20% of the lengths are below 16.5 cm, so Ana's statement is incorrect. **[Or]** Rounding to the nearest whole percent, 20% of the lengths are below 16.5 cm, so Ana's statement is correct.

Answers

Page 119 — Box Plots

Q1

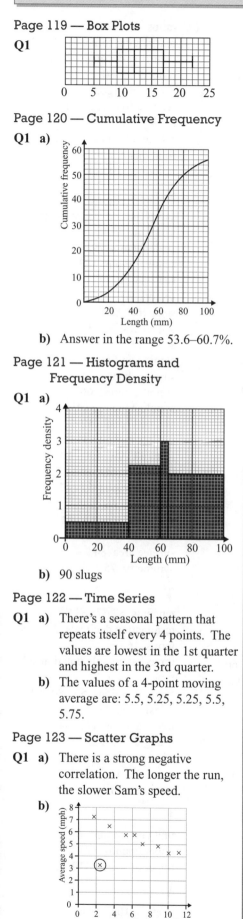

Page 120 — Cumulative Frequency

Q1 a)

b) Answer in the range 53.6–60.7%.

Page 121 — Histograms and Frequency Density

Q1 a)

b) 90 slugs

Page 122 — Time Series

Q1 a) There's a seasonal pattern that repeats itself every 4 points. The values are lowest in the 1st quarter and highest in the 3rd quarter.

b) The values of a 4-point moving average are: 5.5, 5.25, 5.25, 5.5, 5.75.

Page 123 — Scatter Graphs

Q1 a) There is a strong negative correlation. The longer the run, the slower Sam's speed.

b)

c) Approximately 5 mph (±0.5 mph)

d) The estimate should be reliable because **[either]** 8 miles is within the range of the known data **[or]** the graph shows strong correlation.

Page 124 — Comparing Data Sets

Q1 The range of Science scores is the same as the range of English scores, but the IQR for the Science scores is smaller, so Claudia is correct.

Page 125 — Comparing Data Sets

Q1 1) The data classes are unequal, so the columns shouldn't all be the same width. 2) The horizontal axis isn't labelled. 3) The frequency density scale isn't numbered.

Revision Questions — Section Seven

Q1 $\dfrac{8}{50} = \dfrac{4}{25}$

Q2 $\dfrac{1}{y^2}$

Q3 Divide the frequency of each result by the number of times the experiment was tried.

Q4 a)

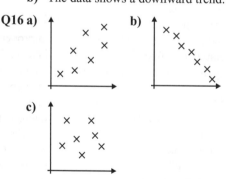

b) Relative frequency of:

pass, pass = $\dfrac{60}{160} = \dfrac{3}{8}$ or 0.375

pass, fail = $\dfrac{45}{160} = \dfrac{9}{32}$ or 0.28125

fail, pass = $\dfrac{30}{160} = \dfrac{3}{16}$ or 0.1875

fail, fail = $\dfrac{25}{160} = \dfrac{5}{32}$ or 0.15625

c) 113 people

Q5 $\dfrac{4}{81}$ **Q6** $\dfrac{12}{20} = \dfrac{3}{5}$

Q7 a) $\dfrac{16}{2704} = \dfrac{1}{169}$

b) $\dfrac{24}{132600} = \dfrac{1}{5525}$

Q8 a)

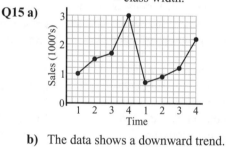

b) $x = 17$

c) $\dfrac{56}{180} = \dfrac{14}{45}$

Q9 A sample is part of a population. Samples need to be representative so that conclusions drawn from sample data can be applied to the whole population.

Q10 Qualitative data

Q11 Mode = 31, Median = 24
Mean = 22, Range = 39

Q12 a) Modal class is: $1.5 \le y < 1.6$.

b) Class containing median is: $1.5 \le y < 1.6$

c) Estimated mean = 1.58 m (to 2 d.p.)

Q13

Q14 Calculate the bar's area or use the formula:
frequency = frequency density × class width.

Q15 a)

b) The data shows a downward trend.

Q16 a) 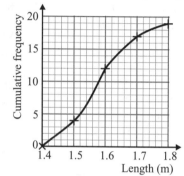 **b)**

c)

Q17 The median time in winter is lower than the median time in summer, so it generally took longer to get to work in the summer.
The range and the IQR for the summer are smaller than those for the winter, so there is less variation in journey times in the summer.

Q18 The runner's mean time after increasing her training hours has decreased from 147 seconds to 138 seconds, so this suggests that her running times have improved.

Index